THE
WORKS OF ARISTOTLE

TRANSLATED INTO ENGLISH
UNDER THE EDITORSHIP

OF

W. D. ROSS, M.A.

FELLOW AND TUTOR OF ORIEL COLLEGE
DEPUTY PROFESSOR OF MORAL PHILOSOPHY IN THE
UNIVERSITY OF OXFORD

VOLUME VII

PROBLEMATA

BY

E. S. FORSTER

OXFORD
AT THE CLARENDON PRESS

Oxford University Press, Amen House, London E.C.4

GLASGOW NEW YORK TORONTO MELBOURNE WELLINGTON
BOMBAY CALCUTTA MADRAS KARACHI LAHORE DACCA
CAPE TOWN SALISBURY NAIROBI IBADAN ACCRA
KUALA LUMPUR HONG KONG

FIRST EDITION 1927
REPRINTED LITHOGRAPHICALLY IN GREAT BRITAIN
AT THE UNIVERSITY PRESS, OXFORD
FROM SHEETS OF THE FIRST EDITION
1953, 1963

PROBLEMATA

BY

E. S. FORSTER, M.A.
Professor of Greek in the University of Sheffield
Formerly Scholar of Oriel College

IN PIAM MEMORIAM PATRIS DILECTI
MICHAELIS SEYMOUR FORSTER
B.C.L., M.A. : COLL. WINTON. ET COLL. NOV. OXON.
QUONDAM SCHOLARIS : OBIIT. ID. MAI. MDCCCCXXI.

Τὸ δυνατὸν γὰρ ἡ φιλία ἐπιζητεῖ, οὐ τὸ κατ' ἀξίαν· οὐδὲ
γὰρ ἔστιν ἐν πᾶσι, καθάπερ ἐν ταῖς πρὸς τοὺς θεοὺς τιμαῖς
καὶ τοὺς γονεῖς· οὐδεὶς γὰρ τὴν ἀξίαν ποτ' ἂν ἀποδοίη.

Aristotle, *Eth. Nic.* 1163^b 15.

PREFACE

THE inclusion of the *Problemata* in the Aristotelian Corpus is no doubt due to the fact that Aristotle is known to have written a work of this kind, to which reference is made in his genuine works and by other writers. An examination of these references shows that some of them can be connected with passages in the *Problemata*, while others cannot; from which it may be concluded that, while the *Problemata* is not the genuine Aristotelian work, it nevertheless contains an element derived from such a work. It is also obviously indebted to other Aristotelian treatises, especially those on Natural History, to the Hippocratean writings, and to Theophrastus. The repetitions and contradictions which occur in the work seem to show that it was a gradual compilation by several hands; and, if one may judge from the late forms of words which occur in several passages, it did not reach its final form until some time after the beginning of the Christian Era. Some critics would date its completion as late as the fifth or sixth century A.D. The doctrine throughout is Peripatetic, and the variety of subjects treated shows the wide interests of that school.

The text used for this translation is that of Ruelle-Knoellinger-Klek (Leipzig, Teubner, 1922). The preface to that edition contains a complete account of the MSS. and a valuable bibliography.[1] Wherever any other reading is adopted the fact is stated in the foot-notes.

---

[1] An important contribution to the text (not mentioned in this bibliography) is that of the late Mr. H. P. Richards in his *Aristotelica* (London, Grant Richards, 1915). This only came into my hands after I had completed the first draft of my translation; it confirmed in several passages conclusions at which I had arrived independently.

Professor W. D. Ross has been good enough to read the translation both in MS. and in proof; a small part of the debt which I owe him is indicated in the foot-notes, but there are innumerable other passages in which his vast knowledge of Aristotelian usage has enabled me to introduce material improvements. I have also to thank Sir Henry Hadow, D.Mus., Vice-Chancellor of the University of Sheffield, and my colleague Mr. G. E. Linfoot, Mus.Bac., B.Sc., for generous assistance in elucidating the Musical Problems.

THE UNIVERSITY,   E. S. FORSTER.
SHEFFIELD,
1 *Feb.* 1926.

CONTENTS

PROBLEMATA

BOOK I

PROBLEMS CONNECTED WITH MEDICINE

1 WHY is it that great excesses cause disease ? Is it because 859ᵃ
they engender excess or defect, and it is in these after all
that disease consists ?

2 But why is it that diseases can often be cured if the
patient indulges in excess of some kind ? And this is the 5
treatment used by some doctors; for they cure by the
excessive use of wine or water or salt, or by over-feeding
or starving the patient. Is it because the causes of the
disease are opposites of one another, so that each reduces
the other to the mean ?

3 Why is it that the changes of the seasons and the winds
intensify or stop diseases and bring them to a crisis and 10
engender them ? Is it because the seasons are hot and cold
and moist and dry, while diseases are due to excess of these
qualities and health to their equality ? In that case, if the
disease is due to moisture or cold, a season which has the
opposite characteristics stops it; but if a season of the
opposite kind[1] follows, the same admixture of qualities
being caused as before intensifies the disease and kills the
patient. For this reason the seasons even cause disease in 15
healthy persons, because by their changes they destroy the
proper admixture of qualities; for it is at the same time
improved by suitable seasons, times of life, and localities. The health therefore requires careful management at
times of change. And what has been said generally as to
the effect of the seasons applies also in detail; for changes
of winds and of age and of locality are to some extent 20
changes of season. These also therefore intensify and stop
diseases and bring them to a crisis and engender them, as

---
[1] i. e. wet or cold.

do the seasons and the risings of certain constellations, such
as Orion and Arcturus and the Pleiads and the Dogstar,[1]
since they cause[2] wind and rain and fine weather and
storms and sunshine.

25   Why ought emetics to be avoided at the changes of the **4**
seasons ? Is it in order that there may be no disturbance
when the excretions[3] are being altered by such changes ?

859ᵇ   Why is it that the feet swell both of those who are **5**
bilious and of those who are suffering from starvation ? Is
it in both cases the effect of wasting ? For those who are
starving waste because they do not receive any nourishment
at all, while the bilious waste because they do not derive
any benefit from the nourishment which they take.

5   Why it is that, though the diseases due to bile occur[4] in **6**
the summer (the season when fevers are at their height),
acute diseases due to bile occur rather in the winter ? Is it
because, being accompanied by fever, they are acute
because they are violent, and violence is unnatural ? For
fervent inflammation is set up when certain parts of the body
10   are moist, and inflammation, being due to an excess of heat,
engenders fevers. In the summer, therefore, diseases are
dry and hot, but in the winter they are moist and consequently acute (for they soon kill the patient), for concoction
will not take place because of the abundance of the excretion.

15   Why is it that the plague alone among diseases infects **7**
particularly persons who come into contact with those who
are under treatment for it ? Is it because it is the only
disease to which all men alike are liable, and so the plague
affects any one who is already in a low state of health ? For

---

[1] Cp. Hippocr. *de aere*, &c., § 11 (Gundermann, p. 26, 24 ff.).

[2] The triple repetition of ὥσπερ points to some corruption in the
text, and the clause ὥσπερ πνευμάτων . . . ἀλέας cannot be translated.
It is probable that ὥσπερ has displaced some such words as αἰτίαι
οὖσαι; Theodore Gaza's version (quoted hereafter as T. G.) renders
*qui flatus imbresque excitant, qui serenitates frigora teporesve solent
afferre.*

[3] For the various excretions see D'A. W. Thompson's note on
H. A. 487ª 5.

[4] Reading νοσημάτων ⟨ὄντων⟩ ἐν τῷ θέρει from T. G.

they quickly become infected by the inflammatory matter caused by the disease which is communicated by the patient. 20

8   Why is it that, when north winds have been prevalent in the winter, if the spring is rainy and characterized by south winds the summer is unhealthy with fever and ophthalmia?[1] Is it because the summer finds the body full of alien humours, and the earth, and any place in which 25 men dwell, becomes moist and resembles localities which are regarded as permanently unhealthy? The result is that, first, ophthalmia occurs when the excretion in the region of the head liquefies, and, secondly, fever ensues. For it is noticeable that anything which admits of extreme 860[a] cold also admits of extreme heat,—water, for example, and a stone, of which the former boils quicker than other things, the latter burns more.[2] As, therefore, in the air a stifling heat occurs when it grows warm owing to its density, so likewise in the body stifling and heat are engendered, and heat in the body is fever and in the eyes ophthalmia. Generally speaking the change which occurs when a warm, 5 dry summer follows immediately on a wet spring, being violent has a deleterious effect upon the body. The effect is still worse if the summer is rainy; for then the sun finds material, which it will cause to boil in the body as in the earth and air; the result is fever and ophthalmia.   10

9   Why is it that, if the winter is characterized by south winds and rainy and if the spring is dry with the wind in the north, both the spring and the summer are unhealthy?[3] Is it because in the winter owing to the heat and moisture 15 the body assimilates its condition to that of the season, since it must necessarily be moist and relaxed? When the body is in this state, the spring being cool congeals and hardens it owing to its dryness. The result is that women who are pregnant run a risk of abortion in the spring because of

---

[1] This problem is clearly derived from Hippocr. *de aere*, &c., § 10 ad fin. (Gundermann, p. 26, 14 ff.).

[2] The sense requires τὸ μὲν ζεῖ, ὁ δὲ κάει for ὁ μὲν ζεῖ, τὸ δὲ κάει. This is clearly the reading which T. G. renders, *fervet etenim illa, urit hic vehementius.*

[3] The source of this problem is Hippocr. *de aere*, &c., § 10 (Gundermann, p. 22, 25 ff.).

20 the inflammation and mortification caused by the dry cold, since the necessary moisture is not secreted, and the foetus in the womb becomes weakly and defective owing to the excess of cold ; for children who are born at this season in fine weather become strong and receive nourishment in the womb. In the case of other persons—because in the 25 spring the phlegm is not purged away owing to its excess (as happens when the weather is warm), but congeals owing to the cold—when the summer and warmth succeeds, setting up violent liquefaction, humours form in those who are bilious and dry because their bodies lack moisture and are naturally parched ; but these humours are slight and so 30 such people suffer from dry ophthalmia. Those on the other hand who are phlegmatic are afflicted with sore throats and catarrh of the lungs. Women suffer from dysentery owing to their natural moisture and cold ; while elderly persons are afflicted with apoplexy, when moisture being all set free at once overcomes them and solidifies owing to the weakness of their natural heat.

35 Why is it that, when the summer is dry and northerly 10 winds prevail and the autumn on the contrary is wet and characterized by south winds, headaches and sore throats and coughs occur in the ensuing winter and then terminate **860ᵇ** in phthisis ?[1] Is it because the winter finds a considerable amount of matter in the body and so it is a difficult task for it to solidify the moisture and form phlegm ?[2] Consequently, when moisture is engendered in the head, it causes 5 a feeling of heaviness, and if it is plenteous and cold, it causes mortification ; but if, owing to its abundance, it does not solidify, it flows into the nearest region of the body,[3] and thus coughs are caused and sore throats and wasting.

But why is it that if the summer and autumn are dry and 11 northerly winds prevail, this weather suits those who are 10 phlegmatic, and women ?[4] Is it because in both cases

[1] This problem is derived from Hippocr. *de aere*, &c., § 10 (Gundermann, p. 24, 29 ff.).
[2] For phlegm see *G. A*. 725ª 15 ff., and A. Platt's note.
[3] i. e. the throat and chest.
[4] This problem is derived from Hippocr. *de aere*, etc., § 10 (Gundermann, p. 26, 3 ff.).

nature tends to an excess in one direction, and so the season exerting its influence in the opposite direction establishes an equable temperament, and they are healthy at the time,[1] unless they themselves do anything which harms them, and, when the winter comes on, they are not in a moist condition, having heat in them with which to resist the cold?

12 Why is it that a dry summer and autumn in which 15 northerly winds prevail is unhealthy for those who are bilious?[2] Is it because their bodily condition and the season have the same tendency and it is like adding fire to fire?[3] For the body becoming dry (the freshest[4] element in it becoming evaporated) and being overheated, dry 20 ophthalmia must necessarily ensue owing to solidification;[5] but because the remaining humours are full of bile[6] and these become overheated, acute fevers must ensue caused by the bile, which is undiluted, and in some cases madness, where black bile is naturally present; for the black bile comes to the surface as the contrary humours are dried up. 25

13 Why do they say that a change of drinking-water is unhealthy, but not a change of air? Is it because water becomes nutriment, with the result that it gets into one's system and has an effect upon one, which is not the case with air? Further there are many kinds of water differing[7] intrinsically from one another, but not of air; this then 30 may also be a reason. For even when we change our place of dwelling we continue to breathe practically the same[8] air, but we drink different waters. It is, therefore,

---

[1] i.e. in the summer and autumn.

[2] This problem is derived from Hippocr. *de aere*, &c., § 10 (Gundermann, p. 26, 5 ff.).

[3] A very common phrase in Aristotle; see Bonitz, *s.v.*, and cp. below, 861[a] 21, 880[a] 21, &c.

[4] γλυκύς here means 'sweet' or 'fresh' in the sense in which water is 'fresh'.

[5] Reading συμπήξεις for συντήξεις, the point being that the effect of a dry summer and autumn is to reduce the liquid matter in the body. T. G. evidently read συμπήξεις, since he renders *dum humor consumitur*.

[6] Reading χολώδεις for χολῶδες. T. G. renders *residuo quod bilosum remanserit*.

[7] Reading διάφορα with Ap, T. G., and Bekker.

[8] Reading αὐτῷ for the misprint αὑτῷ.

probably a right opinion that change of drinking-water is
unhealthy.

Why is it that a change of drinking-water is more **14**
35 unhealthy than a change of food? Is it because we consume more water than anything else? For water is found
in farinaceous and other foods and whatever we drink
consists mainly of water.

861[a]   But why is a change of water unhealthy?[1] Is it because **15**
every change also of season and of age is liable to disturbance? For extremities, such as beginnings and ends, are
particularly liable to disturbance. So too foods, when they
5 are different, corrupt one another;[2] for some have only just
entered the system, while others have not yet done so.
Further, just as a varied diet is unhealthy (for the concoction[3] is then disturbed and not uniform), so those who
change their drinking-water are using a varied diet in what
they drink; and liquid nourishment has more effect than
dry food because it is greater in bulk and because the
moisture from the foods themselves forms nourishment.

10   Why does a change of drinking-water cause an increase **16**
of lice in those who suffer from louse-disease?[4] Is it because,
owing to the disturbance set up by the different water
in those who frequently change their drinking-water, the
unconcocted state of the liquid causes a moist condition,
especially in that part where the conditions are suitable?
15 Now the brain is moist, and therefore the head is always
the moistest part of the body (as is shown by the fact that
hair grows there more than elsewhere),[5] and it is the
moisture of this part which generates lice.[6] This is clear

[1] T. G. here renders, *Sed cur cibi et aquae mutatio gravis est?*
We should perhaps read Διὰ τί ἡ ⟨τῶν σιτίων καὶ τοῦ ὕδατος⟩ μεταβολὴ
νοσώδης ;
[2] The argument, which is somewhat condensed, appears to be as
follows : It is a mechanical truth that the extremities of anything
material (e.g. a plank of wood, cp. *Mech.* 857[a] 27, &c.) are most
liable to movement ; similarly changes of seasons and of a man's age,
and alterations in diet imply a beginning and an end and are therefore more liable to disturbance.   [3] Reading οὐ μία ⟨ἡ⟩ πέψις (Platt).
[4] For the *morbus pedicularis* see *H. A.* 556[b] 27 ff., and D'A. W.
Thompson's note, and Pliny, *N. H.* xi. 39.
[5] Cp. *H. A.* 658[b] 2.   [6] Cp. *H. A.* 557[b] 2.

in the case of children; for their heads are moist and they
frequently have either running at the nose or discharge
of blood, and persons of this age suffer particularly from
lice.[1]

17   Why is it that from the rising of the Pleiads until the 20
west wind blows those who suffer from chronic diseases are
most likely to die, and the old rather than the young? Is
it because two things are fatal to life, excess[2] and cold?
For life is heat, whereas this season has both the above
characteristics, for it is cold, and winter is then at its height,
the subsequent season being spring. Or is it because those 25
who suffer from chronic diseases are in a similar condition to the old?[3] For the occurrence of a long illness
is like premature old age, since in both the body is dry
and cold,—in the one case owing to the time of life, in
the other from disease.[4] Now winter and frosts constitute
an excess of coldness and dryness; therefore to those who 30
are in a condition where a very little will turn the scale,
winter is like ' fire added to fire ' and so causes death.

18   Why is it that in marshy districts sores on the head are
quickly cured, but those on the legs only with difficulty?[5]
Is it because the moisture, owing to the fact that it contains 35
an earthy element, is heavy, and heavy things are carried[6]
downwards? Thus the upper parts of the body are cleared
out[7] because the impurities are carried to the lower parts,
and these become full of excretions which easily putrefy.

19   Why is it that, when a very dry summer follows after **861^b**
northerly winds have prevailed in the winter and the
spring has been damp and rainy, the autumn is universally
fatal, especially to children, while in other people dysentery
and prolonged quartan fevers occur then?[8] Is it because, 5

---

[1] Cp. *H. A.* 557^b 7.   [2] Cp. above, 859^a 2, 3.
[3] Cp. *G. A.* 784^b 32.   [4] *ib.* 25–7.
[5] This problem occurs again in xiv. 6.
[6] Reading ὑποχωρεῖ . . . ὑποκεχωρηκέναι (cp. 909^a 38, 39 and Bonitz,
Arist. Stud. iv, p. 401).
[7] It is doubtful whether ἔκκριτα can mean this. The parallel passage
909^a 38 reads εὔπεπτα, 'easily concocted', which should probably be
restored here.
[8] Cp. Hippocr. *de aere*, &c., § 10 (Gundermann, p. 22, 18 ff.).

when there is a moderate amount of rain in the summer, the moisture boiling within us, which collected in the damp spring, is cooled and becomes quiescent? If on the other hand this does not happen,[1] children, because they are moist and hot, are in a state of excessive boiling, because they are not cooled; and anything which does not as it

10 were[2] boil out in the summer, does so in the autumn. If the excretions do not cause death immediately, but settle round the lungs and windpipe—for they collect first in the upper part of the body, because we are warmed by the air, for it is owing to this that ophthalmia occurs before fever in an unhealthy summer—if then, as I have said, the

15 excretions in the upper parts of the body do not immediately kill the patient, they descend[3] in an unconcocted condition into the stomach; and thus dysentery is caused, because the moisture owing to its abundance is not discharged. If the dysentery ceases, quartan fevers arise in those patients who survive; for the sediment of the unconcocted moisture remains very persistently in the body

20 and becomes active, just like black bile.

Why is it that, if the summer and the autumn have 20 been rainy and damp, the ensuing winter is unhealthy?[4] Is it because the winter finds the body in a very moist state, and also the change from great heat is violent and not

25 gradual,[5] because the autumn as well as the summer has been hot, and so acute diseases are caused in some persons, if they have no rarity in their bodies (for in such persons the moist excretions tend to collect in the upper part of the body, because these parts provide room for them, whereas the lower parts differ in this respect)? Those then whose

30 flesh is solid do not allow of much excretion. When therefore the excretion in the upper parts of the body cools (as happens in drunken persons when they grow cold), the above-mentioned diseases are engendered. On the other

---

[1] i. e. if there is no rain in the summer.   [2] Reading οἷον for ὅσον.

[3] The change from the singular ἀνέλῃ to the plural καταβαίνουσι can hardly stand and we should read καταβαίνει.

[4] This problem is derived from Hippocr. *de aere*, &c., § 10 (Gundermann, p. 24, 25 ff.).

[5] οὐκ ἐκ προσαγωγῆς is a very common Hippocratic term.

hand when fevers are set up in persons in whose bodies there
is more rarity, the fevers caused by a large quantity of
unconcocted moisture become burning fevers,[1] because in
such people the humours are distributed more through the 35
whole body than in solid-fleshed people, and, when the
flesh is contracted by the winter-cold, the humours being
heated cause fever. For excessive heat in the whole body
is fever, and, when it is intensified by the abundance of 862[a]
moisture already present there, it turns into a burning
fever.

21 Why is it that when a large amount of vapour is drawn
    out of the earth by the sun, the year is pestilential? Is it 5
    because it is necessarily a sign that the year is damp and
    rainy and the ground is necessarily damp? The conditions
    of life will then resemble those under which people live in
    a marshy district, and these are unhealthy. The body must
    then have in it an abundance of excretion and so contain
    unhealthy matter in the summer.

22 Why is it that those years are unhealthy in which small 10
    toad-like frogs are produced in abundance? Is it because
    everything flourishes in its natural environment, and these
    frogs are naturally moist and so signify that the year is
    moist and damp? Now such years are unhealthy; for then 15
    the body being moist contains abundant excretion, which is
    a cause of diseases.

23 Why is it that south winds which are dry and do not
    bring rain cause fever?[2] Is it because they cause alien
    moisture and heat[3] (for they are naturally moist and hot),
    and this is what causes fever, for it is due to the combined 20
    excess of moisture and heat? When therefore south winds
    blow without bringing rain, they engender this condition[4]
    in us, whereas, when they bring rain with them, the rain

---

[1] Καῦσος is the remittent bilious fever which is epidemic in the
Levant ; cp. Hippocr. *de aere*, &c. *l. c.*, *Vet. med.* 15, *Aphor.* 1248.

[2] This problem is partly identical with that of Bk. xxvi. 50. The
source is Theoph. *de Ventis*, § 5.

[3] i. e. in the body. The parallel passage 946[a] 5 reads ἐμποιοῦσι
τοῖς σώμασιν.

[4] i. e. heat and moisture.

cools us. Now south winds from the sea are also beneficial
to plants, for they are cooled by the sea before they reach
25 them; whereas blight is due to alien moisture and heat.

Why is it that men feel heavier and weaker when the 24
wind is in the south?[1] Is it because moisture becomes
abundant instead of scanty, being melted by the heat, and
moisture, which is heavy, takes the place of breath, which
30 is light? Further, our strength is in our joints, and they are
relaxed by south winds (as is shown by the fact that things
which have been glued together creak); for the viscous
matter in the joints, if it hardens, prevents us from moving,
whereas, if it is too moist, it prevents us from exerting
ourselves.

Why are people more liable to fall ill in the summer, 25
35 while those who are ill are more liable to die in the winter?[2]
Is it because in the winter, owing to the fact that the hot
matter from its density becomes collected within the body
and we suffer more through the excretions which solidify
in us, if we cannot concoct them,[3] the commencement of
the disease must necessarily be violent, and being of this
862ᵇ character it is likely to prove fatal? In the summer on the
other hand, because the whole body is in a state of rarity
and cool and too much relaxed for great exertion, there
must necessarily be many commencements of disease owing
to fatigue and to the fact that we do not concoct all that we
5 swallow (for summer is the season of fresh fruit); but such
diseases are not so violent, and therefore yield easily to
treatment.

Why is it that deaths are particularly likely to occur 26
during the hundred days following each solstice? Is it
because in each case the excess of heat or cold extends
10 over this period, and excess causes disease[4] and death in
the weakly?

[1] This problem occurs again in Bk. xxiv. 42 (945ᵃ 10 ff.), where it is
more briefly treated. The source is Theoph., *op. cit.*, § 56.
[2] Cp. below, chapter 28.
[3] Taking ποροῦντες as a *nominativus pendens* and reading ⟨διὰ⟩ τῶν
ἐν ἡμῖν κτλ.
[4] Cp. 859ᵃ 1.

27   Why is it that the spring and the autumn are unhealthy?
Is it because changes are unhealthy?[1]   The autumn is more
unhealthy than the spring, because we are more apt to
contract disease when heat turns to cold than when cold
turns to heat, and it is in spring that cold turns to heat and ₁₅
in autumn that heat turns to cold.

28   Why is it that illnesses are rarer in the winter than in
the summer, but more often fatal?[2]   Is it because illnesses
arise from slight causes in the summer but not in the winter?
For in winter we are in a better condition for concoction
and at the very height of our health,[3] so that naturally
illnesses which arise from more serious causes are them- ₂₀
selves more serious and more likely to prove fatal.   We
see the same thing in athletes and generally amongst
those who are in a healthy condition; for they either
are not afflicted with disease, or, if they are, they rapidly
succumb, for they only become ill from some serious
cause.

29   Why is it that in the autumn and winter burning fevers ₂₅
are more likely to occur when the weather is cold, while in
the summer chills are most troublesome when it is hot?   Is
it due to the fact that of the humours in man the bile is hot
and the phlegm cold?   As a result, in summer the cold
matter is set free, and being diffused in the body gives rise
to chill and shivering; in the winter, on the other hand, the ₃₀
hot matter is overpowered by the weather and cooled.
Burning fevers are more troublesome in the winter and
autumn, because, owing to the cold, the hot matter collects
within, and the fever is within and not on the surface; it is
natural therefore that burning fevers should occur during
this part of the year.   This can be well illustrated by con- ₃₅
trasting those who bathe in cold water and those who use
warm water in the winter; those who wash in cold water,
though they feel chilled for a short time whilst they are

---

[1] Cp. 859ᵃ 9.

[2] The problem of chapter 25 is here rather differently stated and
answered.

[3] There is no reason with the Teubner editors to doubt the correct-
ness of the reading here.

actually washing, suffer no ill effects from the cold during
863ᵃ the rest of the day, while those who use hot water continue
to be less able to resist the cold. For the flesh of those who
wash in cold water becomes solid, and the hot matter collects
within ; but the flesh of those who use warm water becomes
5 rare, and the hot matter is diverted to the outside of the
body.[1]

In what does the virtue of a poultice consist?   Would it, 30
owing to its dissolvent action, set up perspiration and
evaporation?

How can the presence of an abscess be diagnosed?   Is it 31
true that, if, when hot water is poured over it, a change
takes place, there is an abscess, but none if there is no
change?

10   In what cases ought cauterization to be employed, and in 32
what cases the surgeon's knife?[2]   Is it true that wounds
which have large openings and do not close up quickly
ought to be cauterized, so that a scab may form?   If this is
done, there will be no festering.

In what does the virtue of a remedy for stanching blood 33
consist?   Is it because it has a drying effect and stops the
discharge of excretions without [3] making a scab or causing
15 decay of the flesh?   If so, the wound must be free from
inflammation and likely to heal up.   For if there is no discharge, it will be free from inflammation, and being dry it
will close up; whereas it will not close up as long as it
is discharging moisture.   Most remedies, therefore, for
stanching blood are pungent, so as to cause contraction.

When ought drugs to be employed and not the knife or 34
20 cauterization?[4]   Ought drugs to be used for the armpits
and groin?   For sores in these parts are sometimes painful
and sometimes dangerous after they are cut open.   Flat
growths and those which project considerably and are

---

[1] Some manuscripts here add a sub-title ὅσα βοηθήματα (or βοηθημα-
τικά, or βοηθηματικὰ προβλήματα) πρὸς ἴασιν.
[2] See below, chapter 34.
[3] The Teubner text omits ἄνευ before ἐσχαρώσεως.
[4] Cp. chapter 32 above.

situated in parts which are venous and not fleshy, should be cauterized; but those which collect at an acute point and are not situated in solid parts of the body should be treated with the knife.

35　Why is it that, if one is cut with a copper instrument, 25 the wound heals more quickly than if the cut is made with iron? Is it because copper is smoother and so tears the flesh and bruises the body less? Or must we reject this explanation, since, if iron takes a better edge, the cleavage is easier and less painful? Yet even so copper has a medicinal power of its own,[1] and 'in all things it is the beginning that is important',[2] and so the copper, by its immediate action[3] as soon as the cut is made, causes the 30 wound to close up.

36　Why is it that burns inflicted by copper heal more quickly than others? Is it because copper contains more rarity and is less substantial, and the more solid a thing is the more heat it contains?

37　Is barley-gruel lighter and better for use in sickness than that made from wheat? For the latter commends itself to 35 some people who argue from the fact that amongst bakers **863^b** those who handle wheaten flour have a much better colour than those who employ barley meal,[4] and furthermore that barley is moister and that which is moister requires[5] more concoction. But is there any reason why barley should not have some qualities which make it more difficult of concoction and others which make it more serviceable because of its lightness? For barley is not only moister than wheat, 5

---

[1] Cp. 890^a 27 and *Mir. Ausc.* 834^b 30, where flower of copper is said to be prescribed for the eyes. For the preference of bronze or copper over iron in antiquity, see Dr. R. Caton in *J. H. S.* xxxiv. (1914), p. 114, who quotes the scholiast on Theocr. ii. 36.

[2] Here the proverbial μέγιστον ἀρχὴ παντός (cp. *Soph. El.* 183^b 22, *E. N.* 1098^b 7, &c.) is used to emphasize the importance of the immediate application of the remedy, which is here supplied by the copper of the surgical instrument.

[3] Reading as suggested by Bekker τῷ οὖν εὐθύς.

[4] Cp. Bk. xxi. 24, and xxxviii. 10.

[5] Ruelle's πλέονος ⟨οὔσης⟩ does not give the required sense. T. G. renders *concoctionem desiderat pleniorem*, and Sylburg's πλέονος ⟨δεῖται⟩ or something similar must be read.

but it is also colder, and porridge and any other food which
is served to one who is in a fever ought to be such that it
will provide him with a little nourishment and also cool
him.   Now barley-gruel has these qualities; for, because it
is moist rather than substantial, it gives nourishment which
10 is small in bulk and at the same time has a cooling effect.

Why do purslane and salt stop inflammation of the 38
gums?[1] Is it because purslane contains some moisture?
This is seen if one chews it or if it is crushed together[2] for
some time; for the moisture is then drawn out of it.   This
glutinous matter sinks into the gum and drives out the
acidity.   For that there is an affinity between the disease
15 and the remedy is shown by the acidity; for the juice of
purslane has a certain acidity.   Salt on the other hand
dissolves and draws out the acidity.   Why then do lye and
soda not have this effect?   Is it because they have an
astringent instead of a dissolvent action?

Why is it that fatigue must be cured in summer by baths, 39
20 in winter by anointing?[3]   Is anointing employed in the
latter case because of the cold and the changes which it
causes in the body?   For the fatigue must be got rid of by
heat which will warm the body, and olive-oil contains heat.
In summer, on the other hand, the body requires moisture,
because the season is then dry and chills are not to be
feared, because the natural inclination is towards heat.
A sparing diet of solid food and a liberal indulgence in
25 liquid nourishment are appropriate to the summer, the
latter being peculiar to summer, while the former is commoner then than at other seasons; for indulgence in drinking
is peculiar to the summer because of the dryness of the
season, but a sparing diet is found at all seasons but is more

---

[1] This problem is repeated in Bk. vi. 9 (887ᵇ 1 ff.). αἱμωδία is
generally applied to a scorbutic affection of the gums, swelling of the
gums being one of the symptoms of scurvy; this can hardly be the
meaning here, since salt would be the last thing to prescribe for
scurvy.

[2] The parallel passage (887ᵇ 3) reads συντεθῇ for συνθλασθῇ. The
latter gives better sense and should be read in both passages.

[3] The same problem is treated in almost identical words in Bk. v.
38; cp. Theophr. *de Lassit.*, § 17.

general in the summer ; for then, owing to the weather, heat is engendered by food.

40   Why do some drugs relax the stomach and not the bladder, others the bladder and not the stomach ? Is it 30 true that anything which is naturally moist and full of water, if it has medicinal properties, relaxes the bladder ? For it is there that the unconcocted moisture settles ; for the bladder is a receptacle for any moisture which is not concocted in the stomach ; and such moisture does not remain there, but passes away without undergoing or causing any change. But anything which partakes of the 35 nature of earth, if it has medicinal properties, relaxes the 864ᵃ stomach ; for it is to the stomach that anything of an earthy nature is carried, so that, if it has any motive power, it causes a disturbance in the stomach.

41   Why is it that some things affect the upper part of the stomach, hellebore for example, others the lower part, for instance scammony,[1] while others like elaterium [2] and the 5 juice of thapsia [3] affect both parts ? Is it because some of the drugs which affect the stomach are hot and others cold, so that some of them, owing to their heat, as soon as they reach the upper part of the stomach are carried thence to the upper region of the body,[4] melting in particular [5] anything there [6] which is most alien to them and least substantial ; and if the drug be powerful or has been administered 10 in a dose stronger than nature can withstand, it carries these liquefactions [7] and any excretions that there may be down into the upper part of the stomach, and by its heat stirring up the breath, which it engenders in great quantity, checks

[1] A species of convolvulus found in Asia yielding a resinous gum.

[2] A drug deriving its name from its medicinal qualities (Hippocr. *Acut.* 383) ; according to Pliny (*N. H.* xx. 1. 3) it was prepared from the wild cucumber. Cp. also Celsus, 5, 12 ; 6, 5.

[3] The *Thapsia Asclepium* of Linnaeus ; in large doses it was a violent poison and was so used by Nero (Pliny, *N. H.* xiii. 22. 43) ; cp. also Theoph. *H. P.* ix. 9. 1.

[4] Cp. *H. A.* 494ᵃ 27.

[5] If the text is sound, μάλιστα μέν is here used without any corresponding δέ.

[6] Reading τἀκεῖθεν (W. D. R.) for κἀκεῖθεν.

[7] ταῦτα, i. e. τὰ ἀλλοτριώτατα καὶ ἥκιστα συμπεφυκότα.

their progress and causes vomiting? Drugs of a cold nature,
15 on the other hand, owing to their weight are carried downwards before undergoing or causing any change and, borne
thence, have the same action as those which affect the upper
part of the body; for passing thence [1] upwards through the
ducts and setting in motion any excretions or liquefactions
over which they prevail, they carry them with them in the
same direction.[2] Drugs which partake of both these kinds
20 and are a mixture of hot and cold, possessing both qualities,
have both these effects, and are the composite drugs which
doctors now make up.

Why is it that drugs have a purgative effect, while other **42**
things, though they surpass them in bitterness and astringency and other such qualities, do not have this effect? Is it
25 because the purgative effect is not due to these qualities but
to the fact that they are unconcocted? For anything which,
though small in bulk, owing to its excessive heat or cold is
unconcocted and of such a nature as to overcome, and not
be overcome by, animal heat, if it is easily dissolved in
30 the two stomachs, is a drug. For when such drugs enter
the stomach and become dissolved, they are carried into the
vein by the ducts through which the food passes, and, not
being concocted but themselves prevailing, they make their
way out, carrying with them anything which gets in their
way; and this is called purging. Copper and silver and
35 the like, although they are not concocted by animal heat,
are not easily dissolved in the stomach.[3] Oil and honey
864[b] and milk and other such foods have a purgative effect; but
this depends, not on any quality which they possess, but on
quantity; for, if they act as a purge, they only do so when
they are unconcocted owing to their quantity. For things
can be unconcocted for two reasons, either because of their
quality or because of their quantity. So none of the above-
5 mentioned foods are drugs, because they do not purge owing
to their quality. Astringency and bitterness and unpleasant
odour are characteristic of drugs, because a drug is the

---

[1] i. e. from the lower part of the stomach.
[2] i. e. cause vomiting, like the drugs which are of a hot nature.
[3] And therefore do not act as drugs.

opposite of a food ; for that which is concocted by a natural process amalgamates with the body and is called a food ; but that whose nature it is to refuse to be overcome[1] and which enters into the veins and causes disturbance there owing to its excess of heat or cold, this is of the nature of a drug.

43 Why is it that pepper if taken in large quantities relaxes the bladder, but if taken in small quantities affects the stomach, whereas scammony[2] if taken in large quantities relaxes the stomach, but if taken in small quantities and when it is old affects the bladder ? Is it because each has more effect on one part of the body ? For pepper promotes urine, while scammony is purgative. Pepper therefore if taken in large quantities is carried into the bladder and does not dissolve in the stomach, but if taken in small quantities it is overcome and relaxes the stomach and acts upon it as a drug. Scammony, on the other hand, if it is taken in large quantities, is overcome to such an extent that it is dissolved, and being dissolved it becomes a drug for the reason mentioned above;[3] but, if it is taken in small quantities, it is swallowed with what is drunk and passes into the ducts and is quickly carried into the bladder before it can cause any disturbance, and there by its own force it carries off all the excretions and liquefactions which are on the surface. When it is taken in large quantities, as has already been remarked, owing to its strength it remains a long time in the stomach and effects an extensive purgation of the earthy element.[4]

44 Why do some cure by cooling the same inflammations which others bring to a head by heating them ? Surely it is because the latter collect the inflammation by applying external heat, the former by cooling the heat already present in the body.

45 Why is it necessary to change poultices ? Is it in order that[5] they may be more felt ? For as, in things which we

---

[1] i. e. which is not subject to the process of concoction.
[2] See note on 864ᵃ 4.   [3] Cp. *ib.* 29, 30.
[4] Cp. 863ᵇ 35-864ᵃ 2.   [5] Reading ὅπως, with Richards, for ὅτι ὡς.

eat, that to which we have grown accustomed no longer
35 acts as a drug but becomes a food, so poultices lose their
effect.

Why does it promote health to reduce one's diet and 46
865[a] increase one's exercise? Is it because an excess of excretion
causes disease, and this occurs when we take too much
nourishment or too little exercise?

Why is it that drugs, and bitter and evil-smelling sub- 47
stances generally, have a purgative effect?[1] Is it because
5 anything which is evil-smelling and bitter does not admit of
concoction? Drugs therefore are bitter and evil-smelling;
for they are drugs because, in addition to being bitter, they
do not admit of concoction and can cause motion; and
if they are administered in too large doses, they are destructive of life. But substances which are destructive of life
even if given in small quantities are not drugs but deadly
poisons. Nor again do we give the name of drugs to those
10 substances which are not purgative through their natural
qualities; for indeed many foods have the effect of drugs,
if taken in sufficient quantity—milk, for example, and
olive oil [2] and unfermented wine; all these things, because
they are not easily concocted, have a purgative effect on
those by whom they are not easily concocted.[3] For
different things are easy or difficult of concoction to
different people; and so the same things do not act upon
15 every one as drugs, but particular things act upon certain
people. For, generally speaking, a drug ought not only to
be difficult of concoction, but also ought to have the power
to produce movement; just as also exercises, whether
external or internal, expel alien matter.

Why is it that sweet-smelling seeds or plants promote 48
the flow of urine?[4] Is it because they contain heat and are

---

[1] This chapter is largely a repetition of chapter 42 in a slightly
different form.

[2] Cp. above, 864[a] 36.

[3] καθαίρει καὶ τούτοις and καθαίρει καὶ τούτους are obviously variants
both of which have come into the text. The next sentence shows that
we should read διὰ τὸ μὴ εἶναι εὔπεπτα, οἷς μὴ εὔπεπτα καθαίρει καὶ τούτους.

[4] This problem with several additional lines is repeated in xii. 12
and xx. 16; the shorter version here given does not complete the

easily concocted, and such things have this effect ? For the heat in them causes quick digestion,[1] and their odour has no corporeal existence; for even strong-smelling [2] plants, such as garlic, promote the flow of urine owing to their heat, though their wasting effect is a still more marked characteristic; but sweet-smelling seeds contain heat.

49 Why is it that unclean and foul sores require to be treated with dry, pungent, and astringent drugs, while clean, healthy sores require moist, porous [3] remedies ? Is it because something must be drawn out from unclean sores, and it is foreign moisture which must be extracted ? Now biting, pungent, and astringent substances have this effect, and the dry rather than the moist. Clean sores, on the other hand, only require to skin over.

50 Why is it that sexual excess is beneficial to diseases caused by phlegm ?[4] Is it because the semen is the secretion of an excrement and in its nature resembles phlegm, and so sexual intercourse is beneficial because it draws off a quantity of phlegm-like matter ?

Is it better to give the patient nourishment at first or later ?[5] Ought nourishment to be given at the beginning, so that the inflammation, when it sets in, may not find the patient already weak ? Or ought the patient to be reduced at once ? Or ought the following to be the treatment, namely, that the patient should first take nourishment in the form of draughts, since food of this kind is milder and **865^b** more readily swallowed and dissolved, and it is easier for a sick person to receive nourishment from this sort of food ? For where [6] the food has first to be acted upon in

---

sense, and the additional matter (907^b 9-12, 924^b 23-6) should probably be restored here.

[1] λεπτύνει is here apparently used in its technical medical sense of 'digest', cp. Hippocr. *Vet. Med.* 16.

[2] The parallel passages 907^b 7 and 924^b 21 read here τὰ μὴ εὐώδη for τὰ ὀσμώδη.

[3] Reading μανοῖς (Monro) for μόνοις.

[4] Cp. iv. 16. τὰ should be read for the misprint τὸ of the Teubner text.

[5] Apparently a new problem begins with this question.

[6] Reading οὗ (Bussemaker) for εὖ.

the stomach,—namely, both dissolved and heated—these
5 processes cause pain to the body.

Why is it that, in order to examine urine to see if it is **51**
concocted, one must stop the flow of urine rather than
continue to pass it? Is it because it is a sign of concoction
if it is reddish in colour, and this is better detected if
the flow is stopped? Or is it because anything that is
10 liquid forms as it were a better mirror of its colour in
a small than in a large quantity? For form is better
discerned in a large quantity, but colour in a small quantity,
in dew, for example, and drops of rain and tears on the
eyelids. If urine, therefore, is allowed to flow it becomes
15 greater in quantity, but, if it is checked, it takes on colour[1]
more readily; and so if it has already taken on this character[2]
by concoction, this can be better observed if the flow of
urine is stopped and light thus refracted and a mirror
formed.

Why should the flesh be made rare rather than dense in **52**
order to promote health?[3] For just as a city or locality is
healthy which is open to the breezes (and this is why the
20 sea too is healthy), so a body is healthier in which the air can
circulate. For either there ought to be no excrement present
in the body or else the body ought to get rid of it as soon
as possible and ought always to be in such a condition that
it can reject the excrement as soon as it receives it, and be
in a state of motion and never at rest. For that which
25 remains stationary putrefies (standing water, for example),
and that which putrefies causes disease; but that which is
rejected passes away before it becomes corrupt. This then
does not occur if the flesh is dense, the ducts being as it
were blocked up, but it does happen if the flesh is rare.
One ought not therefore to walk naked in the sun; for the
flesh thereby solidifies and acquires an absolutely fleshy
30 consistency, and the body becomes moister; for the internal
moisture remains, but the surface moisture is expelled,

---

[1] *sc.* τὰ χρώματα as the object of δέχεται.

[2] Reading with Bekker αὐτὸ τοιοῦτον.

[3] This problem is repeated in v. 34 and is identical with the second
part of xxxvii. 3. ὅτι must be emended to διὰ τί. Cp. 884ᵃ 26.

a process which also takes place in meat when it is roasted rather than boiled. Nor ought one to walk about with the chest bare; for then the sun draws the moisture out of the best constructed parts of the body, which least of all require to be deprived of it. It is rather the inner parts of the body which should be submitted to this process; because 35 they are remote, it is impossible to produce perspiration from them except by violent effort, but it is easy to produce it from the chest because it is near the surface.

53   Why is it that both cold and hot water are beneficial to chilblains? Is it because chilblains are caused by an excess 866^{a} of moisture? If so, the cold water thickens and hardens the moisture, while the hot water causes it to evaporate and enables the vapour to escape by rarefying the flesh.

54   Why is it that cold both causes and stops chilblains, and 5 heat both causes and stops burns? Is the cause the same in both cases, namely, that they cause them by setting up liquefaction and stop them by drying them up?

55   In fevers liquid nourishment ought to be administered often and in small quantities.[1] For a large quantity flows away and is wasted, but a small quantity taken frequently 10 sinks in and penetrates into the flesh. For as the rain, if it comes down upon the earth in torrents, runs to waste, but, if it comes down in small quantities, merely moistens the ground;[2] so the same thing occurs in fever patients. In irrigation, if the water is allowed to flow gradually, the channel sucks it up; whereas, if the same amount of water is allowed to flow all at once, it makes its way wherever it 15 is directed.

Next the patient ought to lie as still as possible, because fire also obviously dies down if one does not stir it. And he ought not to lie in a draught, because the wind stirs up the fire, and, being fanned, it becomes great instead of small. For this reason the patient ought to be well

---

[1] This and the following chapter are not, strictly speaking, problems, but descriptions of treatment. They were apparently extracted from some medical treatise with a view to being put into the form of problems, and this purpose was for some reason never carried out.

[2] Placing a comma after μόνον.

wrapped up,¹ because fire is extinguished if it is not
20 allowed to draw in air; and the garments ought not to be
removed until damp heat is present, for the fire if exposed
to the air dries up the moisture—just as happens also in
nature.²

In the case of intermittent fevers one must make prepara-
tions beforehand by washing³ the patient and applying
25 fomentations to his feet, and he must rest well wrapped up,
in order that there may be as much heat as possible in him
before the attack begins. For a flame will not be able to
burn where there is a great fire; for the great fire will
absorb the little fire. Consequently a great fire must be
prepared beforehand in the body; for fever has but little
30 fire in it, and so the great fire will absorb the little fire.

In quartan fevers⁴ the patient must not be allowed to get 56
thin, and heat must be introduced and engendered in his
body. Exercises must also be employed. On the day on
which the attack is expected he must bathe himself and
avoid sleep. A heating diet is beneficial, because a quartan
35 fever is weak; for if it were not so, it would not occur only
every fourth day. For, mark you, where there is a great
fire, a flame cannot burn; for the great fire attracts and
866ᵇ absorbs the little fire. For this reason it is necessary to
engender great heat in the body, because fever has but
little fire in it. The daily treatment consists in introducing⁵
at one time heat and at another time moisture into the
body. Some diseases are caused by heat, others by moisture; those which are caused by heat are cured by moisture,
5 and those which are due to moisture are cured by heat, for
heat dries up moisture.

¹ Reading with Bonitz περιστελλέσθω for περιστέλλεσθαι, cp. κατα-
κείσθω l. 15, ἀπογυμνούσθω l. 21.
² i. e. it is always the nature of fire to dry up moisture.
³ Reading ἐκλούοντα with the majority of MSS., cp. below, l. 33.
There should be no comma after ἐκλούοντα.
⁴ This chapter is clearly another version of the last part of the
previous chapter (ll. 23-30 above).
⁵ It appears necessary to read εἰσάγειν for εἰσάγοντα.

BOOK II

PROBLEMS CONNECTED WITH PERSPIRATION

1 WHY is it that perspiration is caused neither when the breath is expanded nor when it is held in, but rather when it is relaxed?[1] Is it because, when it is held in, the breath fills out the veins and so does not allow the perspiration to escape, just as the water in a water clock cannot escape if you turn it off when the clock is full?[2] But when the perspiration does come out, it does so in great abundance, because it has gradually collected during the actual period[3] that it has been checked.

2 Why is it that the parts of the body that are immersed in hot water do not perspire, even though they are themselves hot?[4] Is it because the water prevents liquefaction, while perspiration is formed when matter which is not properly attached to the flesh[5] is expelled by heat?

3 Why is perspiration salty?[6] Is it because it is caused by movement and heat which rejects any foreign matter in the process by which nourishment passes into blood and flesh? For such matter quickly separates, because it has no affinity with the body, and evaporates externally. It is salty because the sweetest and lightest part of the food is taken up by the body, while the unsuitable and unconcocted part is discharged. This when it is excreted below is called urine, in the flesh it is sweat; both of these are salty for the same reason.

[1] This problem is derived from Theoph. *de Sud.* 25, 26.
[2] This comparison with the water clock was originally made by Empedocles; cp. *de Respir.* 473ᵇ 1–474ᵃ 5.
[3] Reading αὐτῇ ⟨τῇ⟩ ἐπιληψίᾳ (Bussemaker).
[4] Cp. Theoph., *op. cit.* 30. This problem is cited by Athenaeus (i. 44) as from the *Physical Problems* of Aristotle.
[5] Omitting with Cᵃ Yᵃ ὃ κωλύει τήκεσθαι; this omission is supported by Theoph., *l. c.*, ὁ δὲ ἱδρὼς τῆξίς τίς ἐστι τῶν οἷον κακῶς προσῳκοδομημένων ταῖς σαρξὶν ὅταν ἐκκρίνηται διὰ τὸ θερμόν.
[6] From Theoph., *op. cit.* 2, 3.

Why is it that the upper parts of the body perspire **4**
more freely than the lower?[1] Is it because heat rises
upwards and remains there, and this carries the moisture
30 upwards? Or is it because breath causes sweat, and the
breath is in the upper parts of the body? Or is it because
sweat is unconcocted moisture. and such moisture resides in
the upper parts because the process of its composition takes
place there?

Why is it that sweat is produced most copiously if we **5**
exercise the arms while we keep the other parts of the
body in the same position?[2] Is it because we have most
35 strength in this region of the body? For it is in this
region, which is nearest to the strongest part of us, that we
hold our breath ; and we gain strength by violent exertion,
and, having gained strength, we can hold the breath more
867[a] easily. Furthermore, we feel the effect of friction more
in the arm [3] than when any other part of the body is
rubbed; for it is by holding the breath that we get exercise, both when we are rubbed and when we rub.

Why is it that sweat given off from the head either has **6**
no odour or less than that from the body?[4] Is it because
5 air circulates freely in the region of the head ? That the head
possesses rarity is shown by the fact that it produces hair.
And it is those regions of the body and the substances of
which they are composed through which the air does not
circulate that are malodorous.[5]

Why is it that those who take athletic exercise, if they **7**
wrestle after a period of rest, perspire more freely than if
10 they wrestle continuously?[6] Is it because the sweat collects
while they are resting, and then the wrestling afterwards
brings out this sweat? Continuous exercise. on the other
hand, dries up the sweat, just as does the heat of the sun.

---

[1] From Theoph., *op. cit.* 24, somewhat amplified.
[2] This chapter is Theoph., *op. cit.* 34, cast in problem form.
[3] *sc.* χειρί, which is inserted by Theoph., *l. c.*
[4] This chapter is an almost verbal transcription of Theoph., *op cit.*
9, in problem form.
[5] Cp. 908[b] 20 ff.
[6] This problem is derived from Theoph., *op. cit.* 31.

8   Why is it that one sweats more freely if one has not for
a long time employed means to induce perspiration ?[1]   Is it
because sweat is not caused by moisture alone, but is also
due to the fact that the pores are opened wider and the
body becomes porous ?   In those, therefore, who take no 15
measures to induce perspiration the pores become closed
up, whereas if they do take such measures the pores are
kept open.

9   Why is it that, although the sun warms those who are
naked more than those who are clothed, the latter perspire
more freely ?[2]   Is it because the sun by burning causes the 20
pores to close up ?   Or is it because it dries up the
moisture ?   These processes are less likely to happen in
those who are clothed.

10   Why is it that the face gives off the most perspiration ?[3]
Is it because the sweat can find a way out through[4] parts
which are particularly porous and moist ?   Now the head 25
seems to be the source of moisture, and it is owing to the
presence of copious moisture that the hair grows ; and the
region of the head is rare and porous, and so the sweat
naturally finds a way out.

11   Why is it that one perspires most freely, not when the
heat is applied all at once or when it is gradually diminished,
but when it is gradually increased ?[5]   For those who are in
vapour baths perspire under these conditions more freely
than if all the heat be applied at once.   Is it because it is 30
the presence of anything in proper proportions which
produces each required effect, and so, if it produces this
effect, its presence in greater quantity will not produce
a greater effect, or will rather produce the contrary effect,
for it is because a thing is proportionate[6] that it produces
a certain effect ?   For this reason then increased perspiration

---

[1] The source of this problem is Theoph., *op. cit.* 22.
[2] Cp. Hippocr. *de aere*, &c. 8 (Gundermann, pp. 15, 30 ff.).
[3] From Theoph., *op. cit.* 33 ; cp. below, chapter 17.
[4] Omitting δέ after διά (W.D.R).
[5] Compare below, chapter 32 ; the source of both these problems is
Theoph., *op. cit.* 28, somewhat amplified.
[6] Omitting τὸ after τῷ with most MSS.

is not induced as the result of greater heat; but because to each increment of heat there answers a different proportion, 35 and that which has already produced its effect produces no greater effect, increased perspiration is rather the result of successive additions of heat. For it is not the same cause which prepares the way and creates a favourable condition for a series of effects and then begins to produce the effect, but a different cause. So a small quantity of heat prepares the way and predisposes the body to perspire **867ᵇ** better than a large quantity; but another and a greater proportion is required actually to produce the perspiration, but this does not continue to produce the effect which it originally produced, but must be followed by another application of heat different again in its proportions.[1]

Why does the sweat flow more freely if a scraper be **12** used than if it be allowed to remain on the body? Is it 5 because the presence of external sweat induces cooling? Or is it because the external sweat forms as it were a lid over the pores and so prevents the movement of the internal sweat?

Why is it that rue and certain unguents give the per- **13** spiration an evil odour?[2] Is it because things which 10 have a heavy scent, mixing with the excretory fluids, make the odour of these still more unpleasant?

Why do we perspire more on the back than on the front **14** of the body?[3] Is it because in the front of the body there is an interior region into which the moisture is drained, but this is not the case with the back, but there the excretion of 15 moisture must be external? (It is for the same reason that we perspire less on the stomach than on the chest.) A further reason is the fact that the back and hinder parts hold the perspiration more than the front, because the latter become more cooled than the former. (This is the reason too why 20 the armpits perspire most readily and freely; for they are least subject to cooling.) Further, the regions about the back are fleshier than those in front and therefore moister;

---

[1] Reading τῇ συμμετρίᾳ for τῆς συμμετρίας.
[2] Cp. Theoph., *op. cit.*, § 10. This problem occurs again in xx. 33.
[3] Cp. Theoph., *op. cit.*, § 32.

and there is more moisture in the hinder parts, because the marrow in the spine causes considerable humidity.

15 Why is it that we do not perspire in those parts of the 25 body on which we are lying? Is it because the area with which we come into contact with anything is hot and therefore prevents the perspiration from passing forth, for it dries it up? Furthermore it is compressed, and pressure causes the blood to disperse, and, when this happens, the part tends to become cool. This can be illustrated from numbness, which is a condition due to cooling and is caused 30 by pressure or by a blow.

16 Why do those who are asleep perspire more freely?[1] Is it due to the heat being driven inwards?[2] For the heat collects[3] inside and expels the moisture.

17 Why is it that one perspires most freely on the face, though it is far from being fleshy?[4] Is it because parts 35 which are rather moist and rare perspire freely, and the head has these characteristics? For it possesses an abundance of natural moisture; this is shown by the veins which extend from it and the discharges which it produces and the brain-fluid and the numerous pores. That there are numerous pores extending outwards is shown by the presence of the hair. The perspiration then comes not from **868**^a the lower parts of the body but from the head; and so one perspires most readily and freely on the forehead, for it is the first thing below the top of the head, and moisture flows down and not up.

18 Why is it that those who are perspiring are apt to vomit 5 if they are cooled either by water or by air?[5] Is it because

---

[1] This problem is more fully dealt with in chapter 28; the source in both cases is Theoph., *op. cit.* 40.

[2] The doctrine of ἀντιπερίστασις of heat and cold is very common in the *Problems*; cp. 875ᵃ 11, 888ᵃ 35, 906ᵃ 15, &c. It is a favourite doctrine of Theophrastus; cp. *caus. pl.* i. 12, 3; ii. 9, 8; vi. 7, 8; *de Igne*, 74, &c. For ἀντιπερίστασις in sleep cp. *de Somno* 457ᵇ 2 and Professor Beare's note.

[3] i. e. collects internally because it is driven inward by the external cooling which takes place in sleep.

[4] This problem is repeated verbally in xxvi. 2; cp. also above, chapter 10 and note.

[5] The source of this problem is Theoph., *op. cit.*, § 38.

the moisture when cooled ceases to move and collects together, whereas before it was not at rest because it was in a state of flux? Or is it because the breath which turns into perspiration by being cooled as it passes out, being cooled internally before passing out turns into moisture and attacking the body [1] causes vomiting?

10 Why is it that sweat is given off from the head and feet **19** of those who are heated more freely than from any other part of the body? Is it because the part which is heated attracts the moisture to itself, and the moisture has nowhere where it can expend itself in these regions of the body, because they are bony, and therefore it finds its way out?

15 Why do those who exert themselves perspire when they **20** cease to exert themselves? [2] For since the exertion is the cause, they ought to perspire while they are exerting themselves. Is it because during their exertion the veins, being inflated with breath, cause the pores to close up, whereas, when they stop, the veins contract, and so the pores become 20 wider and the moisture finds an easier outlet? Or is it because during the exertion the motion expels air from the solidified moisture and, owing to the heat caused by the motion, the moisture becomes breath on the surface of the body; while on the other hand, when the exertion ceases, the heat also stops at the same time, and then the moisture, which we call perspiration, is generated from the condensa- 25 tion of the breath?

Is it more necessary to induce perspiration in the summer **21** or in the winter? [3] Is it not more necessary to do so at a time when, unless care be taken, the body would become too moist and in a dangerous condition? If so, it would be more necessary to perspire in the summer,[4] when a violent

---

[1] We should perhaps read from Theoph., *l. c.*, προσπεσὸν ⟨τῷ ἀναπνευ-στικῷ τόπῳ⟩ ποιεῖ.

[2] Reading with Bekker ὅταν παύσωνται. The same subject is treated in chapter 23; the source of both chapters is Theoph., *op. cit.*, §§ 25, 26.

[3] The same subject is treated in chapter 33; see next note.

[4] Chapter 33 shows that perspiration is less necessary in the winter, because concoction then goes on naturally in the body, and this is also stated in l.31 of the present problem. It therefore appears necessary to read θέρους here for χειμῶνος.

change takes place in the body and the excretions are not thoroughly concocted. Again in the winter, since the body 30 is cool, it is also unnatural to perspire. It is clearly, therefore, more necessary to induce perspiration in the summer; for moisture of all kinds is then more apt to putrefy and should therefore be drawn off. This was the opinion of all the ancients and for the above reason.

22   Why is it that, although the body is in a state of continual 35 flux, and effluvia are given off from the excrements, the body is only lightened if it perspires?[1] Is it because the excretion in the form of effluvia is too little? For when liquid is transformed into air, much air is formed out of little liquid; for what is excreted in liquid form is more abundant. **868ᵇ** The process of excretion, therefore, takes longer to begin, both for the above reason[2] and because the excretion takes place through smaller pores. Further, the viscous and adhesive matter is expelled with the moisture, because it mingles with it, but it cannot be expelled with the breath; 5 and it is this thick matter in particular that causes pain. Therefore also vomiting lightens the body more than sweating, because that which is vomited, being thicker and more substantial, carries away this viscous matter with it. Or is there a further reason, namely, that[3] the region in which the viscous and the adhesive matter is, is situated at a distance in relation to the flesh (and so it is difficult to make it change its position), but near the stomach? For it is engendered either in or close to it; and therefore it is difficult to get rid 10 of it in any other way.[4]

23   Why is it that one perspires less during actual exertion than when one ceases?[5] Is it because while one is exerting oneself one is engendering perspiration, but the process of engendering it is only complete when the exertion is ended? This then is naturally the time when it is expelled from the body in greater quantities; for during exertion it is coming into being, but, when the exertion is finished, it actually

---

[1] This problem is almost verbally repeated in xxxvii. 1 and 2.
[2] i. e. because the moisture is more abundant.
[3] Reading ἤ καὶ ὅτι, cp. 965ᵇ 31.
[4] i. e. except through the bowels.   [5] Cp. above, chapter 20.

15 exists. Or is it because during exertion the pores of the flesh are closed, because the breath is held, but when the pressure of the breath is relaxed the pores open again? Consequently one perspires less when one is holding the breath.

Why is it that perspiration is more copious not when one 24 is running and the body is in motion, but when one stops?[1]
20 Is it because the same thing happens as when flowing water is checked by the hand or by some other means and collects from every direction, and, when it is released, flows in greater volume than before; so perspiration can be stopped by the breath—like water in a water clock—and also in the bladder, which keeps the moisture within. So too, while
25 there is considerable movement, the breath is cut off inside the body, and so the veins are distended, the moisture being unable to find its way out. The moisture then, being cut off, collects, and when the breath is relaxed comes all out at once.

Why is it that, when one is drinking, one perspires less 25 if one eats something as well? Is it because the food sucks
30 up the moisture, as though a sponge were applied, and, just as a stream can be stopped by blocking up its channels, so by stopping[2] the pores through administering food it is possible to a large extent to prevent the flowing of moisture?

Why is that the feet of those who are nervous perspire 26
35 and not the face?[3] For it would be more natural that the feet should perspire only when the whole body perspires; for the feet are the coldest region of the body and therefore least liable to perspire. Also in sickness physicians order the feet in particular to be wrapped up, because they are especially susceptible to cold and so readily give rise to
869[a] cold in the rest of the body also. Is it because nervousness does not cause a displacement of heat—such as takes place from the upper to the lower parts of the body under the

---

[1] This problem is derived from Theoph., *op. cit.*, § 29.
[2] Putting a comma after ῥεύμασι and reading τῷ ἐπιλαβεῖν.
[3] The source of this problem and chapter 31 is Theoph., *op. cit.*, § 36.

influence of fear [1] (hence the relaxation of the bowels in those who are alarmed) —but an increase of heat [2] such as is caused by anger? For anger causes the heat round the 5 heart to boil up; and one who is nervous is affected not by fear or cold, but by an increase of heat.[3]

27 How is it that one can become red in the face without perspiring? [4] Is it due to excessive warmth which results in the heat on the surface drying up the moisture in the face, whilst it liquefies the moisture in the feet because, 10 though less than the heat on the surface, it is more powerful than the natural heat already existent in the feet?

28 Why is it that we perspire more when asleep than when awake? [5] Is it because perspiration originates internally, and the interior parts of the body are hotter, and so the internal heat melts and expels the internal moisture? Or [6] 15 is it because in all probability there is always something given off from the body, but it is not apparent because there is nothing with which it can come into contact and by which its escape can be arrested? That this is so is shown by the fact that the hollow parts of the body perspire continually.

29 Why is it that persons in vapour baths perspire more freely when it is cold? [7] Is it because the heat does not 20 find a way out, because it is surrounded by the cold, which prevents its exit, but collects internally, and, remaining there, dissolves the moisture in our body and engenders per-spiration from it?

[1] The distinction between φόβος and ἀγωνία is not always kept up in the *Problems*. They are distinguished here, but in ᵇ7, 8 and 903ᵇ 12 ἀγωνία is φόβος τις. In 903ᵃ 2 and 905ᵃ 8 ἀγωνία is said to be the result of αἰσχύνη.

[2] ἀγωνία is here described as being due to increase of heat; in 903ᵃ 1 it is ascribed to heat rising upwards, while in 903ᵇ 11 it is said to cause coldness.

[3] Reading from Theoph., *l. c.*, διὰ τὸ μᾶλλον ἐκθερμαίνεσθαι for διὰ τὸ μέλλον.

[4] The source of this problem is Theoph., *op. cit.*, § 37.

[5] Cp. above, chapter 16 and note.

[6] Reading with Bonitz, *op. cit.*, p. 408, ⟨ἡ⟩ ὅτι.

[7] Cp. above, chapter 11.

Why is it that perspiration, even though it be less **30**
²⁵ profuse, is more beneficial if it be induced by running naked
rather than clothed?[1] Is it because exertion in general is
better than non-exertion, and perspiration which is induced
by exertion is better than that which is produced without
exertion, and that which is due in a greater degree to
exertion is better than that which is due in a less degree?
Now perspiration involves more exertion if induced by
³⁰ running about naked: for a naked man cannot perspire at
all unless he runs with considerable energy; whereas, if he
be clothed, owing to the heat produced by his garments,
he soon perspires although he runs only moderately fast.
Those too who run naked in the summer have a healthier
colour than those who wear garments; for just as those
³⁵ who live in regions open to the air have a better colour than
those who live in a stifling atmosphere,[2] so too a man, when
he is as it were in a well-aired condition, acquires a better
colour than when he is stifled and surrounded by considerable heat, as he is more likely to be when he runs clothed.
869ᵇ For this reason too those who sleep much have a less healthy
colour than those who sleep a moderate amount; for a man
who is asleep is in a stifled condition.

Why is it that our feet perspire, but not our faces, when **31**
₅ we are in a state of nervousness, whereas under ordinary
conditions our faces perspire most and our feet least?[3] Is
it because nervousness is a kind of fear connected with the
beginning of an action, and fear causes a cooling in the
upper part of the body; this is also why those who are
nervous are pale-faced.[4] On the other hand they move and
₁₀ dance their feet about, thus resembling those who are taking
exercise; therefore they naturally perspire in those parts
which they are exercising. Also they rub their hands together
and bend and stretch themselves and keep jumping up and
can never remain still; for they are eager for action, because
the heat within them is collected in the region of the chest,
₁₅ which is one of the more substantial parts of the body, and

---

[1] Cp. Theoph., *op. cit.*, §§ 39, 40.   [2] Cp. 865ᵃ 19-21.
[3] Cp. above, chapter 26.   [4] Contrast 903ᵃ 3.

this heat and the blood rushing thence through their whole body results in frequent and varied movement. But they perspire most in the feet, because these are being continually exerted, whereas the other parts of the body obtain rest in the changes of position and movement.

32   Why is it that in a vapour bath one perspires most freely [20] not when the heat is applied all at once nor when it is gradually diminished, but when it is gradually increased ?[1] For if the heat is gradually introduced into the vapour bath,[2] one perspires more freely than if the full amount were admitted at first. Is it because heat which is great from the beginning, finding the flesh on the surface dry, burns the [25] skin and bakes it hard, and the flesh when it is in this condition holds the perspiration within ?[3] Less heat on the other hand tends to relax and rarefy the flesh and as it were stimulates the internal moisture to separate itself and come forth. This condition being established, when more heat is gradually introduced and penetrates deep into the flesh owing to its rarity, it vaporizes the already softened humours [30] and separating those which are light expels them with the breath.

33   Is it more necessary to induce perspiration in the summer or in the winter ?[4] In winter does not the heat collecting within the body concoct and vaporize our internal humours, and so, because all or most of them are expended, there is [35] no need to supply an appropriate method of expelling them ? In the summer, on the other hand, because the flesh is in a state of rarity, the heat escapes and our internal humours become less concocted and therefore need to be drawn off. For if they are allowed to remain, they putrefy owing to the season and cause disease ; for anything that **870[a]** putrefies does so owing to heat that is not its own, whereas its own natural heat causes concoction. Consequently in

---

[1] Cp. above, chapter 11 and note.
[2] Reading ἐπεισφερομένου γὰρ ⟨εἰς⟩ τὰ πυριατήρια [so also Richards]. The corruption, however, is probably more serious and ἐπεισφερομένου perhaps belongs to the previous sentence, cp. 867[a] 29.
[3] The sense demands στέγει for τέγγει.
[4] Cp. above, chapter 21 and note.

the summer the external heat prevails, and so everything within the body tends to putrefy; but in the winter the 5 natural heat predominates, and so the winter does not cause putrefaction.

Why is it that, whereas perspiration is due to internal 34 heat or else to heat attacking the body from without, yet we sometimes shiver while we perspire? Is it because, when owing to the internal heat the perspiration is expelled from a large area into a small space,[1] it collects[2] on the 10 surface of the body and entirely blocks up the channels through which the heat circulates, and so shivering ensues? Another reason is that the flesh becomes saturated and the heat escapes. On the other hand the external heat attacking the flesh at first rarefies it, and then the internal natural heat as it is given off[3] causes the shivering.

15 Why are hot sweats considered to be better than cold?[4] 35 Is it because all perspiration is the rejection of some excretion, and it is natural that a small excretion should become heated, whereas a more abundant excretion is less likely to do so, and so a cold sweat would be an indication of a copious excretion; consequently the disease, the presence of which 20 it indicates, is likely to last longer?

Why is it that, although perspiration is caused by heat, 36 we perspire less in front of a large fire?[5] Is it because, when the body is subjected to considerable heat, the[6] humours are dissolved into vapour; or else we do not feel the moisture, because it makes its way out and quickly 25 dies on the surface?

Why is it that, though the sun heats us more if we wear 37 no clothing, yet we perspire[7] more freely when we are

---

[1] i. e. from the whole interior of the body to the surface.

[2] Reading συστελλόμενοι (agreeing with ἱδρῶτες supplied) for συστελλομένοις.

[3] Reading ἀποκρινόμενον (W. D. R.); the middle ἀποκριάμενον in this sense cannot be paralleled.

[4] Cp. 959ᵇ 25 ff., and Hippocr. *de Morb.* i. 25.

[5] Cp. Theoph., *op. cit.*, § 28.   [6] Reading πνεύματα ⟨τὰ⟩ ὑγρά.

[7] The problem here is the same as that of chapter 9: to give point to the question it is therefore necessary to read ἱδρῶτες ⟨μᾶλλον⟩ γίνονται, the omission being due to the occurrence of the same word in the line above.

clothed? To this we shall give the same answer as to the last problem.[1]

38　Why is it that, though brisk movements are generally regarded as more heating than slow movements, walking 30 up a steep hill, which is a slower movement, induces more perspiration and obstructs the breathing, as though it were more heating than walking down hill?[2] Is it because it is natural for weights to be carried downwards and unnatural for them to be carried upwards? Consequently the nature of the heat[3] which carries us along does not undergo any 35 strain when we are going down hill, but has to bear a continual burden when we are walking up hill; and so it grows exceedingly hot by movement of this kind and causes more profuse perspiration and obstructs the breath. The bending, too, of the body involved in walking up hill contributes to **870^b** prevent the free passage of the breath by obstructing it.

39　Why is it that, although more perspiration is induced by additional clothing, it is not those who wear most clothing that perspire most? To this question we shall give the same answer as we gave above.[4]　　　　5

40　Why is it that, although our bodies are drier in the summer than in the winter, we are more disposed to perspire in the summer? Is it because, our bodies being in a condition of rarity in the summer, not much natural heat is contained in them? This, therefore, dissolves the humours into vapour. In the winter on the contrary, our 10 bodies being externally in a dense condition, the considerable amount of natural heat enclosed within does not dissolve the humours into vapour. Moreover, in the summer we swallow liquid in large quantities, but in small quantities in the winter.

41　Why is it that in healthy persons spontaneous perspiration is not considered to be as good as that produced by 15

---

[1] i. e. the case of a person exposed naked to the sun is parallel to that of a person in front of a large fire.
[2] Walking down hill being a brisker movement and therefore *ex hypothesi* more heating.
[3] ἡ τοῦ θερμοῦ φύσις seems merely a periphrasis for τὸ θερμόν.
[4] Cp. above, chapters 36 and 37.

exertion? Is it because exertion continually drains off the
superfluous moisture and makes the flesh drier, so that the
hollows of the pores are healthy and there is no obstruction
to the straining off of the heat? On the other hand the
20 so-called spontaneous perspiration (which really occurs of
necessity when the natural pores are disturbed by excessive
moisture, and the heat [1] is not completely retained, but can
still resist and expel the moisture) is rightly regarded as
a sign of disease. For then, owing to the presence of
25 a more than proportionate amount of moisture, a natural
process of cooling takes place, and the flesh becoming
saturated assumes a most unhealthy condition.

Why is it that in the winter perspiration is given off less **42**
freely and we do not feel the same desire to induce it,
although our bodies are moister in the winter? Do we
30 perspire less, because in winter our humours are congealed
and solidified to a considerable extent, and are consequently
less easily dissolved? The reason why we do not think it
necessary to induce perspiration in the winter is because
the condition in which we are is a healthy one, and any one
who induces perspiration dissolves and upsets that condition; moreover, by creating in the body a condition of
35 greater rarity than it ought to have, he expels and reduces
the natural heat, so that it cannot so effectively resist the
surrounding cold; also external moisture will more easily
burst its way into the body when the pores are rarefied by
process of perspiration.

[1] Reading τὸ θερμὸν (Sylburg).

BOOK III

PROBLEMS CONNECTED WITH THE DRINKING OF WINE AND DRUNKENNESS

1   WHY is it that, though wine is hot, the drunken are [a] unable to endure cold and are very readily attacked by pleurisy and similar diseases?[1]   Is it because a large quantity of moisture, if it be cooled, forms a mass of cold and so overpowers the natural heat?   For this is similar to [5] what happens when, if a garment is soaked in cold water, the flesh beneath it also becomes cold.

2   Why is it that it is not those who are very drunk that are most troublesome in their cups, but those who are only slightly intoxicated?[2]   Is it because they have neither drunk so little that they still resemble the sober nor so [10] much that they are in the incapacitated state of those who have drunk deep?   Further, those who are sober have more power of judgement, while those who are very drunk make no attempt to exercise their judgement; but those who are only slightly intoxicated can still exercise their judgement because they are not very drunk, but they exercise it badly because they are not sober, and they are ready to despise some of their neighbours and imagine that [15] they are being slighted by others.

3   Why is it that those who drink slightly diluted wine suffer more from the after effects than those who drink wine absolutely unmixed?[3]   Is it because owing to its lightness diluted wine penetrates better into more numerous and narrower parts of the body than unmixed wine, and so is less easy to get rid of?   Or is it because those who drink unmixed wine drink a less quantity, because it is impossible [20] to drink more, and vomit more readily?   Furthermore un-

---

[1] This problem is more fully treated in chapter 6.
[2] Cp. below, chapter 27.   This problem is referred to by Plutarch (*Quaest. Conviv.* iii. 8. 1) as Aristotelian.
[3] Cp. chapters 14 and 22.

mixed wine, being hotter, causes concoction in other things and in itself; whereas watery wine has the opposite effect.

Why is the semen of drunkards generally infertile? Is it **4** because the composition of their body has become full of 25 moisture, and the semen is fertile not when it is liquid but when it has body and consistency?[1]

Why do drunkards tremble, and more so the more they **5** drink unmixed wine?[2] Now wine is heating; but trembling is chiefly due to cold, and so those who are chilled tremble 30 very much. Yet many people before now, who have taken unmixed wine as their only form of nourishment, have been seized with such violent trembling as to throw off those who were trying to hold them down; and when they wash in hot water, they have no perception of it. Is it because trembling is due to cooling, and cooling takes place either when the heat is driven within by external cold, as happens 35 in winter, or when the natural heat is extinguished either by its opposite or by lapse of time, as in old age, or by the excess of extraneous heat which is caused in that which is exposed to the sun or to a blazing fire? This occurs also in those who take unmixed wine. The wine, being hot, **871ᵇ** when on mingling with the proper heat of the body it exceeds it in power,[3] quenches the bodily heat; and the heat being thus extinguished and the body cooled, trembling ensues. But there is also another process of cooling differing 5 from all those described above;[4] namely,[5] when the matter whereby the heat in anything is fed, is removed, and, as a result, the heat dies down. This can be illustrated in the inanimate world from the lamp; for when the oil is expended, the light goes out; and in living beings old age 10 and long, wasting diseases have a similar effect. For when that which feeds the heat is removed or diminished, the result is that the heat fails;[6] for heat is fed by moisture,

---

[1] Cp. *G. A.* 765ᵇ 5. This problem is referred to as Aristotelian by Athenaeus (x. 692ᵇ).   [2] Cp. below, chapter 26.

[3] Reading, with Bonitz and Richards, ὑπερτείνῃ τῇ δυνάμει.

[4] i. e. in 871ᵃ 33–8.

[5] Reading δή (W. D. R.) for δέ, and placing a colon after καταψύξεως.

[6] Reading ἐκλείπειν for ἐκλύειν with Bonitz, *op. cit.*, p. 408; cp. l. 16 below.

not, however, by any kind of moisture but by that which is
smooth and fat.[1] In those, therefore, who are suffering from
the diseases mentioned above and in those who are growing
old, when moisture of this kind becomes corrupted and
changed (becoming harsh and dry instead of smooth and 15
oily), as a result the heat fails. A proof of the above is
afforded by the treatment applied to those who are wasting
to death; for, whenever they have any nourishing liquid
administered to them, the result is that their vitality[2] is
revived, which implies that their bodily dissolution is due 20
to the lack of such a substance. The same cause seems to
operate in those who drink unmixed wine. For the wine,
being warm, co-operating with the heat already naturally
present in the body, tends to use up the supply already
present in the body for the natural heat; consequently some
drunkards become dropsical, others rheumatic, whilst in 25
others the stomach is affected. For the other humours in
them are harsh, and what they imbibe, being soft, does not
acquire consistency owing to the weakness of the natural heat.
Their heat is weak because the matter in which it is still
contained is itself weak; like a fire fed by reeds, which, 30
because its material is weak, is weaker than a wood-fire.

6   Why is it that, though wine is hot, the drunken are
unable to endure cold and are very readily attacked by
pleurisy and similar diseases?[3] Is it because a large
quantity of moisture, if it be cooled, forms a mass of cold,
and so overpowers the natural heat? Now the moister 35
anything is the hotter it is by nature, as is shown by the
fact that external agencies cause heat but do not cause
liquefaction; but where there is less heat, it is clear that
either the heat or the moisture is failing too quickly, and
so, cold humours only being left, it is natural that the 872[a]
drunken should be colder and show the usual symptoms of
chill.

   [1] Reading πίονι, suggested by Bekker, for πλείονι.
   [2] Reading, with Richards, τὸ ζωτικὸν for τὸ δὲ ὀπτικὸν, and omitting
the stop after συμβαίνει.
   [3] A fuller treatment of the topic of chapter 1; cp. also Hippocr.
de Morb., § 26.

Why is it that children, who have a hot temperament, **7**
are not fond of wine, although the Scythians and all who
are courageous are fond of wine because they have a hot
5 temperament? Is it because the latter, though they are
hot, are also dry (for this is the natural condition of a
man), whereas children are hot and moist? Now fondness
for drink is due to a desire for moisture; and so their moist
condition prevents children from being thirsty, for desire
implies a lack of something.

Why is it that men are more sensitive to salty and bad **8**
10 water when they are drunk than when they are sober?[1]
Is it because that which is like and similarly constituted is
unaffected by its like, but opposites are very sensitive to
opposites? A drunken man then has sweet liquids in him
(for such seems to be the nature of wine), and so is more
15 sensitive to bad liquids; but the sober man has harsh and
salty liquids in him, and so, when his food becomes concocted, the excretory humours come to the surface and
these are unaffected by their like[2] and cause the man in
whose body they are to be similarly unaffected.

Why is it that to those who are very drunk everything **9**
seems to revolve in a circle, and as soon as the wine takes
hold of them they cannot see objects at a distance, and so
20 this is used by some as a test of drunkenness? Is it because
the vision is continually disturbed by the heat of the wine?
It makes no difference then whether it is the vision that is
disturbed or the object seen; for the result is the same in
producing the above-mentioned effect. And since the vision
of drunken persons is often mistaken about objects near at
25 hand, it is only natural that it should be even more so in
looking at distant objects. So the latter are not visible to
them at all, while objects near at hand are not seen in their
proper places, but appear to revolve in a circle and not to
be near or far, because, firstly, the circular motion makes it
less possible for the sight to be directed towards distant
objects; for it is difficult to do two contrary things at the

---

[1] Cp. below, chapter 19.　　　　　[2] i. e. salty and bad water.

same time.[1] Now the movement of the sight in a straight 30
line [2] towards the distance is strong, but the circular movement of the vision is restricted to the area implied by its
name. For the above-mentioned reasons then the vision
does not travel to a distance. Secondly, if it could travel
to both near and distant objects,[3] it would not see them, for
the next moment the near or distant object at which it was
looking in the same direction would fail, and, if it did so,[4] 35
the eye could not see it. The circular movement is due to the
natural constitution of the sight ; for it is a cone,[5] the base
of which is a circle, and, moving in this circle, the sight
always sees the same thing,[6] because it never fails, but it is 872^b
deceived as to its position, because it never directs the same
glance upon it ; for just the same thing would happen
whether the object moved in relation to the eye or the eye
in relation to the object.

10   Why is it that to those who are drunk one thing at which
they are looking sometimes appears to be many ?[7] Is it
because, as has already been remarked,[8] the vision is dis- 5
turbed, with the result that the same glance does not rest
on the same object for any length of time? Now that
which is seen differently at the same time appears to exist
later in time ; for that which is seen is seen by contact with
the vision, and it is impossible for several objects to be in
contact with the same thing at the same time. But because
the intervening time, during which the vision comes into 10
contact with and passes away from the object seen, is
imperceptible, the moment during which it has been in
contact and passed away seems to be one and the same ;
and so when several glances come into contact with the
same object at the same time, the objects seen appear to be

---

[1] i. e. the sight cannot travel simultaneously straight forward and in
a circle.
[2] Reading, with Bonitz, ἐπ' εὐθείας φορά for ἐπιθυμία σφοδρά.
[3] Omitting τὸ before ἐγγὺς.
[4] Reading ἀπολεῖπον (Richards).
[5] Cp. below, 911^b 5.
[6] Reading ταὐτὸ for τοῦτο : T. G. renders *rem quidem percipit eandem.*
[7] Cp. below, chapter 30.
[8] i. e. in ^a 21.

several, because it is impossible for the glances to be in
contact with the same [1] thing at the same time.[2]

15   Why is it that those who are drunk are incapable of 11
having sexual intercourse?[3]   Is it because to do so a certain
part of the body must be in a state of greater heat than
the rest, and this is impossible in the drunken owing to
the large quantity of heat present in the whole body, for
the heat set up by the movement is extinguished by the
greater surrounding heat, because they have in them a con-
20 siderable quantity of unconcocted moisture?   Furthermore
the semen is derived from food and all food is concocted,
and those who are satiated with food are more inclined for
sexual intercourse.   This is why some people say that with
a view to the sexual act one ought to take a plenteous
midday meal but a light supper, so that there may be less
25 unconcocted than concocted matter in the body.

Why is it that sweet wine and unmixed wine and mead [4] 12
if drunk from time to time during a drinking bout make
men more sober?   And why do those who drink from
large vessels become less drunk?[5]   Is the reason in all
cases the same, namely the repression[6] of heat on the
30 surface of the body?   For drunkenness takes place when
the heat is in the region of the head.

Why is it that, though that which is sweet tends to rise 13
to the surface, if any one who is already drunk takes a sweet
draught the wine which he has drunk before is concocted
and causes less discomfort?   Is it because that which is
sweet is both soothing and adhesive (which is the reason
35 why it blocks up the pores), while that which is bitter has
a roughening effect?   The latter makes it easy for the heat

---

[1] Reading ταὐτοῦ for ταῦτα.

[2] *sc.* and yet produce different sensations.   Reading with K^a χρόνον
for τρόπον.   [3] Cp. below, chapter 33.

[4] There is no exact equivalent for κυκεών, which was a mixture of
wine, barley, cheese, and honey.

[5] This second question and the suggested solution are repeated in
chapter 25, and the two passages can be emended from one another.

[6] Reading κατάκρουσις from 874^b 12, which gives much better sense,
because, as is shown in the next clause, sobriety depends on the heat
of the wine being kept out of the head.

to rise, but the sweet draught keeps it in by blocking up
the pores; and it has already been remarked [1] that drunken- **873**^a
ness is due to the upper parts of the body becoming heated.
Furthermore sweet wine is odourless, but bitter wine is not,
and any odour oppresses the head.

14 Why is it that wine which is mixed but tends towards the
unmixed causes a worse headache the next morning than 5
entirely unmixed wine? [2] Is it because unmixed wine is
composed of heavy particles and so does not find its way
into the pores of the head, which are narrow, but only its
power, namely its odour and heat, reaches the head? Diluted
wine on the other hand, being mixed with water, which is
light, itself penetrates to the head and having body, as well
as much of the power of unmixed wine, is much less easily 10
concocted; for moist things are most difficult of all to
concoct, and actual substances are more difficult of concoction than mere effects.

15 Why is it that those who do not take physical exercise
are better able to drink themselves into a condition of
drunkenness, and throw it off more easily, than those who
take such exercise? Is it because those who have excretions and moisture in their bodies are more inclined to pass 15
urine? This enables them to drink and afterwards to be
relieved of the effects, because much vinous moisture does
not remain in them. Those who take no exercise are
moist and full of excretions; but those who do take exercise
are dry, and so the vinous moisture penetrates into their 20
body, and its impetus immediately checks the flow of urine,
and the moisture remaining afterwards behind forms a
weight in the body.

16 Why has wine the effect both of stupefying and of
driving to frenzy those who drink it? For these are
contrary states, the frenzied being in a state of excessive
movement and the stupid in a condition of too little movement. Is it true, as Chaeremon says, that 25

Wine mingles with the temper of the drinker? [3]

[1] i.e. in l. 30.   [2] Cp. chapters 3 and 22.
[3] Fr. 16 (Nauck², p. 787).

It therefore has the opposite effect not on the same but upon the unlike, just as fire dries up some things but liquefies others, but does not have both these effects on the same things—for instance it melts ice, but hardens
30 salt. So wine, being in its nature moist, excites the slow and makes them quicker, while it enervates the quick. Therefore some of those who are naturally of a melancholic temperament become entirely enervated as the result of a drunken debauch. For just as a bath makes supple those who have a well-knit and hard frame, while it relaxes those
35 who are supple and moist, so wine has this effect, acting as an internal bath.

Why is it that cabbage stops the ill effects of drinking? **17**
873ᵇ Is it because its juice is sweet and has a cleansing effect (and so doctors use it to purge the bowels), while in itself it is cold? This is shown by the fact that doctors use it in cases of acute diarrhoea, boiling it thoroughly and draining off the juice [1] and letting it cool. In those who are suffer-
5 ing from the after effects of drinking the effect of the juice of cabbage is to draw off the internal humours, which are vinous and unconcocted, into the stomach, whilst the cabbage itself remains in the upper part of the stomach and cools the body. As the body cools, the light humours are carried into the bladder. Thus since the humours through-
10 out the body are expelled by these two methods and it becomes cool, the ill effects of drinking naturally vanish; for wine is moist and hot. A further result of the humours being drawn downwards and expelled is that breath is thereby carried down into the body, and it is only from there that breath can be carried from the wine into the
15 head and cause stupor and headache. But if the breath is carried downwards and the body cooled in the manner mentioned above, the pain of the headache is relieved. For the headache is due to a seething and to inflammation as it dies down; but it is more painful than drunkenness, because the latter drives men out of their senses, but the headache
20 causes them pain when they are in full possession of

---

[1] Reading ἀποχυλίζοντες.

their wits. Just as those who are in a fever are delirious rather than in pain, but feel pain when they are relieved of the fever and recover their senses; for just the same thing happens with headache and drunkenness.

18 Why is it that watery wine is more apt to cause vomiting than water and than unmixed wine? Is it because anything 25 that tends to rise to the surface and is unpleasant to the taste is most likely to cause vomiting? Now wine has the effect of repression;[1] while water is light and not unpleasant, and, therefore, being light[2] it quickly penetrates downwards, but, not being unpleasant, it does not cause heartburn. Now excessively diluted wine is not light enough to percolate through quickly, and because it has 30 a little wine in it, it is unpleasant; for it disturbs the sense of taste by setting up two kinds of movement, one produced by the wine and the other by the water, both of which make themselves felt. But the proper mixing of wine does away with the taste of water and gives the wine a soft taste, which makes it pleasant to drink. But watery 35 wine, being unpleasant to the taste, has a tendency to rise, and anything which does this is apt to cause vomiting.

19 Why is it that men are more sensitive to salty and bad water when they are drunk than when they are sober?[3] 874^a Is it because anything which has an unpleasant taste is more perceptible to those who feel no desire, but is not noticed by those who feel desire? A man therefore who is in a state of lacking something[4] resembles one who feels a desire, and the sober man is in this condition; whereas the drunken man is satiated.

20 Why is it that to those who are very drunk everything 5 seems to revolve in a circle, and as soon as the wine takes hold of them they cannot count objects at a distance, and so

---

[1] Cp. 872^b 29 and note, and 874^b 12.
[2] Omitting καὶ οὐκ ἀηδές, which has clearly come in from the previous line.
[3] The same problem is discussed in chapter 8.
[4] Reading ἐνδεῶς for ἡδέως with Bonitz (op. cit., p. 409); cp. 950^a 14, E. N. 1118^b 10, 1153^a 1.

this is used by some as a test of drunkenness?[1] Is it
because the vision is continually disturbed by the heat of
the wine? The same thing then happens to those who are
drunk as when an object appears double if one puts it[2]
10 close to the eye. For it makes no difference if you move
the eye instead of[3] putting the object close to it, and whether
the movement is within the eye or outside it; for the effect
on the vision is the same in both cases. The result will be
that the object seen appears not to be at rest, and more so
if it is at a distance (for it has less hold upon the vision
when the latter is extended to a distance); and this near
15 movement[4] causes a still greater variation at the farthest
point to which the eye reaches; and if the vision is moved
violently and unevenly[5] up and down, it has still less hold
upon the distant object. Now anything which is extended
to a distance moves in a circle, masts,[6] for example, and
objects suspended; and so the same thing happens to the
vision owing to its weakness, as though it were actually
projected to a distance. It makes no difference whether it
20 is the vision which moves or the object seen; for the effect
on the appearance of the object is the same.

Why is it that, when a quantity of wine is drunk at once, 21
the stomach becomes drier, whereas it ought to be rendered
moister by the additional liquid? Is it because the stomach
has no action upon a large amount of liquid swallowed at
25 once, but it goes unaltered to its proper place (and the
proper place for unconcocted liquid is the bladder), whereas
the stomach acts upon a small quantity and concocts it, so
that it remains in the stomach and makes it moist?

Why is it that those who drink wine properly diluted 22
suffer more from the after effects than those who drink
unmixed wine?[7] Is it because diluted wine, being light,
finds its way into more parts of the body (just as it pene-

---

[1] The same problem is the subject of chapter 9 and the treatment
of it is partly identical.
[2] Reading ὑποθῇ ⟨τί⟩ τις (Richards).
[3] Reading μή (W. D. R.) for μέν.
[4] i.e. the movement set up in the eye as an effect of drunkenness.
[5] Reading ἀνωμαλῶς for ὁμαλῶς.
[6] Reading ἱστοὶ for ὀιστοί with Cᵃ Yᵃ.   [7] Cp. chapters 3 and 14.

trates into clothing), and is more difficult to expel (water 30
by itself being of a thinner consistency but easier to
expel)?[1] Or is it because the amount of unmixed wine
which is drunk is less because of the impossibility of
drinking a large quantity, and there is more liability to
vomiting? Moreover unmixed wine concocts everything
else as well as itself.[2]

23 Why is it that death ensues from the drinking of un- 35
mixed wine in large quantities by one who is already in
a lean condition? On the other hand, those who are
addicted to drinking, if they are not in a lean condition,
often become dry from drinking a large quantity at a time;
for both wine and life[3] seem to be of the nature of hot
things, whereas death is a process of cooling. Is it because 874ᵇ
death by drinking resembles death by hemlock, the natural
heat being gradually extinguished? But the process is
different in the two cases; for hemlock by its coldness
congeals the moisture and heat, whereas wine by its own
heat parches up the natural heat. So just as a small fire is 5
extinguished by a large blaze and by the heat of the sun, so
too the heat in the body is extinguished by that in the
wine, if the latter surpasses it in strength.

24 Why are the drunken more easily moved to tears? Is
it because they become hot and moist, and so they have no
command over themselves and are affected by trifling 10
causes?

25ᵃ ⟨Why is it that sweet wine and unmixed wine and mead
if drunk from time to time during a drinking bout make
men more sober? And⟩[4] why do those who drink from

---

[1] This doctrine is quoted as Aristotelian by Plutarch, *Quaest.
Conviv.* vi. 9. 3.

[2] Omitting ταὐτὸ δ' ἐστὶ πρόβλημα, which is not translated by T. G.
and probably introduced a further explanation; cp. 885ᵇ 3 and Prantl,
op. cit., p. 354.

[3] τὸν ζῆν in the Teubner text is a misprint for τὸ ζῆν.

[4] It is obvious from πάντων (l. 12) that several alternatives are
offered in the statement of the problem. The problem is clearly
a repetition of chapter 12 and we must restore διὰ τί ⟨ὁ γλυκὺς καὶ ὁ
ἄκρατος καὶ ὁ κυκεὼν μεταξὺ διαπινόμενοι ἐν τοῖς πότοις νήφειν ποιοῦσιν;
καὶ διὰ τί⟩ ἧττον μεθύσκονται κτλ.

large vessels become less drunk ? Is the reason in all cases[1]
the same, namely the repression of heat ;[2] that is to say,
on the surface of the body ? For drunkenness takes place
in the region of the head.

⟨Why is it that those who drink much unmixed wine fall **25**[b]
asleep easily ?⟩[3] Is it because to induce sleep warm moisture
15 must be present, for it is easily concocted ? But if no moisture
is present, or[4] only a little, or moisture which is difficult of
concoction, sleep does not come on. Therefore men
become sleepiest when they are fatigued and after meat and
drink, owing to the heat. But sleeplessness afflicts the
melancholic and those who are in a high fever,[5] the former
because the moisture in them is cooled, the latter because
20 there is little or no moisture in them ; these facts must
clearly be looked to as the causes of sleeplessness in these
two[6] cases.

Why do drunkards tremble, and the more so the more **26**
they drink unmixed wine ?[7] Now wine is heating, and
trembling is chiefly due to cold ; and so it is prin-
cipally those who are chilled that tremble. Yet many
25 people before now who have taken unmixed wine as their
only form of nourishment, have been seized with such
violent trembling as to throw off those who were trying to
hold them down, and when they wash with hot water they
have no perception of it. Others who live in this way,[8]

---

[1] Reading ἢ πάντων for πάντων γάρ ; cp. 872^b 28.

[2] Reading ἡ κατάκρουσις ⟨τοῦ θερμοῦ⟩, τουτέστιν ; cp. 872^b 29.

[3] It is clear that ἢ ὅτι δεῖ πρὸς τοὺς ὕπνους κτλ. begins the solution
of a new problem the title of which has fallen out. T. G. begins this
new problem with the words, *Cur vinolentis somnus oriri nequeat ?*
But the fact that drunkenness often induces sleep rather than prevents
it and the arguments contained in the solution point to some other
question. That inserted above seems to be the most applicable,
since, as has been already shown, unmixed wine is hot and easily
concocted.

[4] Reading ⟨ἢ⟩ ὀλίγη (Bonitz).

[5] τοῖς μεγάλας πυρίας is untranslatable and a participle appears to
have fallen out ; the sense must be either that given above or else
'those who indulge in strong vapour baths', which seems to be the
meaning of πυρίαι in *de Part. Anim.* 651^a 1. T. G. renders *vehementer
aestuantes.*   [6] Reading ἑκάτερον (Richards) for ἕτερον.

[7] The same problem is treated, and partly in identical words, in
chapter 5.   [8] i. e. who drink much unmixed wine.

but also undergo massage and take meat as part of their diet, have been stricken with apoplectic seizures; these are less subject to trembling, because they are unable to move, 30 but they suffer from violent pain and an inability to rest. Trembling is due to cooling; for, as has been remarked, it is those who are chilled who suffer from it and the very old, the cause being in the former their cold condition, in the latter their age. Wine, on the other hand, is very 35 heating; so that it ought to have the opposite effect. Is there any reason why the same effect should not be produced by contraries working in a different manner? For example, burning[1] is caused both by frost and by heat, when the frost collects the heat in one place. Thus there is a sense in which the same condition is produced[2] both by 875^{a} contrary causes and by the same cause. Now trembling is due to lack of heat,—not, however, of any kind of heat, but of natural heat. Heat perishes either by dying down or by being extinguished; it is extinguished by its contraries, cold and moisture, and it dies down either through 5 lack of material, as lamps do when they have no more fuel or oil, or under the influence of external heat, as the fire goes out in the sunlight and lamps when they are exposed to the fire. Those then who are chilled tremble because the heat in them is extinguished by the cold. This is why the pouring of hot water over a person makes his hair 10 bristle; for the cold being enclosed within and being compressed[3] causes the hair to stand on end. The coldness of one who is beginning to suffer from fever is due to a like cause. In old age the heat dies down because the material which feeds it fails; for moisture is the food of heat, and old age is dry.[4] Now it is because their own 15 heat dies down that drunkards tremble and any others in whom this effect is produced by wine; but they do not do so in the same way as those who tremble from old age, but there is, as we saw, a third way in which the heat is

---

[1] ἀποκαίειν is regularly used both of 'burning off' and of 'frost-bite'.
[2] Reading συμβαίνει (Y^{a}).
[3] For the doctrine of ἀντιπερίστασις cp. 867^{b} 32 and note.
[4] Reading with Bonitz (*op. cit.*, p. 409) ξηρόν for ψυχρόν; cp. *de long. et brev. vit.* 466^{a} 22, ^{b} 14. T. G. renders *senectus autem sicca est.*

destroyed. For when too much wine is taken, the heat
20 being considerable in the body [1] extinguishes or weakens
our own heat, in which our strength consists; for trembling
arises when the motive power loses control over that which
it moves, just as the extremity of a long and large piece of
wood trembles if one has not a good hold [2] upon it, and
this happens because either that which is being held is too
large or that which is moving it is too weak. So, when the
25 heat is extinguished (for heat appears to be the cause of
motion in animals), the natural control of the body is lost.
That this condition is induced in drunkards and the aged
by a process of cooling is proved by the fact that the
trembling is unaccompanied by chill.

Why is it that one who is slightly intoxicated is more **27**
troublesome in his cups than one who is more drunk and
30 than the sober man? [3] Is it because the sober man
exercises his judgement properly, whereas one who is quite
drunk, because his senses are blocked up, being unable to
resist the heaviness which oppresses him, cannot exercise
his judgement at all, and, this being so, he is not troublesome in his cups? But he who is slightly intoxicated uses
his judgement, but, owing to the wine which he has drunk,
he uses it amiss, and so is troublesome in his cups. He is
35 like Satyrus of Clazomenae, who was given to abuse, and
so when he was defendant in a lawsuit, in order that he
might speak to the point and not abuse his adversary, they
stopped up his ears, so that he might not hear anything
and become abusive; but as his adversary was finishing his
speech, they uncovered his ears, and he, hearing a few
words at the end of the speech, could not restrain himself
and began to revile him, because he could use his senses
40 but could not use his judgement aright.

875ᵇ Why is it that men do not become drunkards by being **28**
addicted to sweet wine, which is pleasanter to the taste?
Is it because sweet wine possesses a flavour other than

---

[1] Putting the comma before, instead of after, ἐν τῷ σώματι.
[2] Reading ἐγκρατῶς (Richards).
[3] This problem has already been discussed in chapter 2.

that of wine?[1] He then who is addicted to sweet wine will be a lover of what is sweet rather than of wine.

29 Why is it that drunkards take a particular delight in the warmth of the sun?[2] Is it because they need concoction? Another reason is the fact that they are cooled by the wine; which is also a reason why apoplectic seizures and torpidity very readily occur after drinking.

30 Why is it that drunkards when looking at a single object sometimes see several objects?[3] Is it because the sources of vision (like the whole head) are disturbed internally by the wine, and, this being so, the vision of the two eyes cannot meet at the same point, but as it were moves to different parts of the object seen; consequently the object appears to be two? The same thing happens if one presses one eye from below;[4] for this disturbs the source of its vision, so that it no longer falls upon the same point as the other eye. This then is an external disturbance, while that caused by wine is internal; but there is no real difference, the effect being the same whatever the cause of the disturbance.

31 Why is it that the tongue of those who are drunk stumbles?[5] Is it because, just as the whole body staggers in drunkenness, so also the tongue staggers and stumbles and cannot articulate clearly? Or is it because the flesh of the tongue is spongy? It therefore becomes saturated and swells up, and when this happens it is more difficult to move, owing to the thickness caused by its increased bulk, and it cannot articulate distinctly. Or is it because, just as we cannot speak under water through lack of air, so we cannot speak when we take liquid into the mouth? So in a state of drunkenness we cannot articulate because the tongue is surrounded by a large quantity of moisture; for a stumbling speech is due to inability to articulate. Or is it because in drunkenness the mind is affected and stumbles? If the mind is in this condition, it is only

---

[1] i. e. its sweetness predominates over its vinous quality.
[2] Cp. chapter 32. [3] Cp. chapter 10.
[4] Cp. 959^a 11. [5] Cp. 888^b 7.

30 natural that the tongue should suffer likewise; for the
mind is the source of speech. This is why, apart from
drunkenness, if the mind is affected, the tongue is affected
also, as for example in those who are frightened.

Why is it that drunkards and those who have to do 32
35 with the sea delight in the sun?[1] Is it because drunkards
require concoction and at the same time certain parts of
their bodies have become cooled? This is why apoplectic
seizures and torpor follow after drinking. Those who
have to do with the sea like the sun because they live
always amid moisture.

Why is it that those who are drunk are incapable of 33
40 having sexual intercourse?[2] Is it because to do so a certain
part of the body ought to be in a state of greater heat
876^a than the rest, and this is impossible in the drunken owing
to the large quantity of heat in them; the heat therefore
caused by the movement is extinguished, being heated by
the surrounding heat?[3] Or is it because for sexual intercourse the lower parts of the body must be heated, whereas
wine naturally rises upwards and so creates heat in the
5 upper parts and withdraws it from the lower parts? Also
people are least inclined for sexual intercourse after food
and are recommended to take a heavy midday meal and
a light supper with a view to it, for the heat and moisture
move upwards when the food is unconcocted and downwards when it is concocted; and the semen is formed from
concocted food. Those who are fatigued emit semen during
10 sleep,[4] because fatigue is a moist and hot condition; if
therefore the excretion takes place in this part of the body,
the result is that semen is emitted during sleep. This also
occurs for the same reason in certain forms of illness,[5] and
likewise in those who are frightened and in the dying.[6]

15 Why is it that the young wet their beds more, when 34
they are drunk, than the old? Is it because they are hot
and moist, and so the excretion which collects is abundant,

---

[1] Cp. above, chapter 29.   [2] Cp. above, chapter 11.
[3] An instance of the doctrine of πῦρ ἐπὶ πῦρ.   [4] Cp. v. 3.
[5] Namely in phthisis; cp. 884^a 6.   [6] Cp. 877^a 26 ff.

because the body does not expend the moisture, and so it overflows; but as they become older, the body owing to its dryness absorbs the excess of moisture? Or is it because the young are more inclined to sleep than the old? Con- 20 sequently, without their being aware of it, the flow of urine finds its way out while they are asleep, before they can wake up, whereas the old are aware of it, just as they are more alive to any external movement than the young. This is confirmed by the fact that the young themselves wet their beds most when they are most sound 25 asleep.

35 Why is it that oil is beneficial against drunkenness and sipping it enables one to continue drinking? Is it because it promotes the flow of urine and so prepares a way for the liquor?

BOOK IV

PROBLEMS CONNECTED WITH SEXUAL INTERCOURSE

WHY is it that one who is having sexual intercourse, 1 and also a dying person, casts his eyes upwards, while a sleeper casts them downwards? Is it because the heat going out in an upward direction makes the eyes turn in the direction in which it is itself travelling, whereas during sleep the heat collects in the lower part of the body 35 and so inclines the eyes downwards? The eyes close because there is no moisture left in them.

Why do the eyes and flanks of those who indulge too fre- 2 quently in sexual intercourse sink very noticeably,[1] though the latter are near and the former far from the sexual organs? Is it because these parts co-operate very noticeably in the effort made in the act of coition, contracting at the time **876ᵇ** of the emission of the semen? It is from these parts then in particular that any easily liquefied nourishment which is present there is squeezed out by the pressure. Or is it because these parts become overheated and waste away most, and sexual intercourse operates through heat, and those parts are most heated which are moved in the act 5 of coition? Now the eyes and the parts about the buttocks noticeably co-operate in the sexual act; for it is impossible to emit the semen without drawing the buttocks together and closing [2] the eyes, for the buttocks by their contraction press out the semen (just as the liquid can be expelled from the bladder by the pressure of the hand), while the bringing to-
10 gether of the eyelids presses out the moisture in the brain.

---

[1] Cp. *de Gen. Anim.* 747ª 16.
[2] Unless τῶν ὀφθαλμῶν καταβληθέντων here means merely 'closing the eyes' as is implied by συναγωγή (l. 10), there will be a direct contradiction with 876ᵈ 32, 33. The alternative is to emend καταβληθέντων to ἀναβληθέντων. Platt omits μή as having come from the previous line.

That the eyes and the region near them have considerable
influence in procreation is shown by the fact that childless
and fruitful[1] women alike try the experiment of anointing
them, thinking that strength must pass by this way into
the semen.   These two parts, the fundament and the eyes,
are always in all persons full of fatness; and, because they 15
co-operate in the act of coition, they share in the heat
which it engenders and are made lean thereby, and much
of their substance is excreted into the semen.   For unless
a part of the body is fat, the heat will not melt it properly,
nor will it do so if the part is fat but does not co-operate
in the sexual act, as is the case with the stomach. (The
kidneys, however, have more sensation in sexual intercourse 20
than other parts of the body because of their nearness to
the organs employed.)   Moreover, the mere passage of
the semen through these parts, which is quite perceptible
by these parts, is sufficient to make them lean; for its
proximity takes away something without adding anything
to them.

3   Why is it that both those who indulge in sexual excess
and eunuchs, who never do so, alike[2] lose their sharpness 25
of vision?   Is it because in the former owing to their
desire, and in the latter owing to their mutilation, the
upper parts of the body become drier than they ought
to be, and this is most noticeable in those organs which
have delicate work to do, such as the eye?   So when
the moisture is drawn away downwards, the upper parts
become dry.   It is quite obvious that sexual intercourse 30
has this effect.   In eunuchs the legs swell and the bowels
are easily relaxed, which shows that the moisture has
moved downwards.

4   Why is it that man alone grows hair on the face and
body when he begins to be capable of sexual intercourse,
whereas this does not happen in the other animals which
have hair?   Is it because on coming to maturity the
characteristics of animals change to their opposites?   For 35

[1] ἀγόνων should perhaps be read for γονίμων.
[2] Reading ὁμοίως with some MSS.

the voice becomes deep instead of shrill, and they become hairy instead of bare; it is clear therefore that animals which are hirsute from birth ought to become bare and not continue to be hirsute when they begin to secrete semen. But this is not so, because animals which emit 877ᵃ semen become drier and rarer, conditions which are favourable to the growth of hair. This is shown by the fact that hair does not grow on scars, for scars are of a close texture and not rare; nor does hair grow upon women and children, both of whom are moist and not dry.

5 Why is it that having the feet bare is prejudicial to 5 sexual intercourse? Is it because the body, when it is about to have sexual intercourse, ought to be warm and moist internally? This condition is attained during sleep rather than when one is awake; and so emission of semen takes place readily and without effort during sleep, but requires exertion in those who are awake. When the 10 body is moist and warm, the feet are even more so; as is shown by the fact that the feet of those who are asleep are warm, being in this condition simultaneously with the interior of the body. But bareness of the feet has the opposite effect of causing dryness and cold. So since it is either difficult or impossible to have sexual intercourse when the feet are not warm, bareness of the feet must 15 necessarily be prejudicial to the performance of the sexual act.

Why is it that man is more languid after sexual inter- 6 course than any other animal? Is it because in proportion to his bulk he emits more semen than any other animal? But why does he do so? Is it because man digests his food with less effort and is naturally moister and hotter 20 than all the other animals? His moistness then creates an abundance of semen, while his heat creates a natural condition favourable to it; for the semen must be moist and hot as long as it is kept in the body.

Why is it that, whereas sexual intercourse takes place 7 by means of heat, and fear and death have a cooling effect, 25 yet semen is sometimes emitted by those who are frightened

and by the dying?[1] Is it because, though some parts are
cooled, others become somewhat warmed, since they already
have their own heat and receive additional heat from the
parts which are cooling? So that, though such persons are
growing cold, the emission of semen is due not to cooling
but to the simultaneous heating. Observation proves this
to be so in those who are frightened; for the blood leaves 30
the upper parts of the body, and the lower parts become
moist, and the bowels and bladder are relaxed. Thus under
the influence of fright the heat makes its way downwards,
and at death it travels upwards from below, and, because
it creates a state of moisture by its warmth, it causes the
emission of semen.

8 Why is it that one ought not to have sexual intercourse 35
or vomit or sneeze or emit a deep breath, unless one is
in a turgid state? Is it because if we are not in a turgid
state, we are in the condition of plants torn up from the
earth with which something which does not belong to
them is torn up also, or of which some part is torn off and
left in the ground? Now anything which ought to be
removed, but of which a part is detached and remains **877ᵇ**
behind, will cause trouble for a long while. And if one
disturbs something external to oneself, this will cause
trouble, because it is not in its proper place; and this is
what will happen if we do any of the above-mentioned
things when we are not in a turgid state.

9 Why is it that one can have sexual intercourse more 5
readily when fasting? Is it because the ducts of the body
are emptier in those who are fasting and full in those who
are full? In the latter case they prevent the moisture
from passing through into the semen. This is seen to be
the case with the bladder; for when it is full it is impossible
to have sexual intercourse readily.[2]

10 Why is it that the young, when they first begin to have 10
sexual intercourse, feel loathing after the act for those with
whom they have had intercourse? Is it due to the fact

---

[1] Cp. 876ᵃ 13.   [2] Cp. 878ᵇ 33–5.

that the change caused in them is great? For they are only conscious of the ensuing feeling of discomfort, and so avoid those with whom they have had intercourse as being the cause of this feeling.

15 Why is it that those who are continually on horseback 11 are more inclined for sexual intercourse? Is it because owing to the heat and movement they are in the same condition as during sexual intercourse? So as growth takes place with increasing age in the region of the genital organs, these parts become enlarged. Since then they are always in this state of movement, their bodies become open-pored and in a condition which disposes them for 20 sexual intercourse.

Why is it that when sexual powers begin to be present 12 the flesh has an unpleasant odour which is not present in men or women before puberty?[1] Is it because unconcocted matter always has a worse taste—being more acid or salty or bitter—and a more unpleasant odour, while concocted matter has a pleasant, or less unpleasant, taste 25 and a more agreeable, or less disagreeable, odour? This is clear from an observation of the whole vegetable and animal world. If the properly concocted matter is removed, that which is left is unconcocted,—for instance in ashes, the sweet portion having been consumed, the dust which remains is bitter, and similarly perspiration is salty. 30 Now the natural heat concocts the semen, which though small in amount is very strong, being a large quantity in a concentrated form.[2] When, therefore, it leaves the body, the latter usually becomes languid and cold; and so the juices in it are subject to less concoction, since the pores are opened owing to the excretion of the semen. Consequently the perspiration of adults is saltier and has a more unpleasant odour than that of children, because it is unconcocted; and if their natural condition is such that the residue[3] of their perspiration has an unpleasant odour,

---

[1] Cp. below, chapter 24, and Theoph. *de Odoribus*, § 7.

[2] i.e. the semen, though small in quantity, is concocted from a large amount of nourishment, cp. 879[a] 9, 10.

[3] i.e. what is left when the moisture in the perspiration has evaporated.

it is still more evident in such persons, and particularly [1] in those parts, such as the armpit,[2] in which it is especially evident in other people also.

13 Why is it that we regard the creature which is born [3] **878ᵃ** from our own semen as our offspring, while that which is produced from any other part of us or from any other excretion is not looked upon as our own? For many things are produced by putrefaction, even from semen. Why then is that which resembles us claimed as our own, while that which is alien to us is not so considered? For 5 either all or none ought to belong to us. Is the reason that, in the first place, what is produced from the semen is born from what is our own, but that which is produced otherwise originates from something which is not ours, namely, from what is purged or excreted from us? In a word, nothing in a creature procreates another creature except the semen; and that which is harmful and evil, and also that which is alien, is not claimed by anything as its 10 own; for it is not the same thing to be part of a thing and to be alien to it and other than it and evil. Now our excretions and putrefactions are not our own but are other than us and alien to our nature. For all things that grow in the body must not be considered as belonging to the body, for even boils grow on it and these are removed and cast forth. In a word, all things that are contrary to nature 15 are alien to the body, and many of the things that grow there are contrary to nature. If therefore the semen is the only thing in us from which a creature can be born, we should be right in regarding as our own offspring that only which is produced from the semen. Moreover anything else which is produced from the semen, as for instance, when it putrefies, a worm, or the so-called monstrosities, 20 when there is corruption in the womb, are not to be reckoned as offspring. In a word, anything which is produced from corruption is no longer produced from that which is our own but from that which is alien to us, like

---

[1] The Teubner text wrongly prints μάλισται for μάλιστα.
[2] Cp. 867ᵇ 19.
[3] The Teubner text wrongly prints γένητα for γένηται.

that which is generated from excretions such as ordure. That all such things are produced from corruption is
25 proved by the fact that what is generated from uncorrupted semen is of such a nature as to resemble that from which the semen came, a horse being born from a horse and a man from a man. And [1] we do not value the semen in itself or everything that is being completed in the process of coming into being (for it is sometimes moisture and a mere mass
30 and flesh which is coming into being),[2] because it has not yet its true nature but only so much of its nature as is implied in the fact that it is so disposed as to produce something resembling ourselves; and nothing even of this kind can be produced from corrupted semen. For these reasons we do not regard as our offspring that which is produced either from anything else in us except the semen, or from the semen when it is corrupted or fails to achieve perfection.

35　Why are people less able to have sexual intercourse in 14 the water? Is it because in water none of those things liquefy which liquefy with heat—lead, for example, or wax? Now the semen obviously liquefies with heat, for it does not liquefy until it is warmed by the friction. Fishes, however, have sexual intercourse without friction.

878ᵇ　Why is it that sexual intercourse is the most pleasant of 15 all things to animals, and is it so of necessity or with some purpose in view? Is it pleasant because the semen comes either from the whole body, as some declare,[3] or not from
5 the whole body but only from the area over which all the ducts of the veins extend? The pleasure then of the friction [4] being similar in both cases, the sensation extends as it were over the whole body. Now the friction is pleasant, since it involves the emission of vaporous moisture enclosed unnaturally in the body; but the act of generation

---

[1] Reading καὶ αὐτὸ δὲ (Richards).

[2] Reading in ll. 28-30 περαινόμενον (καὶ γὰρ ὑγρὸν καὶ ὄγκος τις καὶ σάρξ γίγνεταί ποτε), διὰ κτλ.

[3] This is the Hippocratean doctrine denied by Aristotle in G. A. 721ᵇ 13 ff.

[4] For this meaning of κνησμός, see G. A. 723ᵇ 34 and A. Platt's translation.

is an emission of similar matter for its natural purpose. It is pleasant both of necessity and because it has a purpose 10 in view,—of necessity, because the way to a natural result is pleasant, if it is realized by the senses; and because of its purpose, namely, the procreation of animal life. For it is the pleasure more than anything else which incites animals to sexual intercourse.

16   Why is it that sexual excess is beneficial in some diseases caused by phlegm?[1] Is it because it involves the emission 15 of an excretion, and so a considerable amount of excreted matter is rejected with it, and phlegm is an excretion?

17   Why does sexual intercourse cool and dry the stomach? Does it cool it because the heat is expelled in coition? Coition causes dryness, because, as the heat goes out, the moisture[2] is vaporized and finds its way out as the body cools, while at the same time the heat caused by the act of 20 copulation has a drying effect.

18   Why are those whose eyelashes fall off accounted lustful? Is it for the same reason as that for which the bald also are so accounted?[3] For the eyelashes and the hair of the head really belong together. The reason is that all the congenital hair which does not increase as a man gets older, 25 falls off owing to lustfulness. For the hair of the head and the eyebrows and eyelashes are congenital hair; and of these the eyebrows alone sometimes grow thicker with advancing years (the reason for this has been stated elsewhere),[4] while the hair of the head and the eyelashes both fail from the same cause, viz., that lustfulness cools the upper 30 parts of the body which are deficient in blood, and so this portion of the body does not concoct any of the nourishment, and the hair not receiving any nourishment drops off.

19   Why is it that those who wish to pass urine cannot have sexual intercourse?[5] Is it because the ducts become full?

---

[1] This problem has been already treated in i. 50.
[2] It seems necessary to supply τὸ ὑγρόν here as the subject of ἐξατμίζεται.
[3] Cp. *G. A.* 783^b 27 ff.
[4] This appears to be a direct reference to *P. A.* 658^b 19, 20.
[5] Cp. 877^b 6-8.

35 Now that which is full of moisture cannot admit any more moisture.

Why is it that varicocele prevents both man and any 20 other animals which suffer from it from procreating their species? Is it because varicocele is due to a displacement of breath, and this is why it is beneficial to melancholic diseases? Now sexual intercourse also is accompanied by
879^a an emission of breath.[1] If therefore a rush of breath makes its way along when sexual intercourse is taking place, it fails to impart movement to the semen[2] and the latter becomes cold; consequently it enfeebles the erection of the penis.

Why do those who have sexual intercourse usually 21
5 become languid and weaker?[3] Is it because the semen is an excretion from the whole body,[4] and so the composition of the body, like the harmony of a building, is disturbed by the loss of any portion of it—if, for example, all the blood[5] or any other component part of it is removed? So important is that which the body loses in sexual intercourse, being indeed formed from a large amount of nourish-
10 ment though itself small in quantity,[6] just as a cake is made from wheaten flour.

Why is it that the penis is greatly distended in those who 22 have sexual intercourse at a time when they desire to pass urine? Is it because, owing to the ducts being full of moisture, the semen, passing out through a narrower space, swells the bulk of the penis and lifts it up, for it is situated close to the ducts.

15 What is the cause of the erection and swelling of the 23 penis? Are there two reasons, first, that it is raised by a weight applied behind the testicles, the latter acting as the fulcrum, and, secondly, that the pores become full of

---

[1] For the semen is ὑγρὸν πνευματῶδες (cp. 878^b 8).
[2] i.e. the breath passes into the vein instead of helping in the emission of the semen.
[3] This problem is almost identical with that of chapter 6, but there man is compared with other animals.
[4] Cp. 878^b 3 and note.   [5] Omitting ἤ before πᾶν with T. G.
[6] Cp. 877^b 31.

breath? Or does its bulk become greater from the increase
of the moisture and its change of position, or from the
formation of moisture? Now very large objects are less 20
easily moved, because the weight is farther away from the
fulcrum.[1]

24 Why is it that those who have sexual intercourse or are
capable of it have an evil odour and what is called a hircine
smell, whereas children do not?[2] Is it because, as has
already been said,[3] in children the breath concocts the
moisture and perspiration, whereas the perspiration of 25
grown men remains unconcocted?

25 Why is it that in summer men are less capable of sexual
intercourse and women more so?[4] As the poet says,

> Men, when the artichoke blooms, are weaker and women more
> wanton.[5]

Is it because the testicles hang down lower then than in
the winter, and they must be drawn up if sexual intercourse 30
is to take place? Or is it because hot natures collapse in
summer when the heat is excessive, but cold natures are
invigorated[6] by it? Now a man is dry and hot, but a
woman is cold and moist; consequently a man's strength is
impaired, but a woman's force is invigorated, its deficiency 35
being compensated by its opposite.[7]

26 Why is it that some persons find pleasure in submitting
to sexual intercourse, and some take pleasure in performing
the active part, and others do not? Is it because each form
of excretion has a region in which it is naturally secreted
and, when an effort is made, the breath in finding its way 879[b]
out causes the excretion to swell and expels it; for example,
urine collects in the bladder, food from which the moisture
has been extracted in the bowels, tears in the eyes, mucous
matter in the nostrils, and blood in the veins? Similarly 5
the semen collects in the testicles and penis. In those
whose ducts are not in a natural condition, owing either

---

[1] And in this case the object is not large and is therefore easily moved.
[2] Cp. above, chapter 12.   [3] Cp. 877[b] 22 ff.
[4] Cp. below, chapter 28.
[5] Hesiod, *Op.* 582, 586.   [6] Reading θάλλουσιν (Richards).
[7] i. e. heat.

to the blocking up of the ducts leading to the sexual organs
(as in the case of eunuchs or other victims of sexual disable-
ment) or to some other cause, all such moisture collects in
the region of the fundament; for it is by this way that it
10 passes out of the body. That this is so is proved by the
contraction of that part in sexual intercourse and the
wasting of that region of the body.[1] If therefore through
wantonness a man has a superfluity of semen, it all collects
there; and so, when desire comes upon him, the part in
which it is collected desires friction. This desire may be
15 due to diet or to the imagination. When desire is stirred
from any cause, the breath collects and secretion of this
kind flows to its natural place. If the secretion be thin
and full of air, when the breath finds its way out the desire
ceases (just as the erection in boys and older persons sometimes ceases without the discharge of any moisture);[2] and
the same thing happens, if the moisture dries up. But if
20 neither of these things occurs, the desire continues till the
one or the other of them takes place. But those who are
effeminate by nature are so constituted that little or no
semen is secreted where it is secreted by those who are in
a natural state,[3] but it collects in this part of the body.[4]
The reason of this is that they are unnaturally constituted;
for, though male, they are in a condition in which this part
25 of them is necessarily incapacitated. Now incapacity may
involve either complete destruction or else perversion; the
former, however, is impossible, for it would involve a man
becoming a woman. They must therefore become perverted
and aim at something other than the discharge of semen.
The result is that they suffer from unsatisfied desires, like
women; for the moisture is scanty and has not enough
30 force to find its way out and quickly cools. When it finds
its way to the fundament only, there is a desire to submit to
sexual intercourse; but if it settles both there and in the
sexual organs, there is a desire both for performing and

---

[1] Cp. chapter 2.
[2] Enclosing ὥσπερ ... ἐκκριθέντος in a parenthesis and reading
παύονται, ὅταν τε κατασβεσθῇ κτλ.
[3] i.e. εἰς ὄρχεις καὶ αἰδοῖα, cp. above, ll. 5, 6.
[4] i.e. ἐν τοῖς περὶ τὴν ἕδραν.

submitting to the sexual act, and the desire for one or other
is greater as more semen is present in either part. This
condition is sometimes the result of habit; for men take
a pleasure in whatever they are accustomed to do and emit
the semen accordingly. They therefore desire to do the 35
acts by which pleasure and the emission of semen are produced, and habit becomes more and more a second nature.
For this reason those who have been accustomed to submit
to sexual intercourse about the age of puberty and not
before, because recollection of the past presents itself to 880ª
them during the act of copulation and with the recollection
the idea of pleasure, desire to take a passive part owing[1] to
habit, as though it were natural to them to do so; frequent
repetition, however, and habit become a second nature.
All this is more likely to occur in the case of one who is 5
both lustful and effeminate.

27   Why is it that those who desire to submit to sexual
intercourse feel a great shame about confessing it, which
they do not feel in confessing a desire for meat or drink or
anything of that kind? Is it because the desire for most
things is necessary and its non-satisfaction is sometimes
fatal to life, but sexual desires proceed from something 10
beyond mere necessity?

28   Why is it that men are more inclined for sexual intercourse in the winter and women in the summer?[2] Is it
because men are hotter and drier in their nature, and
women moister and cooler? In men therefore during the
winter the moisture and heat[3] are sufficient to cause the 15
impulse (and it is moisture and heat which give rise to
the production of the semen), whereas in women the heat
is less and the moisture is congealed owing to the lack of
fire. But in summer in women[4] the heat is well proportioned, whereas in men it is more than sufficient; for the
excess dissolves much of their strength. For this reason

---

[1] Omitting δέ after διά; the sentence otherwise has no principal verb.
[2] Cp. above, chapter 25.
[3] i. e. the natural heat and the moisture of the season.
[4] Reading τοῦ δὲ θέρους ταῖς μέν ἐστι: Xª reads ἐστι for οὖν.

20 also children are thinner during the summer ; for it is a case of ' fire added to fire '.[1]

Why is it that those who are hot by nature, when they **29** are strong and well nourished, if they do not have sexual intercourse are often oppressed[2] by bile, which makes its way down in a very bitter condition, and a salty phlegm is 25 engendered, and their complexion changes? Is it because some excretion always comes away with the semen? (Wherefore also the semen of some men who emit a large quantity of excretion[3] is said to smell of the water in which fish have been washed.[4]) So when they have sexual intercourse, this excretion comes away with the semen and so causes no inconvenience; but if they abstain from copulation, the excretion becomes bitter or salty.

30 Why are the melancholic particularly inclined for sexual **30** intercourse?[5] Is it because they are full of breath, and the semen is a discharge of breath? If so, those whose semen is full of breath must necessarily often desire to purge themselves of it; for thus they are relieved of it.

35 Why are birds, and men with thick hair, lustful?[6] Is it **31** because they have a large amount of moisture? Or is this not true (for the female sex is moist and not hairy), but is the real reason that the natures both of birds and of thick-haired men are able owing to their heat to concoct a large quantity of moisture? This is indicated by the presence of hair and feathers. Or is it because the moisture is plentiful and is overpowered by the heat? For if the moisture were **880ᵇ** not plentiful or were not overpowered, hair would not grow on human beings nor feathers on birds. Now the semen is formed most plentifully under conditions of locality and at seasons that have these characteristics,[7] in spring for example, which is naturally moist and hot. Birds and

---

[1] Cp. 861ᵃ 31 and note.   [2] Reading προσίσταται (Bussemaker).
[3] Reading περιττωματικῶν for πνευματικῶν ; the Latin version renders *excrementis abundantium.*
[4] ἰχθύων πλύντρου must be taken together (cp. πλύμα ἰχθύων, *H. A.* 534ᵃ 27), and ἰχθύων does not agree with περιττωματικῶν as implied by Bonitz (Index, p. 352, *s. v. ἰχθύς*).
[5] Cp. 953ᵇ 32 ff.   [6] Cp. below, x. 24.
[7] i. e. when moisture is plentiful and is overpowered by heat.

lame men are lustful for the same reason, namely, that in 5
both, owing to the deficiencies of their legs, the nourishment
is carried downwards in small quantities only, while the rest
travels into the upper region of the body and is converted
into semen.

32 Why is it that when a man has sexual intercourse his
eyes grow very weak? Is it not clear that this happens
because the moisture leaves them? This is proved by the 10
fact that the semen is cold; for it does not become moist
unless the heat warms it thoroughly. Nor does it require
melting, for it is dispersed about the body like blood.

BOOK V

PROBLEMS CONNECTED WITH FATIGUE

15 WHY is it that long walks are more fatiguing and short **1** walks less fatiguing over level ground than over uneven country?[1] Is it because much movement and violent movement causes fatigue, and spasmodic movement is violent, and continuous and monotonous movement is much movement? In walking therefore on hilly ground, if the distance be long, 20 the change provides a rest, and the same movement is not continued for long, even in the case of horses, owing to the change. On even ground, on the other hand, the similarity of position continues uninterruptedly and gives the limbs no rest, but helps to make the movement continuous. Now if the distance is short, no fatigue is caused on flat ground by 25 long-continued motion; whereas over hilly ground the violent change to an opposite kind of movement, sometimes uphill and sometimes down, gives rise to fatigue. Such, in our opinion, is movement over hill country, and that over level ground is the contrary.

Why is it that those who faint and those who collapse **2** 30 after physical exertion are generally held to become smaller in bulk and their voices shriller? Is it because their voices, appearing to be less, seem shriller (this can be illustrated by the fact that those who imitate distant voices make shrill sounds),[2] while their bulk appears less (because the blood removes from the upper to the lower parts of the body)?[3]

Why is it that only the stomach becomes thinner in those **3** 35 who take violent physical exercise? Is it because the greatest quantity of fat is found round the stomach?

[1] This problem is derived practically word for word from Theophr. *de lassit.*, § 15.
[2] Cp. 899^a 22 ff.
[3] The MSS. read καὶ οἱ ὄγκοι ἐλάττους without adding any reason, which is necessary to the sense and to the balance of the sentence. The words enclosed in brackets are taken from T. G., who evidently translates a longer text and reads *quod sanguis a summis corporis partibus sevocat ad imas.*

4   Why is it that the fat is consumed in those who exert themselves? Is it because fat melts when heated, and the movement causes heat, whereas flesh does not melt?

5   Why is it that the parts round the belly are fattest? Is it because they are near to the nourishment? While then 881[a] the other parts of the body receive something from the belly, the belly itself often receives something. Or is it because the belly is exerted less than the other parts, because it has no joints?

6   Why is it that fatigue ceases more readily if one mixes water with the oil with which one rubs oneself?[1] Is it 5 because the oil sinks in farther when mixed with water, whereas by itself it does not penetrate so well, because it has a tendency to remain on the surface? If, therefore, it sinks in, the body is more softened; for oil is naturally hot, and hot things have a drying and hardening effect, and dryness and hardness are inexpedient in fatigue; but when 10 applied with water the oil has a less drying effect.

7   Why is it that vomiting is prescribed for those who are suffering from fatigue, although vomiting is itself fatiguing? Is it because fatigue is caused by the crushing and pressure and weariness of the bones, and this can be caused either by some external or by some internal agency, and in the latter 15 case from one of two causes, either because the flesh over-reaches its own strength, or because one bodily constituent mingles in a large quantity with the rest of the body and does not keep to its proper place, as happens with the excretions? For any burdens which are put upon us externally cause more fatigue than our own members, even 20 though they are lighter than these in weight. This can be illustrated by the fact that those who have eaten or drunk somewhat freely, though they have exerted themselves less than when they were fasting, yet feel more fatigue, because the food, being unconcocted, is not in its proper place. And since fatigue causes liquefaction, and liquefaction is an excretion, it is the latter which produces fatigue in us. 25

[1] Cp. Hippocrates, *de Diaet.* ii. 65.

wandering about at random and attacking the bones and
sinews and the interior parts of the flesh, which are rare
and open. Consequently vomiting, by dislodging the
excretion which is the cause of fatigue, naturally makes us
less fatigued; for it leaves the body in the state in which it
was when the exertion began. Vomiting is fatiguing, not
30 because of the excess of movement caused while it is taking
place, but when it does not happen to be thoroughly carried
out; for fatigue caused by vomiting occurs when a considerable amount of food is left behind and this contains
excretions, which, as we have already said,[1] happens in
those who have eaten largely. If, therefore, in the latter it
35 is not exertion which causes fatigue, but they feel fatigue
because of the condition in which they are, so vomiting
could not be the cause of fatigue in those who do not get
rid of all the food which is in them;[2] for in that case every
one who vomited would feel fatigue, whereas many through
vomiting become less fatigued.

Why is it more fatiguing to the arm if one casts with the 8
881ᵇ hand empty than with a stone in it?[3] Is it because the
movement is more spasmodic if the hand be empty, for the
hand has nothing to rest upon,[4] such as the thrower finds
in the missile which he holds in his hand? Similarly the
competitor in the fivefold contest[5] finds resistance in the
weights[6] which he holds, and the runner in his arms which

---

[1] Cp. ll. 21-3 above.

[2] i.e. the cause of fatigue is not the act of vomiting but the fact that
food is sometimes left behind which engenders excrements, and these
cause fatigue.

[3] This problem is clearly derived from Theophr., *op. cit.*, § 13; cp.
also *de Incess. Anim.* 705ª 17 ff.

[4] ἀπερείδειν is practically the same as ἀντερείδειν of *Mech.* 851ᵇ 35,
where τὸ ἀντερείδειν expresses *vis inertiae*, the tendency of a body at
rest to remain at rest. In this case the tendency of the missile to
remain at rest causes resistance and therefore makes the action of the
arm less spasmodic. Cp. also *Mech.* 858ª 9 ἀντιτείνει γὰρ τὸ ἠρεμοῦν.

[5] The *pentathlon* was a combined contest in running, jumping, disk-
throwing, javelin-throwing, and wrestling.

[6] ἁλτῆρες were weights held in the hand and thrown backwards by
the jumper whilst in the air to give him impetus. Several such weights
still exist in the British Museum and elsewhere, cp. Norman Gardiner,
Greek Athletic Sports and Festivals, p. 298 ff., and A. S. L. Farquharson
on *de Incess. Anim.* 705ª 17.

he swings;[1] so the former jumps farther if he holds weights 5
than if he does not, and the latter runs more quickly if he
swings his arms than if he does not do so.

9   Why is it that quick running causes a tendency to disease
in the head both in man and in the other animals? Yet
generally speaking running appears to draw the excretions 10
downwards, as does walking; for which reason also those
who walk much grow fat in the legs, because both the
nourishment and the excretions settle down from the upper
into the lower parts. Is it true that while motion has this[2]
effect, yet quick motion, owing to the strain and the holding
of the breath which it involves, causes heat in the head and
inflates the veins in it and renders them liable to be affected 15
by external influences, such as cold and heat, and by the
contents of the trunk;[3] and that if these can enter the head,
disease is necessarily engendered in that region?

10   Why is it more fatiguing to walk on level than on uneven
ground, whereas one can walk more quickly on an even
than on an uneven road?[4] Is it because it is less fatiguing 20
if one does not move continually in the same position, and
this is the case rather in traversing uneven ground? On
the other hand one progresses more quickly the less one's
movement is contrary to nature. On even ground, therefore,
the raising and planting of the foot is a slight but frequent
movement, while the opposite occurs on uneven ground.
Now to raise the foot is unnatural (for raising anything 25
requires an effort); and the slight movement of raising the
foot at each step becomes considerable when repeated many
times.

11   Why is it more fatiguing to lie down on a flat than on
a concave surface?[5] Is it for the same reason that it is
more fatiguing to lie on a convex than on a flat surface?

---

[1] On the importance attached by the Greeks to arm action, especially
in short races, see N. Gardiner, *op. cit.*, p. 282.

[2] Reading τοῦτο for ταῦτό.

[3] The θώραξ is defined by Aristotle (*H. A.* 491^a 27) as τὸ ἀπ᾽ αὐχένος
μέχρι αἰδοίων κύτος.

[4] This problem is again treated in chapter 23; the source in both
cases is Theophr., *op. cit.*, § 14.

[5] The source of this problem is Theophr., *op. cit.*, § 9.

30 For the weight being concentrated in one place in the sitting or reclining position causes pain owing to the pressure. This is more the case on a convex than on a straight surface, and more on a straight than on a concave ; for our body assumes curved rather than straight lines, and in such circumstances concave surfaces give more points of contact than flat 35 surfaces. For this reason also couches and seats which yield to pressure are less fatiguing than those which do not do so.

Why are short walks fatiguing?[1] Is it because they **12** involve abrupt change, for they necessitate coming often to a standstill? Now frequent change from one extreme to 882ᵃ another is fatiguing, for it does not allow one to become accustomed to either extreme, and this is tiring; and one cannot become accustomed to both things at once.

Why is it that those who ride on horseback water more **13** freely at the eyes the quicker the horse goes?[2] Is it 5 because the stream of air which meets them is colder according as it is for a shorter time in contact with the body (as happens in the case of naked runners), and it is the cold which makes the eyes water?[3] Or is the reason the contrary of this, namely, that heat makes the eyes water (the sun, for instance), and movement engenders heat? 10 Or is it due to the impact of the air? For as blasts of wind coming from an opposite direction trouble the eyes, so the air all the more deals a gentle blow the quicker the horse is driven.

Why is it that the other parts of the body become more **14** fleshy when subjected to friction, but the stomach becomes leaner? Or is it true that the stomach does not become 15 gradually leaner[4] but solider? The flesh, however, is not similarly affected, and this is the point of the problem; for, speaking generally, the stomach does become leaner as the result of exercise and exertion. The reason is that the fat

[1] Cp. below, chapter 35 : the source of both problems is Theophr., *op. cit.*, § 14.
[2] Cp. below, chapter 37. [3] Reading δακρύειν (Richards).
[4] *sc.* λεπτοτέρα γίνεται ; but T. G. appears to translate a different text.

parts, and those which naturally admit of more expansion, liquefy when heated. Now the skin naturally admits of expansion; but, because it very quickly fattens, it always 20 contains some fat, unless any disease is present. The reason of this is that it is near the nourishment.[1] Since, therefore, generally speaking, fat is not natural but adventitious, and is not one of the necessary constituents of the body, as is the flesh, the movements set up by exercise and friction warm and melt it and distribute the superfluous nourishment 25 in the other portions of the body. It is for this reason that sitting still makes the stomach fat and the rest of the body thin; whereas movement and friction make the stomach thin and fill out the rest of the body.

15   Why is it that after long and violent walking or running, if one stands on tiptoe, the heels quiver and are hastily 30 drawn[2] down again? Is it because, owing to the continuity and violence of the movement, the quivering of the muscles in the man does not cease? For the mind often controls the body as a whole, but does not control certain parts of it, when they have been set in motion in a certain way, the heart, for example, and the sexual organ. The reason is 35 that a considerable quantity of breath is consumed by heat round the muscles, which does not cool off immediately a man comes to a standstill. This breath, therefore, is drawn down, making him quiver, as it were dragging at him beneath by its movement, and leaves him little control over the most distant part of his body—in this case over his heels. A similar phenomenon occurs in the trembling of the lower lip in those who are angry.

16   Why is it that those who are not running very hard 882^b respire rhythmically? Is it because every rhythm is measured by a definite movement, and the movement at regular intervals which occurs in running is of this nature? As soon, therefore, as they begin to run they respire; and so the respiration taking place at equal intervals, because it 5 is measured out by a uniform movement, creates a rhythm. Or is it because all respiration without exception takes

---

[1] Cp. 880^b 39 ff.   [2] Reading σπῶνται for σπᾶται.

place at equal intervals in those who respire naturally and
do not hold their breath? The rhythm then is not obvious
in those who are sitting or walking, because the movement
10 of the body is slight; and in those who are running vigorously
we cannot comprehend the rhythm of the respiration, because
our senses cannot follow the movement. But in those who
are running moderately fast the movement allows the measure
observed by the breathing to be perceptible, and so shows
the rhythm.

Why is it that, when we are running, the air seems to **17**
15 turn into breath? Is it because, while we are moving in
the act of running, we set in motion a stream of air
continuous with our bodies, and this is breath? Wherefore
the air not only seems to turn into breath, but actually does
so. Or is it because in running we come into collision with
the air, and, when this happens, we have a more acute
20 perception of the air owing to the movement? It is only
natural, therefore, that it should seem to us to turn into
breath; for the phenomenon occurs through the rush of our
movement.

Why is it that one is more liable to fall when running **18**
than when walking?[1] Is it because in the former case one
raises oneself higher before moving? For this is the
difference between running and walking.

25 Why is it that in ascending a slope our knees feel the **19**
strain, and in descending our thighs?[2] Is it because when
we ascend we throw the body upwards and the jerk of the
body[3] from the knees is considerable, and so we feel the
strain in the knees? But in going downhill, because the
30 weight is carried by the legs, we are supported by our
thighs, and so they feel the strain. Furthermore, whatever
is unnatural causes strain and pain. Now it is natural for
the knees to bend forward and the thighs to bend backwards.
In going uphill then the knees are bent backwards owing

[1] Cp. below, chapter 29.
[2] Cp. below, chapter 24; the source in both cases is Theophr.,
op. cit., §§ 11, 12.
[3] Omitting καί before ἡ ἀπὸ τῶν γονάτων with Bonitz.

to one's desire to support oneself, but in going downhill 35
the thighs are bent forwards because the body has a tendency
to fall forwards.

20   Why is it that on journeys the middle of the thigh is the
part which feels the strain most? Is it because in anything
that is prolonged and continuous and fixed[1] the strain falls
most upon the centre, and so it is most likely to break at
that point? Now the thigh is of this nature, and so it is in 883^a
the middle of it that we feel the strain most.

21   Why is it that persons of a moist temperament easily
choke as a result of exertion and through heat? Is it
because their moisture when heated becomes air and the
excess of it burns more fiercely? When, therefore, it cannot 5
find its way out owing to its abundance, the process of
cooling does not take place; and so it quickly catches fire
owing to the natural and adventitious heat. It is for this
reason that perspiration induced by taking physical exercise,
and by exerting oneself generally, and the emission of breath
are beneficial; for breath is formed by the separation and 10
rarefaction of moisture.

22   Why is it that bodies of an equable temperament often
feel weariness but throw it off more easily? Is the cause
the same in both cases? For that which is equable is
uniform, and that which is uniform is the more subject to
similar influences; so if any part suffers, the whole straightway suffers in sympathy. But that which is not equable,
being more disunited, is not sympathetically affected by its 15
parts. A body of equable temperament therefore often
feels weariness, but throws it off more easily, because the
whole body shares it; for the suffering, being distributed
over a larger area, is weaker and therefore more easily got
rid of. But a body which is not of an equable temperament,
inasmuch as it has no communion with its members, is less
often afflicted with weariness, but has greater difficulty in
shaking it off; for its suffering is acute.   20

---

[1] Inserting a comma after ἐστημιγμένου δέ.

Why is it more fatiguing to walk on level than on uneven **23**
ground, whereas one can walk more quickly on an even
than on an uneven road ?[1]   Is it because it is least fatiguing
if one does not move continually in the same position, and
25 this is the case rather in traversing uneven ground ?[2]   But
one travels more quickly when the foot has to be lifted less
in any equal period of time.   On level ground the raising
of the foot is a slight but frequent movement, on uneven
ground the reverse ; but the slight[3] movement of raising
the foot at each step becomes considerable when repeated
many times.

Why is it that in descending a slope we feel the strain **24**
30 most in the thighs, and in ascending in the legs ?[4]   Is it
because in ascending the strain is due to the raising of the
body ?   For the whole body becomes a burden ; and so
the part upon which it all rests and with which we raise it
(that is, the legs) feels the strain most.   For the leg is an
extremity, having length but not having width, as the foot
has ; consequently it is shaken.   So we may cite in
35 illustration the fact that we move weights with the shoulder
and rest them upon it, and therefore feel the strain most in
the shoulder.   But when we are descending, the strain is
caused by the body falling downwards and thrusting us
forward unnaturally, so that we feel the strain most in the
part on which it falls most and which it shakes.   Now the
40 leg remains unaffected, and the trunk forms the weight ; but
it is the thigh which receives the weight and is shaken,
883[b] because it has extension and is forced from above into a bent
position where the trunk presses on it.

Why is it that a journey seems longer when we traverse **25**
it without knowing its length than when we do know it,
all other conditions being equal ?[5]   Is it because to know

---

[1] A repetition, partly verbal, of the problem of chapter 10.

[2] The text as it stands gives no sense and we must clearly restore
from 881[b] 20, **21** ἢ ὅτι ἀκοπώτατον μὲν τὸ μὴ ἀεὶ ἐν ⟨τῷ αὐτῷ σχήματι
ποιεῖσθαι τὴν κίνησιν, ὃ συμβαίνει ἐν⟩ τῇ ἀνωμάλῳ κτλ., the omission being
due to *homoeoteleuton*.

[3] Reading γινόμενον ⟨μικρὸν⟩ πολύ, cp. 881[b] 26.

[4] Cp. above, chapter 19.

[5] This problem occurs again in xxx. 4.

its length is to be able to connect a number with it, and 5
the indeterminate is always more than the determinate?
Just as, therefore, if one knows that a journey is a certain
length, it must necessarily be finite, so, if one does not know,
as though the proposition was convertible,[1] the mind
draws a false conclusion, and the distance appears infinite.
Furthermore, a quantity is determinate, and that which is
determinate is a quantity; therefore when a thing appears 10
not to be determinate, it appears to be as it were infinite,
because that which is of a nature to be determined, if it is
not so, is infinite; so that what appears not to be determined
necessarily appears in a sense unlimited.

26   Why is it that the thighs feel fatigue more than the legs?[2]
Is it because they are nearer to the part of the body which
contains the excrement, so that, when that part overflows 15
with heat owing to the movement, the thighs contract more
readily and to a greater extent? Or is it because the thighs
are more closely connected by growth with one another,[3]
for they suffer considerably owing to the separation of what
is really continuous?[4] For indeed, If one feels fatigue
when there is no excrement in the body, yet it is the thighs 20
and loins which suffer more than the other parts. Or is it
because, just as swellings in the groin are caused, if one
receives a blow,[5] owing to the close connexion of the veins
and sinews, so the thigh is similarly affected? For the
thigh is nearer than the leg to the source of the veins.[6] Or
is it because the thigh remains more in the same position
than the legs, and this is more fatiguing?[7] Or is it because

---

[1] ἀντιστρέφοντος is here used in its logical sense of transposing the
terms of a proposition (cp. *Pr. Anal.* 25ᵃ 6 ff.); the proposition 'any
journey of which I know the length must be finite' is converted into
'any journey that is finite must be one of which I know the length'.

[2] The source of this problem is Theophr., *op. cit.*, § 10.

[3] Reading συμφυεῖς for συμφυές.

[4] Cp. *Top.* 145ᵇ 2 ἡ ἀλγηδὼν διάστασις τῶν συμφύτων μερῶν μετὰ βίας.

[5] Reading πληγέντος (cp. Bonitz, *Index*, p. 140). The sense is clearer
in the original source (Theophr., *l. c.*), ὅτι δὲ ἡ ἀνάρτησις ποιεῖ συμπάθειαν
τῶν νεύρων καὶ φλεβῶν καὶ ἐκ τῶν βουβώνων δῆλον· πληγέντων γὰρ τῶν
κάτωθεν ἐνταῦθα βουβῶνες.

[6] i. e. the heart, cp. *P. A.* 665ᵇ 15, *de iuv. et sen.* 468ᵇ 31.

[7] Cp. 881ᵇ 20–22.

25 the thigh is fleshy, and therefore the natural heat[1] there is considerable?

Why is it that in some people[2] sores are formed as the **27** result of exertion?[3] Is it because, when the body contains impurities, movement heats it and causes other excretions to exude with the perspiration? These excretions, being 30 thick and containing harmful humours of an acid, bitter, and salty nature, cannot be expelled owing to their thickness, but swell up through the flesh and cause sores owing to the bitterness of the humour which they contain.

Why is it that food is not given immediately after exercise **28** and after medicine has been administered? Is it because 35 the body is still being purged and has not yet rested from its toil, and the excretions have not yet been expelled?

Why is it more difficult to run than to walk?[4] Is it **29** because the runner has a heavier burden, since, when he is raised in the air, he has his whole weight to support? But a man who is walking continues to put his weight on the 40 part of him which is at rest, like a man leaning against a wall.

884[a]   Why is it that one does not feel hungry immediately after **30** exercise? Is it because liquefaction still remains until the concoction of anything is complete?[5] Or is it owing to the breath which the exertion engenders from the moisture? Or is it owing to the thirst which is due to the heat caused 5 by the exertion? All these possible causes are present.

Why is it that those who are fatigued and those who are **31** suffering from phthisis are apt to emit semen during sleep?[6] Is it because generally speaking those who are warm and moist are inclined to do so, since the semen naturally has these characteristics?[7] Now such a thing is most likely to

---

[1] Reading, with Richards, τὸ κατὰ φύσιν ⟨θερμὸν⟩ ἔχειν.
[2] Reading, with Richards, ἔνιοι.
[3] The source of this problem is Theophr. *de Sudore*, § 13; cp. Hippocr. *Epid.* vi. 5. 15.
[4] Cp. chapter 18.   [5] Reading ἕως ἄν τι πεφθῇ (Bussemaker).
[6] Galen, *Epid.* vi. 3 quotes this problem as Aristotelian; cp. also Theophr. *de Lassit.*, § 16.
[7] Cp. 876[a] 9–12.

happen in persons in these conditions, when the heat
engendered by sleep is added; for the body requires a slight 10
impulse only, which must be internal and not external.
This condition is fulfilled in those who are suffering from
phthisis and in those who are fatigued; the latter being full
of hot liquid owing to their fatigue and movement, and the
former owing to their state of flux and the heat engendered
by their inflamed condition.   15

32 Why is it more difficult to apply prolonged friction
oneself to the left leg than to the right? Is it because,
though our right is the side which is capable of exertion,
yet the rubbing of the left leg, since it involves [1] a distorted
attitude, is unnatural, and anything which is unnatural is
difficult? [2] The difficulty of rubbing the right side with 20
the left hand is not obvious, because the left hand has no
strength whichever side it is applied to. [3]

33 Why is it healthy to reduce the amount of nourishment
and to increase the amount of exercise? Is it because
abundance of excretion is the cause of disease? Now this
is due either to excess of nourishment or to lack of 25
exercise.

34 Why should the flesh be made rare rather than dense in
order to promote health? [4] For just as a city or locality is
healthy which is open to the breezes (and that is why the
sea too is healthy), so a body is healthier in which the air
can circulate. For either there ought to be no excrement
present in the body, or else the body ought to get rid of it 30
as soon as possible and ought to be in such a condition that
it can reject the excrement as soon as it receives it and be
always in a state of motion and never at rest. For that
which remains stationary putrefies (standing water, for
example), and that which putrefies and does not move
causes disease; but that which is rejected passes away
before it becomes corrupt. This then does not occur if the 35

---

[1] Reading ἐξεστραμμένως ⟨γὰρ⟩ γίνεται with Bussemaker.
[2] Cp. 882^b 31.
[3] The text here seems corrupt, but the sense is clear.
[4] This problem occurs also in i. 52, and is identical with the second
part of xxxvii. 3.

flesh is dense, the ducts being as it were blocked up, but it does happen if the flesh is rare. One ought not, therefore, to walk naked in the sun ; for the flesh thereby solidifies and acquires an absolutely fleshy consistency, and the body becomes moister, for the internal moisture remains,[1] but the surface moisture is expelled, a process which also takes

884^b place in meat when it is roasted rather than boiled.[2]   Nor ought one to walk about with the chest bare ; for then the sun draws the moisture out of the best constructed parts of the body, which [3] least of all require to be deprived of it. It is rather the inner parts of the body which should be

5 submitted to this process ; for, because they are remote, it is impossible to produce perspiration from them except by violent effort, but it is easy to produce it from the chest because it is near the surface.

Why is it that short walks are fatiguing ? [4]   Is it because 35 one often comes to a standstill and there is no uniform

10 movement in the joints, and this is fatiguing ?

Why do those who stand still in the sun become warmer 36 than those who move, and this although movement is productive of heat ?   Is it true that every kind of movement does not produce heat, but some kinds have a cooling effect, as happens, for example, when one blows upon or

15 keeps in motion kitchen-pots which have boiled up ? If then the heat remains when one stands still and, doing so, heats us more than if it were in motion (for our own body always gives off a warm steam, which heats the neighbouring air, as though there were a burning brand there), then, if we remain motionless, the air surrounding us becomes warm

20 for the reasons already stated ; whereas, if we move, a wind is set up which cools us, for wind always has a cooling effect.

Why is it that those who ride on horseback water more 37 freely at the eyes the quicker the horse goes, and those on foot the quicker they run ? [5]   Is it due to the fact that the

[1] Reading διαμένει for δὴ μένει, cp. 865^b 31.
[2] Reading τὰ ὀπτὰ τῶν ἐφθῶν, cp. 865^b 32, 966^a 28.
[3] Reading ἃ for ὃ, as in 865^b 34.
[4] Cp. above, chapter 12.   [5] Cp. above, chapter 13.

air which meets them is cold? For cold causes the eyes to 25
water; for by contracting and solidifying the flesh it purges
out the moisture. Or is the reason the contrary of this,
namely, that the heat causes perspiration, and watering at
the eyes is a form of perspiration? Therefore both perspiration and watering at the eyes are due to heat and are alike
salty; and it is movement which causes heat. Or is it due 30
to the impact of the air? For as blasts of wind coming
from an opposite direction trouble the eyes, so too the
quicker a man drives or runs the more does the air deal
a gentle blow, and this causes the eyes to water, because
the ducts of the eye are rarefied by the blow; for every
blow has the effect either of cleaving or crushing.   35

38 Why is it that fatigue must be cured in the summer by
baths, in the winter by anointing?[1] Is it because the latter,
owing to the cold and the changes which it causes in the
body, must be got rid of by heat, which will cause warmth,
and olive-oil contains heat? In summer, on the other hand,
the body requires moisture; for the season is dry and chills 885^a
are not engendered, because it is warm. A sparing diet of
solid food and a liberal indulgence in liquid nourishment
are characteristic of the summer, the latter being peculiar
to the summer, while the former is commoner than at other
seasons; for indulgence in drinking is peculiar to the
summer because of the dryness of the season, but a sparing
diet is found at all seasons, but is more general in the
summer; for then owing to the season more heat is 5
engendered by food.

39 Why is it that those who are running vigorously experi-
ence the greatest shock, if any one impedes them in their
course? Is it because a thing is being drawn apart most
vigorously when it is being dragged or moved violently in
a contrary direction? If therefore any one impedes one
who is running and whose limbs are being vigorously 10
thrust forward, the result is that he wrenches him back at
the same time as his limbs are still moving forward, and so

---

[1] A repetition almost word for word of Bk. i. 39.

the more vigorously he is running the more violent is the shock which he receives.

Why is it that walking along roads[1] over uneven ground **40** is less fatiguing than along a flat, straight surface? Is it because an upright carriage is natural to everybody, but walking over even surfaces is more fatiguing than over uneven ground, since walking over even ground causes a continuous strain on the same members, whereas walking over uneven ground distributes the strain over the whole body? Now walking in warm weather tends more to make the body thin than in cold weather; for it causes more strain upon the outer parts, and so causes thinness by engendering perspiration. Walking in cold weather makes the flesh more solid and causes a great desire for food; for it engenders an increase of heat in the inner parts and, since they become less liable to be affected by the cold, it cleanses the inner region by increasing the heat there, while it makes the flesh firm, since it cannot prevail over the whole of it. In like manner walking uphill is a greater exertion and tends more to cause thinness than walking downhill. For walking uphill causes most strain to the loins (whereas walking downhill is most trying to the thighs, for the whole weight falls upon them and so usually causes fatigue in them); for as they are forcibly carried[2] upwards in an unnatural manner, heat is engendered. Walking uphill therefore induces perspiration and causes thinness by heightening the respiration and engenders pain in the loins; for the legs, being lifted with difficulty, cause the loins to bend and draw them up, which naturally causes a very great strain. Walking on hard, resisting ground causes fatigue to the muscles and tendons of the legs; for it causes tension in the sinews and **885ᵇ** muscles, because the pressure upon them is violent. Walking on soft ground is fatiguing to the joints; for it causes frequent bending of the joints, because the surface trodden gives way.[3]

---

[1] Reading τῶν κατὰ τὰς ὁδούς (Richards).

[2] Omitting ὑπὸ τοῦ θερμοῦ, which spoils the sense, and reading φερομένους.

[3] Omitting τὸ δ' αὐτό ἐστι πρόβλημα, cp. 874ᵃ 34 and note.

41 Why do we walk with difficulty up a steep slope? Is it 5 because all progression is made up of raising the feet and putting them down again? Now raising the foot is unnatural and putting it down is natural, while putting the foot forward[1] is a mean between the two. Now in walking up a steep slope the unnatural motion preponderates.

42 [Why are riders on horseback less likely to fall? Is it 10 because owing to their fear they are more careful?][2]

---

[1] Reading προθεῖναι for προσθεῖναι; the Latin version renders *proponere*; so too Bussemaker.

[2] This problem is omitted by C^a and neither makes any sense nor is relevant to a discussion of fatigue.

BOOK VI

PROBLEMS CONNECTED WITH THE POSITIONS ASSUMED IN LYING DOWN AND IN OTHER POSTURES.

15 WHY is it that sitting down makes some persons fat and **1** others lean? Is it because bodily conditions differ, some men being hot, others cold? Those therefore who are hot grow fat (for the body owing to its heat prevails over [1] the nourishment); but those who are cold, owing to the fact that their body requires heat introduced from without and 20 derives it chiefly from movement, cannot concoct their food while they are at rest. Or is it because the hot are full of superfluities and require movement to expend them, while the cold are not so?

Why is it necessary that the parts of the body should be **2** distended, as happens when a man takes athletic exercise? 25 Is it because the ducts must be purged by their own breath?

Why is it better to lie in a curved position and why do **3** many physicians prescribe this? Is it because the stomach concocts food more quickly when it is kept warm, and it keeps warmer in this position? Furthermore it is necessary to give the vapours a place where they can settle; for then 30 there is less likely to be pain from flatulence. (It is on this account that swollen veins and abscesses of all kinds help to restore a healthy condition, because they form hollows in which they receive the vapours.) When the body then is extended no hollow is formed (for the internal organs occupy all the space); but a hollow is formed when the body is curved.

35 Why is dizziness more likely to occur in those who are **4** standing than in those who are sitting? [2] Is it because, when one is still, the moisture all inclines to one part of the body? This is why raw eggs cannot be spun round and round but fall over.[3] The same thing occurs when the

[1] i. e. concocts (πέττει) or digests.
[2] Cp. Theophr. *de Vert.* 12.   [3] *Ib.* 2.

moisture in the body is put in motion. So one stands up after having been at rest, when one is in this condition;[1] 886[a] but one sits down after having been in motion, when the moisture is evenly and uniformly distributed

5   Why is it that sleep comes more readily if one lies on the right side? Is it because the conditions when we are awake and when we are asleep are the contrary of one another? Since, therefore, when we are awake we recline 5 on the left side, the contrary will occur when another principle, namely, the contrary, is at work. Or is it because sleep is the absence of movement? The parts then of the body which are most active must be at rest; and the parts of the body on the right are most active. So, if one is lying on this side, a waking principle is as it were enchained.

6   Why does one feel numbness? And why more in the 10 hands and feet than elsewhere?[2] Is it because numbness is a process of cooling, being due to deprivation of blood and its transference elsewhere? Now these parts, especially the feet, are least fleshy and most muscular, and so they are naturally disposed to cool quickly.

7   Why do we find it comfortable to recline on the left side, 15 but sleep better on the right side?[3] Is it because by turning away we avoid looking towards the light, since in the dark sleep comes on more readily? Or is it because we keep awake when reclining on the left side, and in this position we can easily employ ourselves in any particular function; and so for the contrary purpose[4] the contrary position[5] is advantageous; for each position invites to a particular 20 function.[6]

---

[1] i.e. when the moisture is collected in one place.

[2] Cp. Theophr., fr. 11 (Wimmer), *de Membrorum Solutione.*

[3] Cp. above, chapter 5.   [4] i. e. for rest.

[5] Reading from T. G. πρὸς τὸ ἐναντίον ⟨τὸ ἐναντίον⟩ σχῆμα (so too Bussemaker).

[6] Many MSS. here repeat a shorter and slightly different form of chapter 1: 'Why is it that sitting down makes some persons fat and others lean? Is it because of their bodily condition? For those who are hotter grow fat, for the body prevails over the nourishment owing to its heat, which is not lost (reading ἀφαιρουμένην); but those who are cool, because they require heat introduced from without, cannot concoct their nourishment while they are at rest.'

BOOK VII

PROBLEMS CONNECTED WITH SYMPATHETIC ACTION

WHY do men generally themselves yawn when they see 1 others yawn?[1] Is it because, if they are reminded of it when they feel a desire to perform any function, they then put it into execution, particularly where the desire is easily stirred, for example, that of passing urine? Now a yawn is a breath and a movement of moisture; it is therefore easy of performance, if only one sees some one else yawning; for the yawn is always ready to come.

Why is it that, although we do not imitate the action 2 if we see a man stretching out his hand or foot or doing anything else of the kind, yet we ourselves yawn if we see some one else doing so?[2] Or does this not always occur, but only when the body happens to feel a desire and is in such a condition that its moisture becomes heated? For then it is recollection which gives the impulse, as also in sexual desire and hunger; for it is that which causes recollection to exist[3] that provides the stimulus towards the condition observed in another person.

Why is it that if we stand by a fire we desire to pass 3 urine, and if men stand near water (for example, near **886ᵇ** a river) they actually pass urine? Is it because water in general reminds us of the water in our own bodies, and the neighbourhood of water incites our internal moisture to come out? Fire of itself dissolves anything which is solidified in the body, just as the sun melts the snow.[4]

---

[1] Cp. problems 2 and 6.   [2] Cp. problems 1 and 6.

[3] ἐστὶ καὶ should perhaps be read for εἶναι, 'for that which causes the recollection also provides the stimulus', &c.

[4] This problem is definitely referred to as Aristotelian by Aulus Gellius (xix. 4): 'Aristotelis libri sunt, qui problemata physica inscribuntur, lepidissimi et elegantiarum omne genus referti. In his quaerit . . . cur accidat, ut eum qui propter ignem diutius stetit, libido urinae lacessat . . . De urina crebra ex igne proximo facta, verba haec posuit: τὸ δὲ πῦρ διαχαλᾷ τὸ πεπηγός, ὥσπερ ὁ ἥλιος τὴν χιόνα.'

4   Why is it that those who come into contact with certain diseases become affected by them, but no one ever becomes healthy through contact with health?[1] Is it because 5 disease is a state of movement, while health is a state of rest? If so, disease can set up movement, but health cannot. Or is it because disease comes to us against our will, while health comes by our own wish? Things then which occur against our will are different from those which occur by our wish and deliberate choice.

5   Why is it that not only do some unpleasant sounds make us shudder[2]—for example, when a saw is being 10 sharpened, or pumice-stone cut, or a stone ground[3]—but the signs of effects produced in others conveyed by the sight cause those very effects in ourselves? For our teeth are set on edge when we see others eating anything bitter, and some people faint when they see any one being strangled. Is it because every sound or noise is a breath,[4] and this penetrating into us naturally causes disturbance? 15 Now it will cause greater disturbance if it comes either in great quantity or with an unusually violent impact, setting up a new condition or causing some alteration within us. Wherefore breaths[5] which, though large in bulk, are yet soft, stir the actual seat of sensation, and such have a pleasant effect; but those which are rough, causing a violent impact, shake the seat of sensation and affect a wide area 20 owing to the force of their impact. Now things which are cold also affect a wide area, for coldness is a kind of force; therefore, as has been already said, it causes shuddering. But things which are rough, because they cause a series of frequent impacts, striking on the base of the hair thrust it in the opposite direction;[6] for when the hair is thrust out, its ends must necessarily assume a contrary position, 25 with the result that it stands upright; for hair always naturally lies flat. The direction taken by the breath

---

[1] Cp. 951ᵃ 4 ff.
[2] φρίττειν covers the meanings both of trembling or shuddering and of the hair standing on end.
[3] Cp. 964ᵇ 35 ff.   [4] i.e. sound-vibration.
[5] Cp. 871ᵃ 33, 889ᵃ 28.   [6] i.e. outwards from the head.

which is conveyed to the body by the hearing is downwards
from above. The sounds, therefore, which we have mentioned [1] being harsh, the hair bristles for the reasons stated.
The bristling occurs more on the rest of the body than on
30 the head, because the hair there is weaker and the effect
produced is weaker. The sensation produced by hearing
being blunter than that produced by sight, the effects
produced by it are confined to the surface of the body ;
the bristling of the hair is an effect of this kind, so it occurs
35 from many dissimilar causes. The sensation produced by
sight being very distinct, its results too are correspondingly
more distinct ; therefore the effects actually [2] occurring in
others are reproduced in those who observe them, but
887ᵃ more mildly than in the original.[3] But as a result of
hearing our hair stands on end for fear, not of the actual
sounds, but of the anticipation which they arouse ; for it
is an anticipation of grievous ill.

Why is yawning caused by the sight of others yawning,[4] **6**
5 and so also the passing of urine, particularly in beasts of
burden ? Is it due to recollection ? For when recollection
occurs the part of the body concerned is stimulated. In
men then, because their sensations are finer, when they
see something stimulation and recollection occur simultaneously. But in the beasts the sight is not sufficient
by itself, but they require another sense to be called into
10 activity ; so the sense of smell must also be employed, this
being a more easily stimulated sense in unreasoning animals.
So the other animals always pass urine in the same spot
as the first one ; for the stimulus is most acute when the
sense of smell is employed ; and the sense of smell is called
in play when they are near the spot.

15 Why is it that when we see any one cut or burned or **7**
tortured or undergoing any other painful suffering, we
share mentally in his pain ? Is it because nature is common

---

[1] Cp. ll. 10, 11 above.
[2] Reading with Bonitz αὐτὰ for ταῦτα, cp. above, l. 12.
[3] As in the example given in 886ᵇ 12–14, viz. fainting as the result
of seeing a person strangled.
[4] Cp. chapters 1 and 2.

to us all, and it is this which shares in the sufferer's pain, when we see any of these things happening to him, through kinship with him? Or is it because, just as the nose and hearing according to their particular faculties receive certain 20 emanations, so also the sight does the same as the result of things pleasant and painful?

8 Why is it that those who come into contact with phthisis or ophthalmia or scurvy become affected by them, but there is no contagion from dropsy or fevers or apoplexy and the rest? In ophthalmia is contagion due to the fact that 25 the eye is very easily affected and more than the other senses assimilates itself to that which it sees—for example, it moves when it sees something else moved—and so it very readily becomes disordered when it sees another eye in that condition? In phthisis is the contagion due to the fact that phthisis makes the breath weak and laboured, and those diseases are most quickly contracted which are due to the corruption of the breath, as is seen in plagues? He therefore who comes into contact with the sufferer 30 inhales this corrupted breath, and so himself becomes ill, because the breath is unhealthy; and he catches the disease from one person only, because that person exhales this particular breath, which is different from that which others exhale; and he catches the same disease, because, in inhaling the breath [1] by which he becomes infected, he is inhaling just such breath as he would if he were already suffering from the disease. Scurvy alone is catching among similar diseases,[2] such as leprosy and the like. because it affects the surface of the body and causes a glutinous discharge 35 (for this is the nature of itching diseases), and so this disease,[3] being on the surface of the body and glutinous, can be conveyed by contact. Other similar diseases are not so conveyed, because either they are not on the

---

[1] Reading τοῦτο for τούτῳ, but the corruption of the text has probably gone farther than this and some such reading as τὴν αὐτὴν δὲ νόσον τούτῳ ὃς ἂν ἀσθενήσῃ, ὅτι ἀναπνεῖ κτλ. is perhaps nearer to the original: 'he catches the same disease as the sick man, because he is inhaling', &c.

[2] Reading μόνον with the best MSS.

[3] Reading αὕτη (Richards).

surface, or else, being on the surface, they do not remain there, because they are dry.

887ᵇ   Why do purslane and salt stop inflammation of the 9 gums?[1] Is it because purslane contains some moisture? This is seen to be so if one chews it or if it be crushed together[2] for some time; for the moisture is then drawn out of it. The glutinous matter sinks into the gum and draws out the acidity. For that there is an affinity between 5 the disease and the remedy is shown by the acidity; for the juice of the purslane has a certain acidity. Salt, on the other hand, dissolves and draws out the acidity. Why then do lye and soda not have this effect? Is it because they have an astringent instead of a dissolvent effect?

[1] This problem occurs also in i. 38, where see notes.
[2] Reading συνθλασθῇ for συντεθῇ, see note on 863ᵇ 13.

BOOK VIII

PROBLEMS CONNECTED WITH CHILL AND SHIVERING.

1 WHY is it that those who are chilled become livid? ₁₀ Is it because the blood is congealed by the cold and, as it congeals, becomes black through the absence of heat? (A white colour, on the other hand, is to be attributed to fire.) For this reason also the flesh of the aged is particularly livid, because it contains very little heat.

2 Why is it that those who are chilled cannot sleep?[1] Is ₁₅ it because any one who is chilled tends to hold his breath, but a sleeper exhales rather than inhales, so that it is difficult for one who is cold to sleep, since it is impossible to do contrary things simultaneously?

3 Why is it that those who are ill or in pain or angry become more active under the influence of cold? Is it ₂₀ because a cold condition makes a man stronger?

4 Why is it that athletes in good training do not bear the cold well?[2] Is it because their condition is clean and airy and free from fat? Such a condition is easily accessible to the air, since it is permeable and does not contain any heat; fat, on the other hand, is hot, unless it is saturated ₂₅ with moisture.

5 Why are the extremities most affected by cold? Is it due to their narrow shape? Also the ducts in them, being narrow, hold little blood, and therefore little heat; for the blood is hot.

6 Why are the feet more liable to become chilled when they are suspended in mid air? Is it because the wind blows more underneath then? Or is it because the blood ₃₀ is contracted into a narrower space below, and so the rest

---

[1] Cp. chapter 22.   [2] Cp. chapter 10.

of the foot is more easily chilled, because the heat leaves it?

Why is it that stout persons are especially liable to chill, 7 although fat is warm? Is it because, owing to the greatness of their bulk, their extreme parts are far from the internal heat, while their near parts are far from the external cold?

35 Why do people shiver after sneezing and after passing 8 urine?[1] Is it because in both processes the veins are emptied, and when they are empty the cold air enters, and this causes shivering?

Why is it that ravenous hunger is felt in cold weather 9 and in winter rather than in summer? Is it because 888ᵃ ravenous hunger is brought on through lack of dry nourishment, and in the cold and winter the internal heat contracts into a narrower space and its internal nourishment soon fails, and when this happens ravenous hunger is more likely to occur? The faintness and weakness due to 5 ravenous hunger occur when liquefaction takes place in the body owing to the collection of heat in one place. This liquefied matter flows into the region usually occupied by the nourishment and itself becomes nourishment for the body; if it attacks the seat of respiration, loss of voice and weakness ensue, the loss of voice being due to the obstruction of the passage of the breath, while the weakness is 10 caused by the lack of nourishment in the body and internal liquefaction. Treatment in such cases can be quickly and simply applied, because the cause of the trouble is external; for it is the external[2] cold making our heat contract which causes the ravenous hunger. So just as one trembles and turns pale from fear, but, when freed[3] from the danger, 15 one recovers immediately; so too those who are suffering from ravenous hunger, after taking a little bread, quickly recover,[4] having undergone a violent and unnatural dis-

---

[1] This problem is almost identical with xxxiii. 16.
[2] Reading ἐκτός (W. D. R.) for ἐντός.
[3] Reading ἀφεθέντες for ἀφέντες (so also Richards).
[4] καὶ οἱ βουλιμιῶντες . . . ταχεῖα ἡ ἀποκατάστασις γίνεται is an anacoluthon for οἱ β. ταχέως ἀποκαθίστανται.

turbance, but not having been permanently injured thereby ;
for the same thing which resists the tendency[1] of nature also
restores us to our natural course.　Once relax the force
which is straining against nature, and the body slips back
into its natural state as suddenly as children who are 20
playing at 'tug-of-war' with a rope, if the rope is let go,
fall on their backs.

10　Why is it that those who have undergone athletic training do not bear the cold so well as those who have not
done so?[2]　Is it because the fat is got rid of by their
exercises, and it is the fat which gives warmth, since that
which is oily is hot?　Or is it because the body is in a 25
more airy and rare condition, because the fat and the
excretions have been got rid of, so that there is nothing
to keep out the cold?　Or is it because through the opening[3]
of the pores by perspiration a number of doors are as it
were removed?[4]　It is clear that the same condition does
not conduce both to health and to strength ; for obviously
a condition of health is one of fatness, while a condition 30
of strength is a state of rarity.

11　Why do we shiver both when hot and when cold water
is poured over us?　For it is strange that contraries should
produce the same result.　Is it because, when cold water
is poured over us,[5] the extinguishing of the internal heat
causes shivering, whereas, as the effect of warm water, the
superficial cold is enclosed[6] in one place and massed to- 35
gether by its inward rush?[7]　So both effects are due to
the same cause, but in one case it operates from within and
in the other from without.

12　Why do the hairs bristle upon the skin?[8]　Is it because
they naturally stand erect when the skin is contracted, and

---

[1] Reading τῇ . . . ἀγωγῇ.　　　　　　[2] Cp. chapter 4.

[3] It is doubtful whether ἀποστόμωσιν, a word apparently only occurring here, can mean 'opening', since the verb ἀποστομοῦν means 'to
stop up'; ἀναστόμωσιν should therefore probably be read.

[4] And so let in the cold.

[5] Reading προσχεομένοις for προσχεόμενοι.

[6] See note on 867[b] 32.　　　　　　[7] Cp. de Somno, 457[b] 14-17.

[8] This problem is repeated in xxxv. 5 ; the same subject is treated
in chapters 15 and 21 below.

40 this contraction occurs owing to cold and certain other conditions?

888ᵇ Why is it that one shivers at the last emission of urine? **13** Is it because, whilst the warm liquid is still within, the bladder and the passages round it are full, but when it has passed out they fill up[1] again with cold air, for nothing can be empty, but must be full either of something corporeal 5 or of air? Inasmuch then as cold air enters, shivering is a natural result.

Why is it that the tongue of those who are chilled, like **14** that of the drunken, stumbles? Is it because, as it stiffens and hardens with the cold, it becomes difficult to move, and, when this happens, it cannot speak plainly? Or is it 10 because, the outer parts of the body being solidified by the cold, the moisture flows together within and saturates the tongue, and so it cannot perform its function, as has been already described in the case of the drunken?[2] Or is it because owing to the trembling produced by chill, the movement of the tongue is irregular and it cannot 15 articulate the words which it utters, and consequently it stumbles?

Why do the hairs stand erect on the bodies of those **15** who are chilled?[3] Is it because as a result of cooling the heat collects in the inner region of the body, and the flesh, as the heat leaves it, contracts more and more, and, as it is drawn together, the hairs become more upright? 20 [Or is it because . . .][4]

Why in the winter are we more likely to become chilled **16** through running than through standing still? Is it because the air surrounding the body, when we stand still, no longer causes discomfort when once the body is thoroughly warm, but on the other hand, when we are running, we are continually encountering more and more cold air, and so 25 are more liable to become chilled? Moreover also air is

---

[1] Reading ἐνέπλησθεν.
[2] Cp. 875ᵇ 27 ff.   [3] Cp. chapters 12 and 21.
[4] A further reason has been accidentally omitted.

cold when it is in motion, and it is for the most part such
air that meets us in running.

17   Why is it that it is colder at dawn, although[1] the sun
is nearer to us? Is it because the period of the sun's
absence is then at its longest, so that the earth has become
more cooled? Or is it because towards daybreak the dew
falls, as does the hoar-frost, and both of these are cold? 30
Or do they too fall because the heat which rises from the
earth is overpowered, the reason that it is overpowered
being the absence of the sun? So that they do not fall
when the sun is farther away, but when it is nearer they
fall and become congealed,[2] because the longer the sun
is absent the cooler the ground becomes.[3] Or is it because
the nocturnal breezes tend to cause cold[4] towards day- 35
break? Or do we only imagine that it is colder because
then the food within us is concocted and, the stomach
being emptier, we are more liable to feel the cold? This
can be illustrated by the fact that we feel very cold after
vomiting.

18   Why is it that those who are chilled feel pain if they
are taken straight to the fire, whereas they do not do so
if they are warmed gradually? Is it because one contrary 40
immediately succeeding another contrary always sets up 889^a
a violent change? We may compare the fact that if one
bends a tree by degrees, it does not suffer, but if one bends
it with greater violence and not gradually, it breaks off.
If therefore like is unaffected by like, and the heat of
a man who is chilled collects and concentrates within him, 5
and the moisture and cold are left behind, and a contrary
is destructive of its contrary, it follows that, if one is
warmed by degrees, the heat comes out gradually and less

---

[1] Omitting ἤ, or else reading ἢ ⟨νυκτὸς⟩ from 938ᵃ 32, where the same
problem is treated more briefly ; cp. below, l. 33, which clearly states
that the dew and the hoar-frost, which fall at dawn, fall when the sun
is near the earth. T. G. renders *cur tempore matutino frigus acrius
est, cum tamen sol propius adsit?*

[2] Putting a comma after πήγνυται instead of a semicolon.

[3] i.e. it so happens that the time when the dew and hoar-frost fall
is the time when the sun is nearest to the earth, but the cause is not
the position of the sun but the fact that the ground is coldest at dawn.

[4] Reading, with Richards, πνεύματα ⟨αἴτια⟩ τῆς ψύξεως.

pain is caused, but, if the warming is not gradual, the
heat is rather drawn out.[1]

10   Why is it that when we are chilled the same heat causes **19**
more burning and pain?[2] Is it because owing to its
density the flesh holds the heat which comes into contact
with it? This is the reason why lead becomes hotter than
wool. Or is the passage of the heat violent because the
pores are congealed by the cold?

15   Why is it that those who are angry do not become **20**
cold? Is it because anger and wrath are the opposite
of cowardice? Now anger is the result of fiery heat, for
by retaining a large quantity of fiery heat within us we
become warm. This is particularly noticeable in children.
For grown-up men when angry become distracted,[3] but
children first of all take in breath in large quantities and
20 then blush; for the amount of heat in them being very
great and causing liquefaction makes them blush, since,
if one were to pour a quantity of cold water on them, they
would cease[4] from their wrath, for their heat would be
quenched. The opposite occurs in cowards and those
who are afraid;[5] for they are chilled and become cold
25 and pale; for the heat leaves the superficial region of
their bodies.

    Why is it that when we shiver, the hairs stand erect?[6] **21**
Do they lie down[7] because they grow in moisture? For
the weight[8] of the hair prevails over the moisture. Now
shivering is caused by the cold, for the cold naturally
30 congeals the moisture. When therefore the moisture, out

---

[1] The text of the whole of this passage is unsatisfactory though the
general meaning is plain.

[2] i.e. more than it would if we were not chilled. This problem is
repeated in xxxvii. 4.

[3] It is improbable that βλάπτονται can mean this by itself without
the addition of ταῖς φρέσι or something similar; it is almost certainly
corrupt. Some verb meaning 'suppress their feelings' or 'escape
notice' would be expected. T. G. does not render οἱ μὲν γὰρ ἄνδρες
βλάπτονται.

[4] Reading παύσαιντ' ἂν (Richards).

[5] The Teubner text prints φοβούμενο for φοβούμενοι.

[6] Cp. chapters 12 and 15.

[7] Reading κατακέκλινται (W. D. R.) for κατακεκλεῖσθαι, cp. below, l. 35.

[8] Reading, with Bonitz, βάρος for βάθος, cp. below, l. 34.

of which the hair grows, undergoes a change and congeals,
it is natural that the hair should undergo a change also.
If therefore it changes into a contrary condition, it either
remains permanently in that condition, or else the hair
will again prevail over the moisture. It is not, however,
likely that the hair can by its weight overpower the
moisture when it is congealed and condensed; and if it is
impossible for the hair to lie down anywhere because the 35
moisture is congealed, the only thing left for it to do is
to stand erect. Or is it because, as a result of cooling,
the heat collects in the interior region of the body, and
the flesh, as the heat leaves it, contracts more and more,
and, as it draws together, the hair grows more upright,[1]
just as when one fixes a twig or some other object into **889**[b]
the ground and fills the space round it and collects the
soil on every side, it is more likely to remain erect than if
one leaves the soil loose round it?

22   Why is it that those who are chilled find it particularly
difficult to go to sleep?[2] Is it because one who is chilled
holds his breath rather than exhales, and a sleeper exhales 5
rather than inhales? Chill therefore induces a condition
which is directly opposed to sleep.

[1] Down to this point the sentence is a repetition of 888[b] 17–21.
[2] Cp. chapter 2

BOOK IX

PROBLEMS CONNECTED WITH BRUISES, SCARS, AND WEALS [1]

10 WHY is it that weals can be prevented by the application **1** of newly flayed hides, particularly those of rams, and by breaking eggs over the part affected? Is it because both these things prevent the collection of moisture and the consequent swelling? For the wounded place attracts the moisture and swells owing to the inflammation.[2] Now eggs owing to their glutinous consistency cause adhesion 15 and prevent swelling (their effect resembling that of cautery [3]), acting as a kind of glue. The hide owing to its glutinous condition adheres and at the same time by its heat sets up concoction and stops the inflammation, for they do not remove it for several days. Rubbing with salt and vinegar is also employed with the object of drawing out the inflammation.

20 Why is it that scars are black on the rest of the body but **2** white on the eye? [4] Is it because a scar, like everything else which is diseased, takes on the contrary of its original colour, and it is in the black part of the eye that wounds are inflicted? However, scars on the body do not become 25 black immediately, but are white at first; nor are scars in the eye always white,[5] but it is only after a while that they become absolutely or comparatively so.

Why does a fennel-stalk [6] make the parts round the place **3** which is struck red and the centre of it white? Is it

---

[1] Some MSS. read τραύματα, wounds, for μώλωπας.
[2] Bekker's reading ἕλκει ἐπαίρεται makes no sense. T. G. renders *pars enim collisa humorem trahit intumescitque.* We clearly should read ἕλκει ⟨τὸ ὑγρὸν καὶ⟩ ἐπαίρεται, the omission being due to *homoeoteleuton.* The sentence then explains τὴν ἄθροισιν τοῦ ὑγροῦ καὶ τὴν ἔπαρσιν of the previous sentence. [3] Cp. 862[a] 10, 11.
[4] This subject is also treated in chapter 7.
[5] Reading λευκαί for μέλαιναι (Bonitz).
[6] Fennel-stalks were used as canes by ancient schoolmasters, cp. Xen. *Cyrop.* ii. 3. 20.

because it presses the blood away from the middle, at the point where, being round, it strikes deepest? Or would one not expect the blood for this reason to return there again, the redness being due to the rush of blood and such a rush taking place towards the part which is struck?

4 Why is it that, when a violent blow is struck with a fennel-stalk, the middle of the flesh which is struck turns white and the surrounding parts red, whereas, if an ordinary stick is used, the middle is the reddest part?[1] Is it because the fennel-stalk owing to its lightness, if it strikes a hard blow, disperses the blood on the surface, and so the part from which the blood has retired has a white appearance, but the parts to which it flows in greater quantities become redder? When the part struck swells up, the dispersed blood does not readily return to its place, because it is scanty and the course which it must follow is upwards;[2] for it needs the force imparted by mass to make it follow an unnatural course. But blows dealt with hard objects owing to their weight and strength cause compression and crushing. The compression, therefore, produces a hollow, while the crushing causes rarity; for crushing is a mild form of cutting and cleaving. The middle of the part struck becoming hollow and rare, the blood flows into it from the surrounding surface; for it naturally flows downwards and into the rare parts, because they give way before it. The blood collecting there naturally makes this part red, whilst the surrounding regions, from which the blood retires, turn white.

5 Why do those who are splenetic have black scars? Is it because their blood is corrupted by the admixture of vitiated and watery blood from the spleen? Now the scar occupies only a small depth of the skin on the surface, but the blood, which is black because it is watery and hot, shows through the skin and gives the scar also a black appearance. Moreover, very often the scar meanwhile becomes blacker and blacker; this is due to the same cause, for owing to

---

[1] A fuller and more satisfactory treatment of the problem of the previous chapter.

[2] i.e. the blood must flow uphill in order to reach the centre of the swelling.

the weakness of the skin the blood cools, and as the heat
evaporates, turns blacker. Similarly in the aged the flesh
becomes blacker,[1] and their congenital scars are blacker
20 than those of the young; for their whole body assumes as
it were the condition of a bruise owing not to the thinness
of their skin but to the fact that their heat fails.

Do things which cause the same effect possess the same **6**
power for the production of that effect, or not? For
25 example, seeing that copper and radishes and mashed beans
and 'sea-lungs'[2] and clay and various other things take
away bruises, do they do so in virtue of the same power?
Or does copper produce this effect because of its rust, which
has a medicinal value,[3] and beans and 'sea-lungs' and clay
because they have an attractive force owing to their rarity,
30 and other things for various other reasons? Or is the
ultimate effect the same in all these cases (for many of them
possess contrary qualities, for example heat and cold[4]),
while the earlier effects may nevertheless be different?

Why do all other scars turn black, while those in the eye **7**
are white?[5] Is it because they cause a change in respect
35 of colour in the parts in which they occur, and so scars
which occur in the eye, which is black, must necessarily be
white?

Why is the blow of a fennel-stalk more painful than that **8**
of some much harder instruments, if in dealing the blow
one considers their comparative effects? For it would be
much more natural to suppose that the stroke of a harder
instrument would be more painful, for it deals a heavier
890ᵇ blow. Is it because the flesh is pained not only by receiving
a blow but also by dealing one? When it is struck by

---

[1] Cp. 967ᵇ 13 ff.

[2] Apparently the marine animal of *de Part. Anim.* 681ᵃ 18 and *Hist. Anim.* 548ᵃ 11.

[3] For the supposed medicinal value of copper cp. 863ᵃ 28 and note.

[4] This is explained by 890ᵇ 7–10, where particular examples are given in illustration of the same problem. There the instances of contraries are χαλκός, which is cold, and θαψία, which is hot. Of the examples given in this chapter ῥαφανίς corresponds most nearly to θαψία.

[5] Cp. above, chapter 2.

hard substances, it only receives a blow (for it yields to them because they are hard); but when it is struck by a fennel-stalk, two effects are produced—it receives a blow and it also deals one, because it does not yield owing to the 5 lightness of the weight imposed upon it; and so the blow is of a double nature.

9   Why are thapsia [1] and metal ladles used to stop bruises, (the former being applied immediately, the latter at a later stage), containing as they do opposite qualities? [2] For a ladle is cold, as the poet says,

> Between his teeth the chilly bronze he bit; [3]

whilst thapsia is hot and burning. Does the ladle have the 10 same effect that water has upon the fainting? For its coldness encounters the heat and prevents it from escaping out of the blood, which collects on the surface owing to the blow and congeals when the heat passes out. For just as would happen if it congealed outside, so the blood congeals near the outer surface while it is still under the skin; but [4] 15 if the heat is prevented from escaping by the coldness of the bronze, the blood does not congeal, but disperses again and returns to the area from which it was collected. Thapsia being hot has the same effect; for by its heat it prevents congelation.

10   Why are bruises dispersed by the application of copper 20 objects such as ladles and the like? [5] Is it because copper is cold? It therefore prevents the escape of the heat from the blood which collects as the result of the blow, and it is the loss of heat from the surface which causes the bruise. The ladle must therefore be applied quickly [6] before congelation takes place. Thapsia, too, mixed with honey is 25 a good remedy for the same reason; for being hot it prevents the blood from becoming cold.

[1] Cp. 864^a 5 and note.
[2] Cp. above, chapter 6.   [3] Homer, *Iliad*, v. 75.
[4] Reading δὲ ἐξιέναι (W. D. R.) for διεξιέναι and putting a colon before κωλυθέντος, and deleting the comma after θερμοῦ.
[5] Cp. above, chapter 9.
[6] This hardly agrees with 890^b 8.

Why is it that if a wound occurs several times in the 11
same place, the scar turns black ?　Is it because, whenever
a wound is dealt, the part affected is always weak and
30 becomes weaker the more often it is wounded ?　Now that
which is weak is chilled and full of moisture ; therefore it
has a black appearance.　Again [1] large and inveterate
wounds form black scars, and to receive frequent wounds is
equivalent to having one wound for a long time.

Why do we apply metal ladles to bruises ? [2]　Is it because, 12
35 when we are struck, the part affected is cooled and the heat
leaves it ?　So the application of the ladle, the material of
which, being copper, is cold, prevents the heat from escaping.

Why is it that hairs do not grow on scars ?　Is it because 13
the pores, from which the hairs grow, become blocked up
and displaced ?

891^a　Why do blows cause swelling and discoloration ?　Is it 14
because the moisture in the part affected is dispersed and,
after breaking its way into the adjoining regions, recoils
again and collects owing to the conglutination of the
moisture ?　Also if any small veins are burst, a collection of
5 bloodshot matter is formed.

---

[1] Putting a full stop after φαίνεται and reading εἶτα ⟨τὰ⟩ for εἰ τὰ
(C^a according to Bekker reads εἶτα).
[2] Cp. above, chapters 9 and 10.

BOOK X

A SUMMARY OF PHYSICAL PROBLEMS

1   WHY is it that some animals cough, while others do not, for example a man coughs, but an ox does not? Is it because in most animals ·the excretion is directed to some other part, but in man to this part? Or is it because in man the matter in the brain is very copious and liquid, and coughing occurs when phlegm flows down?

2   Why is it that in man alone of the animals blood flows from the nostrils? Is it because the matter in his brain is very copious and liquid, whence the veins, becoming full of excretion, send forth a stream through the ducts? For unhealthy blood (that is, blood which is mixed with excretions from the brain) is thinner than pure blood and resembles lymph.[1]

3   Why is it that some animals are fat under the flesh, others in the flesh, and others in both these places? Is it because in those whose flesh is dense the moisture collects between the skin and the flesh, because the skin there is naturally loose,[2] and this moisture being concocted turns into fat? Those, on the other hand, who have rare flesh and a tightly fitting[3] skin, become fat in the flesh; while those who have both these characteristics are fat both in and under the flesh.

4   Why are boys and women less liable to white leprosy than men, and middled-aged women more than young? Is it because white leprosy is due to the escape of breath, and the bodies of boys are dense and do not allow the passage of breath, and those of women do so less than those of men, for the breath is diverted into the *catamenia*? The density

[1] Cp. *P. A.* 651[a] 17.
[2] Reading διὰ τὸ ταύτῃ εἶναι τὸ δέρμα ἀφεστὸς φύσει (Bekker).
[3] Reading with Bussemaker προσεστός for προεστός.

of their flesh is shown by its smoothness. But the bodies of middle-aged and old women allow the passage of breath; for they alone, like old buildings, have a loose structure of their component parts.

35   Why is it that man alone has white leprosy?[1] Is it **5** because he is the thinnest-skinned and at the same time the fullest of breath[2] amongst the animals? An indication of this is the fact that leprosy appears most abundantly and soonest on the parts of the body where the skin is thinnest. Or, while this is true, is there a further reason, namely, that 891[b] in man alone of the animals the hair turns grey? For in leprosy the hair becomes grey,[3] and so it is impossible for leprosy to occur in those in whom the hair does not turn grey.

   Why is it that goats and sheep yield the most milk, **6** 5 although their bodies are not the largest, whereas women and cows produce proportionately less? Is it because in the latter two cases the available material is used up to form bulk, whilst in the other animals it goes into excretions, and in sheep and goats the residue of the excretion all becomes milk? Or is it because sheep and goats are more prolific than the large animals, and so draw off more 10 excretion, because they have more offspring to nourish? Or is it because owing to the weakness of their bodies more excretion is formed during the period of gestation, and the milk comes from the excretion?

   Why is it that in some animals (goats, for example) **7** a change of water causes a change in their colour, which assimilates to that of other animals in the new locality, 15 whereas with other animals (man, for example) this is not so? Or, to put the question generally, why do some animals change and others not (the crow, for example)? Do those animals not change in whom the element of moisture does not predominate, birds, for example, which consequently have no bladder?[4] Why is it that while such creatures do

---

[1] Cp. below, chapter 33.
[2] Reading πνευματωδέστατον (Richards).
[3] Cp. *G. A.* 784[a] 26.   [4] Cp. *P. A.* 671[a] 15 and W. Ogle's note.

not themselves change, yet their offspring do so? Is it ₂₀
because the offspring is weaker than its parents?

8   Why are males usually larger than females? Is it because
they are hotter,[1] and heat is productive of growth? Or is
it because the male is complete in all its parts, whereas the
female is defective? Or is it because the male takes a long
time to attain perfection, the female a short time?

9   Why is it that some animals bear their young quickly, ₂₅
but in others the period of gestation is a long one? Is it
because the longer-lived animals come to perfection more
slowly? It is the longer-lived animals that take a long time
to bear their young. This is not, however, true of the
longest lived of all animals; for example, the horse is
slower in bearing its young but shorter-lived than man.
The reason of this is the hardness of the uterus; for the ₃₀
uterus of a mare may be compared to a dry soil which does
not readily bring the crops to maturity.

10   Why is it that the young of all other animals resemble
their parents in nature more closely than do those of man?
Is it because man's mental condition is more varied at the
moment of sexual intercourse, and so the offspring varies
according to the condition of the male [2] and female parents? ₃₅
The other animals, or most of them, are wholly absorbed in
the sexual act;[3] further, owing to this avidity, impregnation
does not usually take place.

11   Why is it that fair men and white horses usually have 892^a
grey eyes? Is it because there are three colours in eyes,
black, greenish,[4] and grey, and the colour of the eyes
follows that of the body, resulting in this case in greyness? ₅

12   For what reason are there dwarfs? Or to put the question
more generally, why are some creatures quite large, others
small? Let us examine the latter question. The causes of
smallness are two, either space or nourishment—space, if it

---

[1] A much-disputed point, cp. *P. A.* 648^a 30 ff.
[2] The Teubner text prints ὅτε for ὅ τε.
[3] Reading πρὸς αὐτῷ τούτῳ (Richards).
[4] Lit. 'as in goats' eyes'; for the meaning of αἰγωπός see D'A. W.
Thompson's note on *H. A.* 492^a 3.

be narrow, and nourishment, if it be scanty; as happens
10 when attempts are made to make animals small after their
birth, for example by keeping puppies in quail-cages.
Those who suffer from lack of space become pygmies; for
they have width and depth corresponding to the dimensions
of their parents, but they are quite small in stature. The
reason of this is that owing to the narrowness of the space
15 in which they are confined the straight lines become crushed
and bent. So pygmies are like figures painted on shops
which are short in stature but are seen to be of ordinary
width and depth. Those who fail to come to perfection
from lack of nourishment clearly have the limbs of children,
20 and one sometimes sees persons who are very small and yet
perfectly proportioned, like Melitaean terriers.[1] The reason
is that the process of growth has a different effect from that
of space.

Why is it that some animals come into being from the 13
sexual intercourse of animals with one another, others
from the compounding of certain elements—a process
resembling the original production of their species?[2] Just
25 as the writers on natural phenomena explain the first
origin of animals as being due to powerful changes
and movements in the world and universe;[3] so now, if
it is to happen again, some similar movements must
take place.[4] For the beginning of anything is the most
30 important part, being indeed half of the whole;[5] and in
this case the seed is the beginning. The reason then why [6]

---

[1] Also mentioned in *H. A.* 612ᵇ 10, where D'A. W. Thompson
renders 'Maltese dogs'; but according to Pliny (*N. H.* iii. 26. 30)
they came originally from an island off Dalmatia (now called Meleda).
They were a common form of lap-dog; cp. Theophr. *Char.* 21,
Anth. Pal. vii. 211. They frequently appear on vases, e.g. one
figured in *Ann. dell' Inst.* 1852, which has the inscription Μελιταίε,
and shows a long-haired dog with a bushy tail and a sharp nose,
rather of the type of a 'Spitz' or 'Pomeranian': such dogs also figure
on coins and gems, see Imhoof-Blumer and Keller, *Tier- und Pflan-
zenbilder des klass. Altertums*, Plates I. 45; II. 29; XV. 33, 34.

[2] Cp. below, chapter 65.

[3] Omitting the comma after γενέσθαι and reading παντὸς ⟨τὰς⟩ μεγάλας, οὕτω καὶ νῦν.   [4] Putting a full stop after κινήσεις.

[5] Hesiod, *Works and Days*, 40.

[6] Reading αἴτιον ⟨τοῦ⟩ τοιαῦτα (Richards).

small animals which are not produced by sexual intercourse resemble the species as it originally came into
being, is the smallness of the seed; for the smaller a thing
is, the smaller is its first beginning. So the changes even
of this are sufficient to produce a seed for it.[1] And this
is what actually happens; for it is under conditions of 35
change[2] that such creatures usually come into being. In
the larger animals a greater change is necessary for their
production.

14 Why is it that some animals are prolific, such as the
pig, the dog, and the hare, whilst others are not so, for 892ᵇ
instance man and the lion?[3] Is it because the former
class has a number of wombs which they desire to fill and
moulds into which[4] the semen is distributed, while with
the latter the opposite is the case?

15 Why has man a smaller distance between his eyes in
proportion to his size than any other animal? Is it because 5
man follows the law of nature most closely[5] and perception
is naturally of that which is in front,[6] since it is necessary
to see beforehand that to which the movement is directed?
Now the greater the distance between the eyes, the more
will the sight incline sideways. So if the sight is to accord
with the law of nature, the distance between the eyes 10
ought to be as small as possible, for then it will travel
most directly forward. Further, the other animals must
necessarily turn their gaze sideways, since they do not
possess hands; their eyes therefore are farther apart, especially those of sheep, because they generally advance
bending their heads downwards.

16 Why is it that the other animals seldom or never emit 15
semen during sleep? Is it because no animal except man
sleeps on its back and no emission of semen takes place
except in that position?[7] Or is it because the other

---

[1] The text here appears to be corrupt and gives no very satisfactory
sense.
[2] i.e. by decay, cp. *G. A.* 715ª 25.　　　　[3] Cp. *G. A.* 771ª 14 ff.
[4] Reading εἰς ἃς (W. D. R.)　　　[5] Cp. *de Incess. Anim.* 706ᵇ 10.
[6] Reading τοῦ ἔμπροσθεν (so also Richards).
[7] Cp. Theophr. *de Lassit.*, § 16.

animals dream less than man, and the emission of semen only takes place when the imagination is stirred?

Why is it that some animals move their heads and others **17** not? Is it because some have no necks[1] and so cannot move their heads?

Why does man sneeze more than the other animals?[2] **18** Is it because in him the ducts are wide through which the breath and scent pass in? For it is with these, when they fill with breath, that he sneezes. That these ducts are wide is shown by the fact that man has a weaker sense of smell than any other animal; and the narrower the ducts, the keener is the sense of smell. Since, therefore, the moisture, the evaporation of which causes sneezing, enters in larger quantities and more often into wide ducts, and man more than any other animal has such ducts, he might naturally be expected to sneeze[3] most often. Or is it because his nostrils are particularly short and so the heated moisture can quickly turn into breath, whereas in the other animals, owing to the length of their nostrils, it cools before it can evaporate?

Why is it that in no animal is the tongue of a fatty **19** consistency? Is it because that which is fat is dense, whereas the tongue is naturally rare in order that it may recognize different flavours?

Why is it that females pass urine with an effort, but **20** males without an effort? Is it because in the female the bladder is farther away both in depth of position and in distance, since the womb is situated between the fundament **893^a** and the bladder? It therefore requires a greater effort to drive the urine owing to the distance of the womb; and the requisite force is exercised by an effort of the breath.

Why is it that all such animals as do not fly shed their **21** winter coats, except the pig? The dog, for example, does so, and the ox. Is it because the pig is very hot and

---

[1] e. g. fishes and serpents, cp. *P. A.* 664^a 20, 686^a 1, 691^b 30.
[2] This problem is more fully treated in chapter 54; it is repeated in xxxiii. 10.
[3] Reading πταρνύοιντο for πτάρνοιντο.

its hairs grow out of a hot substance (for that which is
fat is hot)? In the other animals the hair is shed because
either the moisture cools or else the natural heat cannot
concoct the[1] nourishment. But the pig[2] does not shed
its hair, either because the moisture in it undergoes no 10
change or because its nourishment is properly concocted;
for whenever any cause is present to make it shed its hair,
the fat is sufficient to prevent it. Sheep and men are
unaffected owing to the quantity and density of their hair;
for the cold cannot penetrate deep enough to congeal the 15
moisture or to prevent the heat from concocting it.

22 Why is it that in sheep the hair grows again softer
when it is plucked out, but in man it is harder? Is it
because the hair of sheep grows out of the surface, and
so can be plucked out without causing pain, the source 20
of its nourishment, which is in the flesh, remaining un-
impaired? So the pores[3] being opened, the excretions
evaporate more readily, and the wool receives the natural
nourishment of the flesh, the latter being fed by soft, sweet
nourishment. The hair of man, on the other hand, since
it grows from a great depth, can only be plucked out by 25
force and painfully. This is shown by the fact that it
draws blood with it. The place therefore from which it
is plucked is wounded and scarred. So at last the hair
ceases to grow on those who pluck it out, and as long
as it does grow again, it grows hard, because all the
nourishing food in the flesh fails, and it is from the excre- 30
tions of this food that the hair grows. This can be
illustrated by the fact that in all those who inhabit a
southerly clime the hair is hard, because the exterior heat
penetrates deeply and vaporizes the well-concocted nourishment; but the hair of those who dwell in northern climes
is soft, because in them the blood and sweet humours are
nearer the surface, for which reason also they have a 35
healthy complexion.

---

[1] Reading πέττειν ⟨τὴν⟩ τροφήν (Bussemaker).
[2] Reading ⟨ἡ δὲ ὑς⟩ ἢ διὰ ... ⟨ἢ⟩ διὰ κτλ. These changes are
demanded by the sense and supported by the Latin version of T. G.
[3] ἀνοιχθέντων seems to require a substantive such as τῶν πόρων in
agreement with it. The Latin version renders *meatibus patefactis*.

Why is it that in sheep the longer the hair grows the **23** harder it is, whereas in man it is softer? Is it because the hair of sheep, obtaining the nourishment described above,[1] receives less food because it is far removed from 40 the source of it, and the nourishment already present in **893ᵇ** it easily evaporates out of it owing to the heat as a result of incomplete concoction?[2] And as the hair dries it becomes harder;[3] for it is the moisture which makes it soft. Human hair, on the other hand, receives less nourishment but is situated nearer to the source of it;[4] and the nourishment is more thoroughly concocted because it is less abundant, and, being concocted, it makes the hair 5 softer, because anything that is concocted is softer than that which is unconcocted; for human hair is derived more[5] from excretion than that of sheep. That concocted matter is softer than unconcocted[6] is shown by the fact that the wool of young sheep is softer than that of old.

10 Why is it that thick-haired men and birds with thick **24** feathers are lustful?[7] Is it because they are naturally hot and moist? Now both these characteristics are necessary for sexual intercourse; for the heat causes excretion, and the moisture is the form which the excretion takes. Lame men are lustful for the same reason as birds;[8] for, owing to the deficiencies of their legs, the nourishment is carried 15 downwards in small quantities only, but travels into the

---

[1] i.e. in ll. 22–4 above.

[2] Reading ἀπεψίαν with Bussemaker.

[3] Reading σκληρότεραι (T. G. has *duriores*).

[4] The sentence αἱ δὲ τῶν ἀνθρώπων ἐλάττω μέν, μᾶλλον δὲ τῆς ἀρχῆς is obviously incomplete as it stands and the required sense must be supplied from the Latin version of T. G. and the implied contrast with the hair of sheep given in ᵃ 38 ff., and something like αἱ δὲ τῶν ἀνθρώπων ἐλάττω μὲν ⟨ἔχουσι τὴν τροφήν⟩, μᾶλλον δὲ τῆς ἀρχῆς ⟨ἐγγίζονται⟩ must be restored.

[5] Reading πλεῖον for πλείστου.

[6] This σημεῖον cannot refer to the sentence immediately preceding it, with which it has no connexion; it must therefore refer to πάντα γὰρ τὰ πεπεμμένα κτλ; the Latin version of T. G. inverts the order of the last two sentences.

[7] This problem is partly identical with iv. 31; cp. also *Physiogn.* 806ᵇ 18.

[8] Reading διὰ τὸ αὐτὸ δὲ καὶ οἱ ⟨ὄρνιθες λάγνοι καὶ οἱ⟩ χωλοὶ ἄνδρες; cp. 880ᵇ 4.

upper region of the body in large quantities, and is there converted into semen.

25 Why has man no mane? Is it because he has a beard, and so the nourishment consisting of the necessary excretion, which in animals goes into the mane, in man goes into the beard?

26 Why is it that all animals have an even number of feet?[1] Is it because it is impossible to move (except by jumping), unless some part is at rest? Since, then, progression involves two things,[2] namely, movement and rest, we immediately get here a pair[3] and an even number. Quadrupeds have two more legs;[4] for they move two, while the other two are at rest.[5] Six-footed animals have an additional pair,[6] of which one moves while the other is at rest.

27 Why is it that in horses and asses hair grows out of scars, but not in man?[7] Is it because in the other animals the skin is part of the flesh, but in man it is only as it were a condition of the flesh? For in man the surface of the flesh seems to become harder through cooling and resembles what we call the crust of boiled meal;[8] just, then, as this crust is really only boiled meal, so what is called man's skin would really be only flesh. Now when a man receives a wound or is chafed, the result is that his flesh becomes denser; and so, the surface of the flesh having undergone a change, the wounded parts do not assume the same nature as the original skin; and, as the flesh has undergone a change, it is not to be wondered at that what grew from it no longer does so—a phenomenon also occurring in what is called baldness, which

---

[1] Cp. below, chapter 30; also *H. A.* 489^b 22, and *de Incessu Anim.* 708^a 21 ff., which is clearly the source of this problem.

[2] Reading ἐκ δυοῖν τινοῖν ἀνάγκη τὴν πορείαν εἶναι.

[3] δὲ must be omitted as a dittograph of δύο.

[4] Reading καὶ τετράποδα δύο ἔτι (for διότι) πλείους, cp. l. 25.

[5] Placing a full stop after ἑστήκασι.

[6] οἱ ἕξ is clearly corrupt, since οἱ can only agree with πόδες understood, which gives no sense. οἱ is perhaps a corruption due to the influence of οἱ δὲ δύο. What the sense requires is καὶ ἑξάποδα καὶ ἄλλους δύο ἔτι, and this has been translated above.

[7] Cp. below, chapter 29.   [8] Cp. *G. A.* 743^b 7.

is also due to a corruption and change in the surface of
40 the flesh. When, however, beasts of burden have been
894ᵃ chafed and recover again, the parts of the body affected
fill out again with the same substance, but it is weaker
than it was before; and since their skin too is a part
of them, the hair (which grows out of the skin) must
come forth and grow, but it is white, because the skin
5 which was formed is weaker than the original skin, and
white hair is the weakest kind of hair.

Why is it that among the other animals twins though **28**
differing in sex are just as likely to survive, but this is
not so with the young of man?[1] Is it because human
twins are particularly weak, for man naturally produces
10 only one offspring at a time? Now in twins it is unnatural
to find a diversity of sex; and so what is most contrary
to nature is also weakest.

Why is it that in horses and asses hair grows out of **29**
scars, but not in man?[2] Is it because the scar impedes
the growth of the hair, either owing to the condensation
of the flesh or because its nutrition is impaired? In man,
15 therefore, it absolutely prevents the growth owing to the
weakness of the hair; but in horses it does not prevent,
but merely impairs, the growth.

Why have animals an even number of feet?[3] Is it **30**
because in anything that moves something must necessarily
be at rest, and this could not happen if there were an odd
20 number of feet (for[4] it was the arrangement of the feet in
pairs which originally made movement possible)?

Why is it that animals are asleep for a shorter time than **31**
they are awake, and their sleep is not continuous? Is it
because all the excretion is not concocted at the same
time, but, when some is concocted, the animal is relieved
and wakes up? Again, they more often wake up when
the region in which the excretion is concocted becomes
25 cold; for it quickly and frequently ceases to do its work,

---

[1] Cp. *H. A.* 584ᵇ 36 ff.   [2] Cp. above, chapter 27.
[3] Cp. above, chapter 26.   [4] Reading εἴπερ for ὅπερ (Richards).

and this cessation causes awakening. Sleep not unnaturally [1] seems to be pleasant, because it gives us rest; but the rest which we take in sleep does not last longer than the time taken by our natural activities, nor do we eat for a longer period than that during which we abstain from food, in spite of the fact that eating is pleasanter than fasting.

32 Why is it that some animals imitate their parents imme- [30] diately after birth, whilst others, like man, do so late, or hardly at all, or never? Is it because some quickly attain a state of physical perfection,[2] whilst others are late in doing so, and some are without a perception of what is for their good, whilst others possess such a perception? Those therefore which possess both these qualities, namely, perception of what is for their good and physical perfec- [35] tion, imitate their parents, but those who have not both these qualities do not do so; for physical and perceptive powers are both requisite.

33 Why is it that white leprosy does not occur in animals other than man?[3] Is it because, while it is a disease which afflicts other animals, only in man does the hair and skin turn partially white? (But, if so, one might raise the question 894ᵇ why diversity of colour in animals occurs at birth and not afterwards.) Or is it because the skin of other animals is hard, whereas man has naturally very thin skin? Now white leprosy is an excretion of breath,[4] which in the other animals is prevented from escaping by the thickness of their skin. [5]

34 Why is it that in white leprosy the hair turns grey, but it does not necessarily follow that leprosy is always present where there is grey hair?[5] Is it because the hair grows from the skin, and greyness is as it were a corruption of the hair? When therefore the skin is in a morbid condition, the hair that grows from it is necessarily affected; but when [10] the hair is unhealthy the skin is not necessarily so.

----

[1] Reading ὡς εἰκός for οὐδὲ εἰκός: the Latin version renders *non immerito*.

[2] τὸ γνωρίζειν is certainly corrupt and has probably come into the text as a gloss upon αἴσθησιν. τὴν ἐπιτέλεσιν τοῦ σώματος or its equivalent must be restored from l. 35. (Richards suggests τὸ βαδίζειν.)

[3] Cp. above, chapter 5.   [4] Cp. 891ᵃ 28.

[5] The source of this problem appears to be *G. A.* 784ᵃ 25.

Why is it that some animals are ill-tempered after bearing 35 young, dogs, for example, and pigs, but others are not noticeably so, for instance women and sheep? Is it because those animals which are full of excretions[1] are mild-tempered, for that which causes them pain passes out at the 15 time of birth? Those,[2] on the other hand, who in bearing young lose healthy material, are made irritable by the reduced condition in which they are; just as hens are bad-tempered, not just when they have laid, but when they are sitting, from want of food.

Why is it that eunuchs, when they are emasculated, in 36 20 other respects change into the likeness of the female,—for they have the voice, the shapelessness,[3] and the looseness of joints which characterize women, and so undergo a violent change, as do other animals when castrated (in bulls and rams, however, we find the horns assuming contrary forms, the reason being that their females have contrary kinds of 25 horns, and so bulls when they are castrated grow larger horns and rams smaller horns)—in respect of size, however, alone eunuchs change into the likeness of the male, for they become larger? Now size is characteristic of the male, for the female is smaller than the male. Or is it not after all a change into the likeness of the female rather than the male? For it is not a change in every dimension, but only in height, whereas the male is characterized by width and 30 depth as well; for this is what his full growth involves. Furthermore, as is the female to the male, so within the female sex is the maiden to the woman; for the latter has reached the full nobility of form, while the former has not yet done so. It is into the likeness of *their* nature[4] then that the eunuch changes; for their growth is in height. So Homer well says,

> Stature chaste Artemis gave them,[5]

---

[1] Such as women and sheep, cp. *H. A.* 584ᵃ 6.
[2] Omitting ὥστε or reading τούτοις in its place.
[3] Xᵃ clearly preserves the right reading here, ἀμορφίαν. ὀξύτητα has come into the text as a gloss upon φωνὴν θηλυκήν.
[4] Reading εἰς τὴν τούτων οὖν ⟨φύσιν⟩ μεταβάλλει (Richards).
[5] Homer, *Od.* xx. 71.

as being able to give what, being a maiden, she herself 35 possessed. When, therefore, a eunuch changes in size, he does not change into the likeness of the male; for the change is not in the direction of physical perfection, but eunuchs increase in size only in respect of height.

37 Why is it that eunuchs either never suffer from varicocele, or do so less than others? Is it because, by their being 895[a] castrated, their nature changes into that of persons lacking generative power? Now boys and women lack this power, and neither has varicose veins except women very occasionally.

38 Why is man better able to utter many voices, while other 5 animals of one and the same species utter only one voice? Has man too[1] really only one voice, but many forms of speech?[2]

39 And why has man different forms of speech in different places,[3] while the other animals have not? Is it because men in their speech make use of a number of letters, but the other animals employ either none or only two or three consonants? (Now it is consonants combined with vowels that form 10 speech.) Now speaking is signifying something not merely by the voice but by certain conditions of the voice, and not merely to signify pain or pleasure; and it is the letters which regulate these conditions. But children express what they want to say just in the same way as wild beasts; for young children cannot yet make use of the letters in speech.

40 Why is it that of all animals man alone is apt to hesitate 15 in his speech?[4] Is it because he is also liable to be dumb, and hesitancy of speech is a form of dumbness, or at any rate the organ of speech is not perfect? Or is it because man partakes more of rational speech, while the other animals only possess voice, and hesitancy of speech, as its

---

[1] Reading ⟨ἢ⟩ καὶ κτλ. (So also Richards.) T. G. has *an hominum etiam vox una est?*

[2] On διάλεκτος and φωνή see 898[b] 30, and cp. *H. A.* 536[b] 1.

[3] Reading αὕτη ⟨ἄλλη⟩ ἄλλη (W. D. R.).

[4] Cp. below, Book xi. 55.

name implies,[1] is simply[2] being unable to explain one's meaning continuously?

20 Why is it that man more than the other animals is apt to **41** be lame from birth? Is it because the legs of animals are strong (for quadrupeds and birds have bony and sinewy legs), but human legs are fleshy, and so owing to their softness they more easily become damaged through movement?[3] Or is it because in man alone of animals the period 25 of gestation varies? For he may be born after the seventh or the eighth or the tenth month.[4] For the other animals there is one fixed time for coming to perfection without any further delay;[5] but in man the period of delay[6] is long, and so, when the foetus moves, its extremities being soft 30 are more[7] liable to become broken in the longer period.

Why have eunuchs sore and ulcerated legs? Is it because **42** this is also characteristic of women, and eunuchs are effeminate? Or, while this is true, is the cause in women as well this, that the heat has a downward tendency? (Menstruation shows that this is so.) So neither eunuchs 35 nor women grow thick hair, owing to the presence of copious moisture in them.

Why is it that no animal except man suffers from gall- **43** stones?[8] Is it because in beasts of burden and cloven-hoofed animals the ducts of the bladder are wide? Those animals which produce their young alive not immediately but after **895ᵇ** an interval, like certain of the fishes,[9] never have bladders, but the sediment which might form gall-stones is forced into the bowels (as happens also in birds), and so easily passes out with the excrement. But man has a bladder and a stalk[10] to the bladder, which is narrow in proportion to his

---

[1] i.e. ἰσχνόφωνος from ἴσχειν and φωνή, cp. 903ᵃ 38 f. οἱ ἰσχνόφωνοι ἴσχονται τοῦ φωνεῖν.

[2] Reading κατὰ τὸ ὄνομα οὐδὲν ἢ οὐ for οὐ κατὰ τὸ ὄνομα ἐν ᾗ οὐδέ.

[3] i.e. in the uterus before birth.

[4] Cp. *G. A.* 772ᵇ 7 ff.   [5] Reading οὐ διατρίψασι (Richards).

[6] ἐν πλήθει, if retained, must be used here of time, but some such reading as ἐν τῇ μήτρᾳ, 'in the uterus', seems to be demanded by the context. (Richards makes the same suggestion.)

[7] Reading πλεῖον for πλείω.   [8] Cp. *G. A.* 519ᵇ 20.

[9] Cp. *P. A.* 670ᵇ 10, 671ᵃ 15, 676ᵃ 30.

[10] Cp. *H. A.* 497ᵃ 20, 24.

size; so, because he has this part, the earthy matter is 5
forced into the bladder (and so chamber-pots become
discoloured by it) and, owing to the heat in that region, it
becomes concocted and thickens still more and remains
there and increases owing to the narrowness of the urethra;
for the earthy sediment, being unable to make its way out 10
easily, coheres together and forms a gall-stone.

44   Why is it that beasts of burden and cattle and horned
animals and birds do not eruct?[1] Is it owing to the dryness
of their stomachs? For the moisture is quickly used up
and percolates through; whereas eructation results when
the moisture remains and evaporates. In animals with long 15
manes and tails,[2] owing to the length of their necks, the
breath tends to travel downwards, and therefore they
generally break wind backwards. Birds and horned
animals neither eruct nor break wind; and ruminating
animals do not eruct, because they have several stomachs
and the so-called 'reticulum';[3] and so the breath finds
a passage up and down through many channels, and the 20
moisture is taken up before it can become vaporized and
cause either eructation or breaking of wind.

45   Why is it that tame animals are invariably found also in
a wild state, but wild animals are not always found also
in a tame condition?[4] For even men certainly exist in
a wild state in some places,[5] and wild dogs are found in 25
India and horses elsewhere; but lions and leopards and
vipers and many other animals are never found in a tame
state. Is it because the inferior condition is more easily
acquired at first and it is easier to degenerate into it, since it
is not the original but the ultimate nature which is difficult
to attain to at once?[6] For this reason all tame animals are

---

[1] This problem is quoted by Apollonius, *Hist. Mirab.*, as from the
φυσικὰ προβλήματα of Aristotle.
[2] This class is enumerated in *H. A.* 491ᵃ 1 ff.
[3] Or 'second stomach', see *H. A.* 507ᵇ 4-8.   [4] Cp. *H. A.* 488ᵃ 30.
[5] Cp. *P. A.* 643ᵇ 5 (but in *H. A.* 488ᵃ 27 man is said never to be
'wild'). Darwin (*Descent of Man*, pp. 41, 42) insists on the fact that
it is erroneous to regard man as more domesticated than the other
animals.
[6] This statement seems to contain a glimmering of the Doctrine of
Evolution.

30 at first wild rather than tame (for example the child is
greedier and more quick-tempered than the man), but
physically weaker. So we find the same state of affairs in
the products of nature as in those of the arts. For among
the latter there are always badly made objects, and the bad
are more numerous than the good, beds for instance and
35 garments and the like ; and, where a good object is produced,
it is always possible to find also a bad one, but, where a bad
object is produced, it is not also possible always to find
a good one. This can be seen from an examination of the
works of the primitive painters and sculptors ; for in their
day there was not yet any good painting or sculpture anywhere, but only inferior work. So likewise nature always
896^a produces inferior specimens and in a greater number,[1] and
superior specimens in a smaller number and in some cases
not at all. Now the tame is superior and the wild inferior.
It is, I suppose, easier for nature—not the primitive nature
but that towards which animals develop —to make the good
kinds also tame ;[2] but the opposite kinds never, or scarcely
ever, become tame, and it is only under certain conditions of
5 locality and time that sooner[3] or later owing to a general
admixture of circumstances all animals can become tame.
The same thing happens in plants of all kinds ;[4] those
which are garden plants are also found in a wild state, but
it is impossible for all to be cultivated, but some are so
peculiarly conditioned in many respects in their natural soil
10 that, though neglected and left wild, they grow better and
more like cultivated plants than those which are carefully
tilled in other soil.

Why is it that men have large navels, whereas in the **46**
other animals they are inconspicuous ? Is it because in the
latter, owing to the long period of gestation,[5] they wither

---

[1] Omitting καὶ πλείους.

[2] Reading φύσει δὲ οὐ τῇ ἐξ ἀρχῆς ἀλλ' ἐφ' ἥν, οἶμαι, ῥᾷον ποιεῖν ⟨τὰ⟩
υπουδαια καὶ ἥμερα.

[3] Reading ἄρτι for ἀρτίου, and placing the comma after ποτὲ instead
of after ἀρτίου.

[4] With the whole of this passage cp. *de Plantis*, 819^b 29 ff., and
Theophr. *H. P.* iii. 2. 2.

[5] i. e. the period of gestation is longer in proportion to the time
from conception to the full maturity of the young.

off and project outwards and swell all up into sores, and so 15 the navel sometimes even becomes mis-shapen? [1] Now man comes forth from the womb in an imperfect condition, and so his navel comes away still full of moisture and blood. That some animals are perfect and others imperfect at birth is shown by the fact that some animals can fend for themselves, but children require looking after.

47   Why is it that some animals copulate only once, others 20 frequently, and some only at certain seasons of the year and others at no fixed time? [2] For example, man does so at all times but wild animals only occasionally, and the wild boar only does so once but the domesticated pig frequently.   Is it the effect of nourishment and warmth and exercise, since 'Cypris depends on fullness'? [3] Again, the same species bears young once in some localities but several times in 25 others; for instance, the sheep in Magnesia and Libya have young twice a year. [4] The reason is the prolonged period of gestation; for animals, when their desire is satisfied, feel desire no longer, just as, when they have fed, they no longer desire food.   Also animals when pregnant feel less desire for sexual intercourse, because the menstrual purgation does not take place.

48   Why is it that men who have porous teeth are generally 30 short-lived? [5] Is it a sign that the skull is thick?   For the brain is weak if it is not well ventilated, and so, being moist, it quickly decays, just as all other things decay if they are not in motion and cannot evaporate.   For this reason too man has very thick hair upon the head, and the male is longer-lived than the female because of the sutures in his skull. [6] 35

---

[1] The sense is unsatisfactory, since the latter part of the sentence seems to contain arguments which imply a prominence of the navel.

[2] Cp. Plutarch, *Quaest. Nat.* 21.

[3] A quotation from a lost play of Euripides; cp. Nauck², p. 647, no. 895.

[4] Cp. *H. A.* 573ᵇ 30.

[5] Cp. xxxiv. 1.

[6] Which permit more evaporation; cp. *P. A.* 653ᵇ 1 ff. and W. Ogle's note.

But we must next consider length of life in relation to other conditions.[1]

Why then are men long-lived who have a cut right across **49** their hands?[2] Is it because animals whose limbs are badly articulated are shortest-lived, aquatic animals for example? **896ᵇ** And if those which are badly articulated are short-lived, clearly those that are well articulated must be the opposite. Now the latter are those in which even those parts are best articulated which are by nature badly articulated; and the inside of the hand is the least well articulated part of the body.

5   Why is it that man alone squints, or at any rate does so **50** more than any other animal?[3] Is it because he alone, or more than other animals, is liable to epilepsy[4] in infancy, when distortion of the vision also always begins?

Why is man more affected by smoke than other animals? **51** Is it because he is most prone to shed tears, and shedding tears is one of the effects of smoke?

10   Why does horse take pleasure in and desire horse, and **52** man take pleasure in man, and generally why do animals delight in animals which are akin to and like them? For every[5] animal is not equally beautiful, and desire is of the beautiful. The beautiful then ought to be pleasanter; but in actual fact it is truer that not every kind of beauty is pleasant,[6] nor are pleasure and the beautiful equally[7]
15 pleasing to all men; for example, one creature takes greater pleasure in eating or drinking and another in sexual intercourse. The question why each creature prefers and takes

---

[1] The Latin version of T. G is no doubt right in rendering here, *an in ceteris quoque idem est cogitandum*; the reference being to the following problem, which is coupled to the present chapter by the connecting particle δέ, and probably also chapter 64.

[2] i.e. the so-called 'line of life', cp. also xxxiv. 10.

[3] Cp. xxxi. 26, 27.

[4] ἐπίληπτον should probably be read here for ληπτόν, cp. 960ᵃ 10 and note.

[5] Reading ὁτιοῦν (Platt) for ὅτι πᾶν.

[6] Omitting τὸ καλὸν καὶ τὸ ἡδύ, which in its original form, τὸ καλὸν καὶ ἡδύ, was doubtless a marginal variant of κάλλος ἡδύ.

[7] Reading πᾶσιν ⟨ὁμοίως⟩ ἡ ἡδονή to complete the sense.

greatest pleasure in sexual intercourse with a creature that is akin to it is dealt with elsewhere;[1] but to add that what is akin is also most beautiful is not true.[2] But we regard as beautiful that which is pleasing with a view to sexual intercourse, because, when we feel desire, we delight in looking upon the object of our desire. And indeed the same thing happens in other forms of desire; for example, when we are thirsty we take greater pleasure in the sight of something to drink. So that which is beautiful in view of a certain use of it seems to be most pleasant because we particularly desire it. (But this is not true of that which is beautiful in itself, as is proved by the fact that even grown men appear to us beautiful, when we look at them without[3] any idea of sexual intercourse. Do they then appear beautiful in such a way as to give our eyes more pleasure than those who are of an age for sexual intercourse? There is no reason why they should not, provided we do not happen to feel a desire for sexual intercourse.) Thus something to drink appears to us as particularly good; for, if we happen to be thirsty, we shall see it with considerable pleasure.

53   Why is it that in man the front of the body is more thickly covered with hair than the posterior portion, but in quadrupeds the posterior part is hairiest?[4] Is it because all two-footed animals have the front part of the body more thickly covered? For the birds resemble man in this respect. Or is nature always wont to protect the weaker parts and is every creature weak in some respect?[5] Now in all quadrupeds the posterior portions are weaker than the front parts owing to their position; for they are more liable to suffer from cold and heat; but in man the front portions of the body are weaker and suffer likewise under these conditions.

[1] Viz. in iv. 15 and 26.

[2] Restoring the MS. reading οὐκέτι, which is more idiomatic than οὐκ ἔστι.

[3] To make sense of this passage we must read ⟨οὐ⟩ πρὸς τὴν συνουσίαν βλέψασι, the negative here being implied by εἰ μὴ ἐπιθυμοῦντες τύχοιμεν in l. 27. (So too Sylburg and Bussemaker.)

[4] The source of this problem is clearly *P. A.* 658[a] 16 ff.

[5] τόπον should perhaps be read for τρόπον.

897ᵃ   Why is it that man sneezes more than any other animal?[1] **54**
Is it because he also suffers most from running at the nose?
The reason of this is that, the heat being situated in the
region of the heart and being naturally disposed to rise
upwards, in the other animals its natural direction is to-
5 wards the shoulders and thence, splitting up owing to
refraction, it travels partly into the neck and head and
partly into the backbone and flanks, because these parts
are all in the same straight line and parallel to the ground
on which the animal stands. Now the heat,[2] as it travels
along, distributes the moisture uniformly to these parts
10 alike; for the moisture follows the heat. Four-footed
animals therefore do not suffer either much from running
at the nose or sneeze; for sneezing is due to the rush
either of a mass of breath, when moisture evaporates more
quickly than the body, or of unconcocted moisture (hence
it precedes a cold in the head);[3] and these forms of
moisture are not found in the other animals, because the
15 rush of heat is equally distributed between the fore and
hind parts of an animal. Man being naturally, like the
plants, at a right angle to the ground on which he stands,
the result is that a very copious and violent rush of heat
takes place in the direction of the head, and the heat in
its course thither rarefies and heats the ducts in the region
of the head. Now these ducts being in this condition
20 are better able to receive the moisture than those leading
downwards from the heart. When, therefore, a man happens to have become in too moist a condition and to have
been cooled off externally,[4] the result is that the heat
obtaining nourishment and collecting within increases, and
as it does so it is carried to the head and the ducts there.
25 Into these the moisture, which is thin and unconcocted,
follows the heat and fills them up and causes cold in the
head and likewise sneezing. For at the beginning of
a cold the heat, being carried along in advance of the

---

[1] Cp. above, chapter 18, and xxxiii. 10.

[2] Omitting τὸ σῶμα, which has probably come in as a gloss.

[3] Punctuating ἀπέπτων (διὸ πρὸ τῶν κατάρρων γίγνεται), ἃ κτλ., and taking ὑγρῶν as the antecedent of ἅ.

[4] Putting the comma after instead of before ἔξωθεν.

moisture and inflating the ducts, causes sneezing by the expulsion of the breath and by the drawing off[1] of those humours which are light and pungent. Hence it happens 30 that after sneezing from a cold in the head one wipes away watery matter. These all[2] having been set in motion, the continuous and solid[3] humours follow closely upon them and block up the ducts in the region of the head and nostrils. If they become swollen and distended, they 35 cause pain in the region of the head. That the ducts are blocked is shown by the fact that no breath can pass out through them;[4] so those who suffer from running at the nose neither sneeze nor can they use their sense of smell. Sneezing unaccompanied by running at the nose is due to the same causes, but has some slight and insignificant origin; and so the humours, being collected by 897ᵇ the heat and vaporized by it owing to their small mass, are precipitated down the nostrils. The noise made by the breath is due quite as much to the violence of its rush as to its quantity. For the heat, being carried along in a direct line to the brain and rushing into it, is refracted 5 into the nostrils, because the ducts there lead out from the brain. The rush made by the breath in breaking out into the nostrils, being unnatural, is consequently violent, and therefore makes loud noises. Amongst the other animals birds are most liable to running at the nose, because they 10 most resemble man in form; but they are less liable to it than man, because they usually hold their heads down, since they derive their food from the ground.

55 Why are marine animals larger and better nourished than land animals? Is it because the sun consumes the 15 outer surface of the earth and takes the nourishment out

---

[1] Omitting πρό. T. G., who has *ductuque humoris tenuis acrisque*, does not render it, and its insertion destroys the sense of the passage, since the light humours are expelled in sneezing while the solider humours remain.

[2] i. e. the breath and the light humours.

[3] Reading πάχος ἔχοντα (cp. 871ᵃ 26 and *G. A.* 739ᵃ 12) for πάθος ἔχοντα. The Latin version renders *crassi*.

[4] Reading τὸ μηδὲν ἐκτὸς δι' αὐτῶν. τὸ μήτ' ἐκτὸς ἢ δι' αὐτῶν neither is Greek nor does it make sense. The required meaning, however, is clear. ἀφίεσθαι should probably be read for ἀφεῖσθαι.

of it? (For this reason too those animals which are enclosed in the earth are better nourished.) Marine animals then are free from all these disadvantages.

Why is it that the other animals provide themselves **56** more often with dry than with moist food, but man takes more moist than dry nourishment?[1] Is it because man is naturally very hot and therefore requires most cooling?

Why is it that eunuchs do not become bald?[2] Is it **57** because they have a large amount of brain-matter? Now this is the result of their not having sexual intercourse with women;[3] for the semen passes from the brain through the spine. For this reason too bulls which have been castrated appear to have large horns after castration. For the same reason also, apparently, women and children are not bald.

Why is it that some animals are able to feed themselves **58** directly after birth, while others cannot? Are those who can do so the shorter-lived among those animals which are capable of memory? It is for this reason that they always die sooner.

Why does man produce more moist than dry excrement, **59** but horses and asses more dry than moist? Is it because the latter animals take more dry food, whereas man takes more moist than dry nourishment?[4] For all excrement comes from food, and a greater amount of food produces a greater quantity of excrement.[5] Some animals then take more moist food, others more dry food, because some are **898**[a] naturally dry and others moist. Animals then which are naturally dry feel more desire for moist food, since they require it more; but those which are naturally moist desire dry food, for they stand more in need of it.

Why is it that birds and men and the courageous animals **60** have hard frames? Is it because high spirit is accompanied

---

[1] Cp. below, ll. 35, 36.
[2] Cp. *H. A.* 632[b] 4, *G. A.* 784[a] 6, and Hippocr. *Aph.* 6.
[3] *G. A.* 783[b] 27.   [4] Cp. above, ll. 19-22.
[5] Reading πλείων (Richards) for πλείω.

by bodily heat, since fear is a process of cooling? Those
then whose blood is hot are also courageous and high-
spirited; for the blood gives them sustenance. Plants too
which are watered with warm water become harder.

61 Why is it that quadrupeds of a small size most often
give birth to monstrosities, whereas man and the larger 10
quadrupeds, such as horses and asses, do so less often?[1]
Is it because the small quadrupeds, such as dogs, pigs,
goats, and sheep, have much more abundant progeny than
the larger animals, which either always or usually produce
only one offspring at a time? Monstrosities come into
being when the semen becomes confused[2] and disturbed 15
either in the emission of the seminal fluid or in the mingling
which takes place in the uterus of the female. So birds
too produce monstrosities; for they lay twin[3] eggs, and
their monstrosities are born from such eggs in which the
yolk is not separated by the membrane.[4]

62 Why is the head in man more hairy than the rest of the 20
body[5]—in fact quite disproportionately so—while in the
other animals the opposite is the case? Is it because some
of the other animals send an excessive amount of their
nutritive material into teeth, others into horns, others into
hair? Those who expend their nourishment on horns
have less thick hair on the head; for the available material
is used up in the horns. Those whose nourishment goes 25
into teeth have thicker hair on the head than horned
animals (for they have crests or manes),[6] but less thick
than such creatures as[7] birds. For birds have the same
sort of covering as man;[8] but,[9] whereas in birds the

---

[1] Cp. *G. A.* 770^a 10 ff.

[2] For ἐπαλλάττειν cp. *G. A.* 769^b 34, 36.   [3] i. e. double-yolked.

[4] Cp. *H. A.* 562^a 24 ff., *G. A.* 770^b 16, and A. Platt's notes.

[5] Cp. *H. A.* 498^b 17 ff., *P. A.* 658^b 1.

[6] λοφιά includes both crest and mane.

[7] Reading, with Richards, οἴων ὀρνέων.

[8] The sense here is clear and is that of T. G.'s version (*his enim
illud etiam, quod homini, genus integendi natura tribuit*), but the
reading is doubtful. τὴν τῶν ἀνθρώπων seems to require a noun, and
Richards suggests ἔκδοσιν; but (1) is ἔχουσι τὴν τῶν ἀνθρώπων ἔκδοσιν
good Greek for 'have the same distribution of hair as men', and (2) is
not this contradicted by what follows? ἔχουσι γὰρ τὴν αὐτὴν χαίτην τῷ
ἀνθρώπῳ is perhaps preferable.

[9] Reading ὁ ⟨δ'⟩ ἐκείνοις (so also Richards).

covering is distributed all over the body owing to its abundance, in man[1] it breaks out only on the head; for man is neither[2] on the one hand devoid of hair, nor on 30 the other hand has he sufficient to cover the whole body.

Why is it that in man alone of the animals the hair 63 turns white?[3] Is it because most of the animals shed their coats every year, for instance the horse and the ox, while others, though they do not do so, are short-lived, such as sheep and others (in which case the hair does not 35 turn white, because it does not as it were grow old)? But man does not change his hair and is long-lived, and so he grows white owing to age.

Why is it that those in whom the distance from the 64 navel downwards is longer than that from the navel to 898ᵇ the chest are short-lived and weak? Is it because their stomach is cold owing to its small size, and therefore it tends to cause excretion rather than concoction? Now such persons are unhealthy.

Why is it that some animals come into being not only 65 from the sexual intercourse of animals with one another 5 but also spontaneously, while others, such as man and the horse, can only be born as the result of sexual intercourse?[4] Is it due, if to no other cause, at any rate to the fact that the former have a short period of coming to birth, so that the moment of birth is not protracted and can take place at the change of the seasons;[5] but of the latter class the coming to birth is much protracted, 10 since they are born after a year or ten months, so that they must necessarily be born from the intercourse of animals with each other or not at all?[6]

[1] Reading τούτῳ (Richards); Yᵃ has τούτω.
[2] Reading οὔτε . . . οὔτε (Richards).
[3] Cp. 891ᵇ 1, *G. A.* 778ᵃ 25, 780ᵇ 4, 782ᵃ 11.
[4] Cp. chapter 13.
[5] Which sets up the process of decay necessary for spontaneous generation, cp. 892ᵃ 35, 36 and *G. A.* 715ᵃ 25.
[6] The text as it stands makes no sense. Since, however, the Latin version of T. G. renders *quapropter vel nullo pacto vel ex coitu procreentur illa necesse est*, we should certainly read with Bussemaker ⟨ἢ μή⟩ γίνεσθαι ἢ κτλ.

66   Why is it that the teeth of Ethiopians are white—indeed whiter than those of other nations, but their nails are not correspondingly white? Are their nails dark because their skin also is black and blacker than that of others, and the nails grow out of the skin? But why are their teeth white? Is it because those things turn white out of which the sun extracts the moisture without adding any colour to them, as happens in the case of wax? Now the sun colours¹ the skin, but it does not colour the teeth, but the moisture is evaporated out of them by the heat.

67   Why is it that, when the head is removed, some animals die immediately or very soon, while others do not? Does death occur less quickly in the bloodless animals, which require little nourishment, since they do not need food immediately and the heat in them is not diffused in moisture, whereas full-blooded animals cannot live without food and heat? The former can live after their heads are cut off, for they can live longer without breathing. The reason for this has been stated elsewhere.²

¹ i.e. tans.
² This appears to be a direct reference to *de Respir.* 475ᵃ 20 ff.

BOOK XI

PROBLEMS CONNECTED WITH THE VOICE

WHY is it that of all the senses the hearing is most liable 1
to be defective from birth? Is it because the sense of
hearing and the voice may be held to arise from the same
30 source?[1] Now language, which is a kind of voice,[2] seems
to be very easily destroyed and to be very difficult to
perfect; this is indicated by the fact that we are dumb
for a long time after our birth, for at first we simply do
not talk at all and then at length begin only to lisp. And
35 because language is easily destroyed, and language (being
a kind of voice) and hearing both have the same source,
hearing is, as it were, *per accidens*, though not *per se*,
the most easily destroyed of the senses.[3] Further evidence
899^a of the fact that the source of language is eminently easy
to destroy may be taken from the other animals; for no
animal other than man talks, and even he begins to do
so late, as has already been remarked.

Why is it that the deaf always speak through their 2
5 nostrils?[4] Is it because they are near to being dumb?[5]
Now the dumb make sounds through their nostrils; for
the breath escapes by that way because their mouth is
closed, and it is closed because they make no use of their
tongue for vocal purposes.

10 Why have all hot-natured men big voices? Is it because 3
they necessarily have a large amount of cold air[6] in them?

---

[1] Cp. *de Anim.* 426ª 27.   [2] Cp. above, 895ª 5.

[3] Reading ἐκ for εἰ before συμβεβηκότος and punctuating as follows:
διά τε τὸ τὴν διάλεκτον εὔφθαρτον εἶναι, τὴν αὐτὴν δὲ ἀρχὴν ἀμφοτέρων
εἶναι, καὶ τῆς διαλέκτου (φωνὴ γάρ τις) καὶ τῆς ἀκοῆς, ὥσπερ καὶ ἐκ
συμβεβηκότος ῥᾷστα τῶν αἰσθήσεων φθείρεται καὶ οὐ καθ᾽ αὑτὴν ἡ ἀκοή.

[4] Cp. chapter 4 and xxxiii. 14.   [5] Cp. *H. A.* 536ᵇ 3 ff

[6] T. G. evidently translates from a text which read θερμὸν for ψυχρόν,
for he renders *perfervidum*. If ψυχρόν is retained the meaning is that
the heat inside the body attracts a quantity of cold air from without;
there is therefore more air to expel and consequently the voice is big

For their breath, which is hot, attracts the air to itself,
and the more of it there is the more it attracts.   Now a big
voice arises from setting in motion a large quantity of air,
and when the motion is swift, the voice is shrill, and when
it is slow, it is deep.

4   Why do the deaf always speak through their nostrils?[1] 15
Is it because the deaf breathe more violently?   For they
are near to being dumb; the passage therefore of the
nostrils is distended by the breath, and those who are in
this condition speak through the nostrils.

5   Why are sounds more audible at night?[2]   Is it because
there is more quiet then owing to the absence of great 20
heat?   For this reason too there is usually less disturbance;
for it is the sun which is the source of movement.

6   Why do voices sound shriller at a distance?[3]   For
example, those who try to imitate persons shouting from
a very great distance utter shrill noises, like those of an
echo; and the sound of an echo is distinctly shriller,[4] and
it is a distant sound, being the result of refraction.   Since 25
then in sound the swift is shrill and the slow is deep,
one would have expected voices to seem deeper from a
distance, for all moving bodies move more slowly the
farther they progress from their starting-point, and at last
fall.   May not the explanation be that these mimics use
a feeble and thin voice[5] when they imitate a distant 30
sound?   Now a thin voice is not deep, and it is impossible
to emit a small and feeble sound that is deep, but such
a sound is necessarily shrill.   Or is it true that not only
do the mimics imitate for this reason, but also the sounds
themselves become shriller?   The reason is that the air
which travels makes the sound; and just as that which
first sets the air in motion causes the sound, so the air 35

in volume.   The reading ψυχρὸν is borne out by Hippocr. *Epid.* vi. 4. 19
ἐν οἷς πλεῖστον τὸ θερμόν, μεγαλοφωνότατοι·   καὶ γὰρ ψυχρὸς ἀὴρ πλεῖστος.
   [1] A repetition of chapter 2 in a slightly different form; cp. also
xxxiii. 14.
   [2] For a more elaborate treatment of this problem see chapter 33.
   [3] Cp. chapters 20 and 47, and xix. 11.
   [4] i. e. shriller than the sound which it echoes.
   [5] Reading μιμοῦνται καὶ λεπτῇ.

in its turn must do likewise and be partly a motive power and partly itself set in motion.[1] That is why sound is continuous, motive power continually succeeding to **899^b** motive power, until the force is spent, which results in falling in the case of bodies, when the air can no longer impel the missile, while in the case of sound the air can no longer impel other air. Continuous sound is produced when air is impelled by air, while the missile continues its progress as long as there is air to keep a body in 5 motion. In the latter it is always the same body that is carried along until it drops, in the former it is always different air. Smaller objects travel more quickly at first, but do not go far. Therefore voices are shriller and thinner at a distance; for that which moves more quickly is shrill —a question which we have already raised.[2] It is for the 10 same reason that children and invalids have shrill voices, whereas grown men and healthy persons have deep voices.[3] That[4] from near at hand one cannot clearly distinguish degrees of deepness and shrillness and that altogether the conditions are not the same as those of heavy bodies thrown, is due to the fact that the body thrown is one and preserves its identity throughout; whereas sound is 15 air impelled by air. Consequently a body falls in one particular spot, while the voice scatters in every direction, just as though a body thrown were, in the course of its flight, to be broken into infinitesimally small pieces, some particles even returning on their track.

Why are newly plastered houses more resonant? Is it **7** because their smoothness gives greater facility for refraction? They are smoother because they are free from cracks 20 and their surface is continuous. One must, however, take a house which is already dry and not one which is still quite wet; for damp clay gives no refraction of sound. It is for this reason that stucco[5] has a higher degree of

---

[1] Cp. *de Aud.* 800^a 1-11.   [2] i.e. in 899^a 13 and 26.
[3] Cp. chapter 16.   [4] Reading τοῦ δέ (Richards).
[5] Apparently a smoother and more expensive material than ordinary plaster: it was used for coating the inside of reservoirs, cp. *de Col.* 794^b 31, 32.

resonance.   Perhaps the absence of disturbance in the air
also contributes something; for when the air is[1] massed
together it beats back the air that strikes against it.

8   Why is it that if a large jar or empty earthenware 25
vessels are buried in the ground[2] and lids placed on them,
the buildings in which they are have more resonance,
and the same is true if there is a well or cistern in the
house?   Is it because, since an echo is due to refraction,
the air when enclosed is necessarily massed together, and
so the sound has something dense and smooth upon which
it can strike[3] and from which it can be refracted, these
being the most favourable conditions for an echo?   A well, 30
then, or a cistern causes the contraction and massing
together of air, and jars and earthenware vessels also have
dense surrounding walls, and so the phenomenon in question results in both cases.   For anything which is hollow
is particularly resonant; for which reason bronze vessels
are particularly so.   That resonance still continues when
the vessels are buried need not surprise us; for the voice
is carried downwards as much as in any other direction—
indeed one conceives of it as being carried in a circle in 35
every direction.

9   But why is it that there is more resonance where vessels
are buried than where they are not?   Is it because covered 900^a
vessels receive the air and retain it better?   The result is
that the impact of sound upon them is more violent.

10   Why does cold water poured out of a jug make a shriller
sound than hot water poured from the same vessel?   Is it
because the cold water falls at a greater speed, being heavier, 5
and the greater speed causes the sound to be shriller?

¹ It is quite clear from a comparison with the next problem (ll. 27–
34 below) that ὤν must be read for ἰών.   The meaning is that a mass
of undisturbed air collected in an enclosed space (in this case in a
room, in the next problem in an earthenware vessel, well, or cistern)
is a good medium for the refraction of sound, and therefore gives an
echo.   For another instance of the confusion of ὤν and ἰών see
904ᵇ 16 and note.
² The custom of burying storage vessels in the floors of houses is
amply borne out by excavations on ancient sites from the earliest
periods onwards.
³ Omitting the comma after ἀνακλασθήσεται, and reading προσπίπτων.

Heat, on the other hand, makes water lighter by rarefying it and causing it to rise.[1] We may compare the phenomenon that torches deal softer blows when they are alight.

10   Why is it that the voice is rougher when one has passed **11** a sleepless night? Is it because the body, owing to absence of concoction, is moister than usual, especially in its upper part (which is also the cause of heaviness in the head), and moisture in the region of the windpipe necessarily makes the voice rougher? For roughness is due to unevenness, 15 whilst depth is due to congestion; for the passage of sound is then slower.

Why does the voice become broken very readily after **12** meals?[2] Is it because the region in which it is produced is thoroughly heated by constant impacts, and, becoming heated, attracts the moisture? The moisture too is itself more copious and readier to hand when food is being taken.

20   Why is the sound of weeping shrill, whereas that of **13** laughing is deep?[3] Is it because those who weep[4] either set only a little breath in motion, because they are weak, or else exhale violently, which makes their breath travel quickly? Now speed makes for shrillness; for that which is hurled from a body which is tense travels quickly. (On the other hand, a man who is laughing is in a relaxed condition.[5]) Those who are weak make shrill sounds, for they set only 25 a little air in motion, in some cases merely on the surface.[6] Further, the air emitted by those who are laughing is warm, while the breath of those who are weeping is colder, just as

---

[1] i. e. by evaporation.

[2] Cp. chapter 22. On 'broken' voices cp. *de Aud.* 804ᵇ 11 ff.

[3] Cp. chapters 15 and 50.

[4] οἱ μὲν ὀλίγον κινοῦσι πνεῦμα δι' ἀσθένειαν must refer to the weepers, not to the laughers, for (1) those who weep are weaker (cp. 904ᵃ 25, 26), and (2) laughers emit large quantities of air (cp. ll. 25-9 below). οἱ δὲ σφοδρῶς, ὃ ποιεῖ ταχὺ φέρεσθαι τὸ πνεῦμα must also refer to weeping, for breath which is quickly and violently expelled makes a shrill sound. The whole sentence therefore refers to two different cases of οἱ κλαίοντες. Any other way of taking the passage involves hopeless confusion in this problem and contradicts chapters 15 and 50. Greater clearness would be obtained by reading ἢ ὅτι ⟨οἱ κλαίοντες⟩ οἱ μὲν κτλ. Richards (*op. cit.*, p. 18) suggests σφοδρῶς δὲ for οἱ δὲ σφοδρῶς.

[5] Reading διαλελυμένος for διαλελυμένως.

[6] Richards (*loc. cit.*) suggests that οἱ δ' ἀσθενεῖς ... ἐπιπολῆς is a gloss.

pain is a chilling of the region round the breast. Now heat
sets a great mass of air in motion, so that its progress is
slow,[1] whereas cold imparts movement to a little air only. 30
The same thing happens with flutes; when the player's
breath is hot,[2] the sound produced is much deeper.

14   Why do children[3] and the young of other animals have
shriller voices than the full-grown of their species, and that
though shrillness involves a quality of violence? Is it
because[4] the voice is a movement of the air, and the swifter
the movement the shriller is the sound? Now a little air 35
can be moved more easily and quickly than a large quantity,
and it is set in motion owing either to its concretion or to its
dissolution by heat. Now since we draw in cold air when we
inhale, the air within us can become concreted by the act of
inhalation; but exhalation, when heat sets air in motion, can
become voice, for it is when we are exhaling that we speak,
not when we are inhaling. And since the young are hotter 900^b
than their elders, and their interior passages are narrower,
they may well have less air in them. So, as there is less
in them of that which is moved[5] and more motive power,
namely heat, for both reasons the movement of the air may 5
be quicker; and, for the reasons already stated,[6] the quicker
the movement the shriller the voice.

15   Why is the sound of weeping shrill and of laughter
deep?[7] Is it because those who weep, in uttering their
cries, strain and contract the mouth? Owing to the tension
the air that is in them is impelled into swift motion, and the 10
contraction of the mouth, through which it passes, makes
its speed still greater. For both these reasons the voice
becomes shrill. On the other hand, those who laugh relax
the tension in doing so and open the mouth. Since then
for this reason they emit the air from the mouth through
a wide aperture and slowly, their voice is naturally deep.

[1] And therefore deep.
[2] Reading θερμῷ (Platt); all MSS. have θερμοί.
[3] Cp. chapters 16, 34, 62.
[4] Reading ἡ ⟨ὅτι⟩ ἡ φωνή, suggested by Ruelle.
[5] i.e. air.   [6] 899^a 13, ^b 8, &c.
[7] Cf. chapters 13 and 50.

₁₅ Why is it that persons without generative power, such **16** as boys, women, men grown old, and eunuchs, have shrill voices, while adult men have deep voices?[1] Is it because[2] the thin voice has only one dimension, just as the line and other thin things have one dimension, while thick things have more than one? Now it is easier to create and set in ₂₀ motion one thing than several things. Now the breathing of the persons mentioned above is feeble and sets little air in motion; and the air which has only one dimension is very small in quantity, for it will be thin for the reasons already stated. And the voice produced from it will be of the same quality, and a thin voice is shrill. This then is the reason why persons without generative power have shrill voices; ₂₅ whereas men who are vigorous set a large quantity of air in motion with their breath, and the air, being large in quantity, is likely to move slowly and causes the voice to be deep. For shrillness of voice is, as we have seen, produced by a movement at once swift and thin, neither of which conditions is fulfilled in an adult man.

Why are our voices deeper in the winter?[3] Is it because **17** ₃₀ then the air both inside and outside us is thicker, and, being such, its movement is slower and the voice therefore deeper? Further, we are drowsier in the winter than in the summer and sleep longer, and we are heavier after sleeping. In the period then during which we sleep for a longer time than we are awake (namely, the winter), we may expect to have ₃₅ deeper voices than in the season when the contrary happens. For during the short interval of wakefulness the condition set up during sleep persists and causes a tendency to drowsiness.

Why is the voice deeper as a result of drinking and **18** **901^a** vomiting and cold weather? Is it due to the congestion of the larynx[4] caused by phlegm, which makes fluid matter collect in it? In some people vomiting and drinking, in others the season and the constriction resulting therefrom,

---

[1] Cf. chapters 14, 34, and 62, and *de Aud.* 803^b 18 ff.
[2] Reading ἢ ⟨ὅτι⟩ καθάπερ.   [3] Cp. chapter 61.
[4] Greek φάρυγξ, cp. *P. A.* 664^a 16 and Ogle's note.

make the larynx narrower, so that the passage of breath is 5 slower; and its slow passage makes the voice deep.

19 Why is it that a deeper voice is more audible close at hand, but less so at a distance? Is it because a deeper voice sets a greater amount of air in motion, but not at a distance? So we hear it less well at a distance, because it travels less far, but better from near at hand, because a greater mass 10 of air strikes upon our sensory organ. A shrill sound is audible at a distance, because it is thinner; and that which is thin has greater longitudinal extension. It might also be said that the motion which causes it is quicker; this would be so, if the breath which sets the air in motion were at the same time dense and narrow. For, in the first place, 15 air which is small in bulk moves more readily (for the air which is set in motion by that which is narrow is small in bulk); and, secondly, that which is dense deals more impacts, and it is these which cause the sound. This can be illustrated from musical instruments; for, all other conditions being the same, it is the thinner strings that give shriller sounds.[1]

20 Why does the voice seem shriller to those standing at 20 a distance, whereas shrillness depends on the rapidity at which the voice travels, and that which travels moves more slowly the farther it goes?[2] Is it because the shrillness of the voice depends not only on the rapidity with which it travels but also on the attenuation of sound?[3] The farther one is away the more attenuated is the voice when it reaches 25 one, because very little air is set in motion. For the motion gradually diminishes; and just as number in diminishing terminates in the unit, so a body terminates in a single dimension, and this in a body is tenuity. So it is also with the voice.

21 Why is it that both those who have taken violent exercise 30 and those who are ill speak shrilly?[4] Is it because those who are ill set only a little air in motion, and a little air

---

[1] Cp. *de Aud.* 803ᵇ 23 ff.   [2] Cp. chapters 6 and 47.

[3] Reading λεπτὸν τὸν (Richards) for λεπτότατον.

[4] Cp. chapter 40.

travels more quickly than a larger quantity? Those who have taken violent exercise, on the other hand, set the air in vigorous motion, and air which is in vigorous motion travels more quickly, and in the voice quickness of motion causes shrillness.

35   Why do those who shout after meals spoil their voices?[1] **22** **901ᵇ** Indeed, we can see how those who are training their voices, such as actors and chorus-men and all such persons, practice early in the morning and on an empty stomach. Is it because the spoiling of the voice is simply the spoiling of 5 the region through which the voice passes out? So too those who have sore throats have their voices spoilt, not because the breath which causes the voice is any worse, but because the windpipe is roughened. This region by its nature is especially liable to be roughened by violent heat;[2] and so neither can those who are in a fever sing, nor can 10 those who have been suffering from a violent fever sing immediately after it leaves them; for their larynx is roughened by the heat. The consumption of food naturally increases and heats the breath, and it is reasonable to suppose that the breath being in this state makes the windpipe sore and rough as it passes through; and when this 15 happens the voice is naturally spoilt.

Why is it that the voice, which is air that has taken **23** a certain form and is carried along, often loses its form by dissolution, but an echo, which is caused by such air striking on something hard, does not become dissolved, but we hear it distinctly?[3] Is it because in an echo refraction takes 20 place and not dispersion? This being so, the whole continues to exist and there are two parts of it of similar form;[4] for refraction takes place at the same angle. So the voice of the echo is similar to the original voice.

[1] This problem clearly continues the topic raised in chapter 12.
[2] In 900ª 12-14 moisture is said to be the cause of roughness, not heat as here.
[3] This problem is repeated, in part verbally, in chapter 51.
[4] The two 'parts' into which τὸ ὅλον is divided are (1) the voice on its way to the hard object from which it is refracted, and (2) the voice after refraction, i.e. the echo.

24   Why is it that, although the young of all other animals and infants have shriller voices than the full-grown of their ₂₅ species,[1] calves have deeper voices than full-grown oxen?[2] Is it because in each species the young resembles the female of the same kind? Now among cattle cows have deeper voices[3] than bulls, and the calves resemble the former rather than the latter; but in all other species the males have deeper voices.

25   Why is it that when the orchestra of a theatre is spread ₃₀ with straw, the chorus makes less sound? Is it because, owing to the unevenness of the surface, the voice does not find the ground smooth when it strikes upon it and is therefore less uniform, and so is less in bulk, because it is not continuous? Similarly light too shines more on smooth surfaces, because it is not cut off by anything which inter- ₃₅ cepts it.

26   Why does salt make a noise when it is thrown on fire?[4] **902^a** Is it because salt has a little moisture in it which is evaporated by the heat and violently bursting forth rends the salt? Now anything which is rent makes a noise.

27   Why is it that some children, before they reach the age ₅ at which it is time for them to express themselves clearly, find voice and say something distinctly, and then go on as before[5] until the usual age for speaking arrives? Some regard such incidents as portents; and before now cases have been reported of children who spoke immediately after birth. Is it because generally the majority of children at ₁₀ birth[6] follow the usual course of nature (and so the pheno- menon in question occurs only in a few), and their faculties keep pace with one another; and so they hear [and find voice][7] and understand what they hear and speak and express themselves clearly all at the same time? Sometimes,

---

[1] As has already been stated in 900^a 32 ff.
[2] Cp. *G. A.* 786^b 15, *H. A.* 545^a 19.
[3] Cp. *G. A.* 786^b 22, *H. A.* 538^b 14.
[4] Cp. chapters 42 and 43.   [5] i. e. do not speak again.
[6] Retaining the MS. reading γινομένων.
[7] καὶ φωνεῖ is hardly necessary here, its meaning being more appro- priately expressed by καὶ λέγει following.

however, these things[1] do not go together, but some
15 children understand before the faculty by which they
converse is set free for use, while in others the opposite
happens.   The latter, then, would not converse intelligently
(for they merely repeat what they hear) ; but when the time
comes at which they can both speak and understand, they
make a natural use of both functions.   But in those in whose
20 souls perception through hearing has been perfected before
the organ[2] by which the voice is first set in motion and
speech is formed, the full power and freeing of the organ of
speech sometimes comes to pass when they already
understand a great deal.   This is especially likely to happen
after sleep—the reason being that sleep makes the body
and the faculties more sluggish by giving them a rest—or,
if not after sleep, after some other similar change has taken
25 place.   We can do many things of this sort which require
some short-lived opportunity—after which the conditions
are no longer suitable—when the organ of speech is in this
state of freedom ; and[3] when there has been obviously
present to their sensation something by which thought was
stirred, in virtue of having heard it the child returns to it
and utters it.   Now tunes and phrases often occur to us
30 without our deliberate intention, but if we originally utter
them deliberately, we afterwards speak or sing them without
deliberate intention and cannot get rid of them from our
lips.   So too when this happens in children, they speak,[4]
and then the faculty involved relapses again into its natural
condition, until the time comes for it to become strong and
35 to be separately constituted.

Why do some objects, chests for example, suddenly make 28
a noise and move, when nothing perceptible sets them in
motion ?   Yet that which causes motion is stronger than
that which is moved.   The same question arises in connexion

---

[1] Reading ταῦτα (Richards).
[2] Reading with Bussemaker ⟨ἢ⟩ ᾧ.
[3] Reading with Richards ὅταν ⟨δ'⟩ . . . ᾧ.
[4] Reading οὕτω καὶ τοῖς παιδίοις ὅταν συμβῇ τοῦτο, εἶπον, εἶτα πάλιν
κατέστη κτλ. (cp. above, ll. 7, 8) ; this is supported by the Latin version
of T. G.. *ita fieri potest ut pueri aliquid dicant, rursusque membrum
. . redeat ad suam naturam.*

with corruption and old age; for everything which is said
to be 'destroyed by time' is destroyed by something
imperceptible. Is it similar to dripping water and stones 902ᵇ
lifted by the growth of plants, namely, that it is not the
final effort but its continuity which raises or moves the
object? This continuity of effort is imperceptible, but it
results in a movement which is perceptible. So too that
which is contained within perceptible spaces of time 5
moves and can be divided into imperceptible portions,
but these cause motion and corruption by their sum
and their continuity.[1] Now continuity is not in the
present time but in the period of time terminated by the
present.

29 Why does one hear less well when one is yawning?[2] Is
it because a quantity of breath emitted in the yawn finds its 10
way also into the ears, so that the motion which it sets up
in the neighbourhood of the ears makes a distinct impression
on the perception, especially after sleep? Now sound is
air or a certain condition of it. The sound then from outside enters the ear, and that from within comes into collision
with it, and the movement thus caused checks the progress 15
of the sound from without.

30 Why do children hesitate more in their speech than grown
men? Is it because, just as, when we are children, we
always have less control over our hands and feet and at
a still earlier age cannot walk at all, so the young cannot
control their tongue? Now when they are quite small, they 20
cannot speak at all but can only make sounds like the
animals, because they lack control. This is the cause not
only of hesitancy in speech but also of lisping and stammering. Lisping is due to the inability to master a letter—not
any letter but some particular one; stammering is due to

---

[1] i.e. it takes a considerable period for the growth of a tree to move
a stone, and if it is examined at any particular moment the movement
is imperceptible; but there is a perceptible difference between the
position of the stone at the beginning and at the end of the period,
and this is the effect of the sum of the continuous but imperceptible
movement.

[2] Cp. chapter 44 and *G. A.* 781ᵃ 30.

the dropping out of some particular letter or syllable;[1]
25 hesitancy is due to the inability to join one syllable to
another sufficiently quickly. All three are due to want of
power; for the tongue is not an efficient servant of the
intelligence. The same thing occurs in those who are
drunken and in the old; but always to a less extent than in
children.

30   Why is it that the voice trembles in those who are nervous[2] **31**
or afraid?[3] Is it because the heart is shaken by the passing
out of the heat? For this happens in both conditions,
being an effect both of nervousness and of fear.[4] When the
heart is shaken, the impact[5] is not one but many, like that
35 from strings which are not properly stretched.[6]

Why is it that those who are nervous have deep voices, **32**
but those who are afraid speak shrilly?[7] Is it because in
those who are afraid the region about the heart is chilled,[8]
because the heat passes downwards, and so they set only
a little air in motion? For the force which sets the air in
motion is derived from heat. In those who are nervous the
903ᵃ heat travels upwards,[9] as happens in those who are ashamed;
for it is through shame[10] that nervousness is felt. In those
who are ashamed the heat travels upwards to the face, as is
shown by the fact that they tend to blush.[11] The heat
therefore dissolves and thickens the air with which they
5 speak, and such air can only be propelled slowly; and in
the voice that which is slow is deep.

---

  [1] Cp. *de Aud.* 804ᵇ 26–33.
  [2] For a definition of ἀγωνία see 869ᵇ 6; see also note on *ib.* ᵃ 2 for
the difference between ἀγωνία and φόβος.
  [3] Cp. xxvii. 1, 6, and 7.
  [4] καὶ γὰρ ... φοβουμένοις has perhaps come into the text as a gloss
upon ἀμφοτεράκις δὲ πάσχουσι τοῦτο. The doctrine here agrees with
that of ii. 31 as far as the effect of fear is concerned (ὁ δὲ φόβος κατάψυξις τῶν ἄνω, 869ᵇ 7), but the effect of nervousness is there said to be
τὸ τὸ θερμὸν αὐτῶν ἠθροῖσθαι εἰς τὸν περὶ τὸ στῆθος τόπον (*ib.* 13).
  [5] i. e. of the voice upon the air.
  [6] Cp. *de Aud.* 804ᵃ 38 ff.   [7] Cp. chapter 53.
  [8] Cp. 869ᵇ 7 (quoted in note on l. 32 above).
  [9] In 869ᵃ 4 ἀγωνία is called αὔξησις θερμοῦ.
  [10] Cp. 905ᵃ 8.
  [11] Contrast 869ᵃ 8, where those who are nervous are said to turn pale.

33   Why are sounds more audible in the night than in the day? [1] Is it for the reason that Anaxagoras [2] gives, namely, that in the day-time the air, heated by the sun, hisses and roars, but at night it is still because the heat has ceased, 10 and that when there is no noise hearing is easier? Or is it because one hears more easily through a comparative void than through a *plenum*? Now in the day the air is dense, being full of light and of the sun's rays; but at night it is rarer, for then the fire and the rays, which are bodies, have gone 15 out of it. Or is it because in the day-time the various bodies around us [3] distract our intelligence, and so it is less able to distinguish [4] what it hears? Also because we do all that we have to do preferably in the day rather than at night, our intelligence [5] too is busy then; and the perception apart from intelligence does, if one may say so, [6] only an imperceptible amount of work—as the saying is, 'It is the mind 20 which sees, the mind which hears'. [7] But at night when our sight has no work to do and our intelligence is more at liberty, the channel of hearing, being wider open, is just as receptive of sounds [8] and better able to report them to the intelligence, because the latter is neither busy nor distracted 25 by the sight, as it is in the day-time.

34   Why is it that persons without generative power, such as boys, women, men grown old, and eunuchs, have shrill voices, while adult men have deeper voices? [9] Is it because of the weakness of the organ which sets the air in motion? For that which is weak sets only a little in motion; and 30 a little air travels quickly, and that which travels quickly is shrill. Or is it because the first passage through which the air passes is narrow in those who are without generative power, so that that which expels the air from it has little force,

---

[1] A more elaborate statement of the problem already briefly treated in chapter 5.

[2] Diels, *Vorsokr.*[3], p. 392.

[3] i. e. visible objects.   [4] Reading εὐκρινής (Richards).

[5] Reading αὐτὴ (sc. ἡ διάνοια) for αὐτὰ; so also Richards.

[6] καθάπερ is inserted to apologize for the play upon the words αἴσθησις and ἀναίσθητον.

[7] Epicharmus, fr. 2.

[8] Omitting καθάπερ τῆς ἡμέρας (Platt) as having come from l. 26.

[9] Cp. chapters 14, 16, and 62.

and the air, being small in volume, travels quickly through the larynx above, which is wide? But in the adult and
35 fully developed men this passage is wide (just as also is that[1] leading to the testicles), and so the quantity of the air expelled is also greater; and so passing through more slowly it makes a deeper sound.

Why is it that those who hesitate in their speech cannot **35**
903^b speak in a low voice? Is it because they are hindered from using their voice by some impediment? Since, then, there is[2] not equal force exerted and similar movement set up when there is some impediment to the movement and when there is none, a violent effort is required. Now the voice is a movement, and those who use more force
5 speak louder; and so, since they have to force the hindrance out of the way, those who hesitate in their speech must necessarily speak louder.

Why do those who hesitate in their speech become worse **36** when they are nervous, but better under the influence of drunkenness? Is it because their condition is a state resembling apoplexy[3] of some interior part of the body
10 which they cannot move and which by its coldness hinders their speech?[4] Wine then, being naturally hot, tends to get rid of the coldness, but nervousness creates coldness; for it is a form of fear, and fear is a chilling condition.[5]

Why is it easier to hear sounds from outside in a house **37** than those from inside a house outside it? Is it because the sound from inside becomes dispersed because it travels
15 over an immense space, so that each component part of the sound is not sufficiently strong to make itself heard, or at any rate is less audible? On the other hand, a voice from without entering within into a smaller space and into stagnant air arrives in a close mass, and so being greater in bulk is more audible.

---

[1] Reading ὥσπερ καὶ ⟨ὁ⟩ ἐπὶ (Platt).
[2] Reading κινήσεως ⟨οὔσης⟩ (Richards).
[3] Reading ἀποπληξίᾳ (Bekker).
[4] Apoplexy is accompanied by loss of heat, cp. 860^a 34
[5] See note on 869^a 2.

38   Why are those who hesitate in their speech melancholic? Is it because melancholy is due to their responding too 20 quickly to the imagination? Now this is characteristic of those who hesitate in their speech; for the impulse to speak outstrips their power to do so, the mind responding too quickly to that which is presented to it. The same thing occurs in those who lisp;[1] for in them the organs employed in speech are too slow.[2] This is shown by the fact that men under the influence of wine become lispers, 25 since then they respond most to the objects presented to their vision and not so much to the mind.

39   Why do leeks contribute to loudness of the voice (for we find that this is so even with partridges)? Is it because, whereas boiled garlic makes the throat smooth, leeks contain a certain amount of adhesive matter, and this cleanses the larynx?

40   Why is it that in all other creatures the sounds made 30 are shriller when more violence is used, but man speaks more shrilly when he is weak?[3]   Is it because then he sets less air in motion, and this passes along quickly, and its speed makes the sound shrill?

41   Why can one hear better when one holds one's breath than when one exhales?[4]   This is why people when 35 hunting tell one another not to breathe. Is it because the power of perception rises into the upper parts of the body when the veins are distended? For it sinks when one is asleep; and so those who are sleeping exhale rather than inhale, and lose the sense of hearing. Or does the blood rise upwards when one exhales, so that the lower 904[a] parts of the body become void, and one can hear better in a void? Or is it because breathing is a noise, and when it takes place in the act of exhaling it impedes the hearing?

---

[1] Cp. Hippocr. *Epid.* ii. 5. I νοσήματα δὲ ἔχουσι τραυλὸς . . . ἢ ἰσχνόφωνος . . . μελαγχολικά.

[2] Reading βραδύτερα.

[3] Cp. chapter 21.   [4] Cp. chapter 48.

Why do small quantities of salt make a noise and ex- **42**
plode more quickly, but large quantities more violently?[1]
Is it because in the former case the particles burst quickly
because they are small (for the fire does not have far to
penetrate), but in the latter case slowly, since a large mass
is more difficult to burst than a small? A small quantity
makes a small noise because the impact is small, whereas
10 a large quantity makes a loud noise because the impact
is greater; and sound is an impact. The stronger an
object is, the greater is the explosion if it is struck;[2] for
it is less yielding.

Why is it that if the same quantity of salt is thrown **43**
on to a large fire, it makes less noise than if thrown on
a small fire, or else makes no noise at all? Is it because
it is burnt up before it can burst? For it burns because
15 the moisture is used up,[3] and it makes a noise because
it bursts.

Why does one hear less well when one is yawning?[4] **44**
Is it because the action of yawning cuts off the breath
internally and the breath so cut off accumulates in the
region of the ears? This is shown by the fact that there
is a noise in the ears when one yawns. Now the breath
20 thus cut off hinders the hearing. Further one also makes
a noise when one yawns, and this tends to impede the
hearing. Also the organs of hearing must necessarily
become compressed by the distension of the mouth in
yawning.

Why is it that though the voice, since it is a kind of **45**
stream, is naturally inclined to travel upwards, yet it is
more audible below from above than above from below?
25 Is it because the voice is a kind of air mingled with
moisture, and this air being weighed down by the moisture
is carried downwards instead of upwards, since it is the
natural characteristic of moisture to be carried downwards?
For this reason one hears better when one is below. Or

[1] *Sc.* when thrown upon the fire, as in chapters 26 and 43.
[2] Reading πληγῇ.   [3] Cp. 902ᵃ 2, 3.
[4] This is the same problem as that of chapter 29, somewhat
differently treated.

is such a result characteristic only of the voice of a living
creature (for it contains moisture), while the phenomenon
which we are discussing is found also in other sounds?
Just as the sight then, if it be allowed to fall from a higher ₃₀
to a lower object, makes an upward reflexion and vice
versa,[1] so the voice, which has a natural tendency to rise,
coming into collision with the air which bars its progress,
cannot overpower the air, which is greater in mass and
heavier, but the air which is set in motion by the voice, ₃₅
being refracted, is carried in a contrary direction and downwards, and so, being scattered in a downward direction,
it is more audible below. Somewhat similar is that which
happens in an echo, which is due to the refraction of the
voice in a contrary direction.

46   Why are the voices of drunken persons more broken **904ᵇ**
than those of the sober? Is it because their voice breaks
easily owing to their state of repletion? This can be
illustrated by the fact that chorus-men and actors practise
not after a meal but on an empty stomach.[2] Now since
a person in a state of drunkenness is in a condition of ₅
greater repletion, his voice is naturally more broken.

47   Why can one hear shriller voices at a greater distance?
Is it because shrillness in the voice is rapidity, and what
is carried forcibly along moves more rapidly, and what is
carried violently along is carried farther?[3]   ₁₀

48   Why can we hear better if we hold the breath?[4] Is it
because breathing makes a noise? It is only natural therefore that we should hear better when the noise is less; for
the noise is less when we hold the breath.

[1] The reference here seems to be to the fact that if one gazes at an
object and then lowers or raises the eyes, a momentary image is
retained of the object first looked at. It is difficult to see the exact
force of this comparison between the voice and the sight; there is
perhaps some confusion due to the use of the word ἀνάκλασις in two
senses, viz. refraction of sound and reflection of light.
[2] Cp. 901ª 35–ᵇ 3.
[3] This is a condensed form of the answer given to the same problem
in chapter 6; cp. also chapter 20.
[4] This problem has been more fully treated in chapter 41.

15   Why is it that light cannot penetrate through dense 49 objects, whereas sound can do so, although light is rarer and travels[1] farther and quicker than sound?[2] Is it because light travels in a straight line, and so, if anything blocks its direct course, it is completely cut off, but sound, because it is a breath, can also travel in a line that is not 20 direct? So we can hear those who make sounds from any direction and not only those who are in a straight line with our ears.

Why is the sound of laughing deep, whereas that of 50 weeping is shrill?[3] Is it because a voice which comes from those who are in a state of tension is shrill, and that which is shrill is weak? Now both these characteristics 25 are found rather in those who are weeping; for they are in a state of greater tension and they are weaker.

Why is it that the voice, being air which has assumed 51 a certain form and is carried along,[4] often loses its form by dissolution, but an echo, which is formed by such air striking on something hard, does not become dissolved, 30 but we hear it distinctly?[5] Is it because in an echo refraction takes place, not dispersion? It starts then as a complete whole and continues to be so.[6] Also, the effect produced upon it is due to a similar agency;[7] for it is refracted from the air in the hollow, not from the hollow itself.

Why is it that when one person makes a sound and 52 a number of persons make the same sound simultaneously, 35 the sound produced is not equal nor does it reach correspondingly farther?[8] Is it because each of them thrusts forward his own portion of air and they do not all impel the same air, except to a very small extent? The result

---

[1] Reading with Bonitz (*op. cit.*, p. 412) ἰόν for ὄν; see also note on 899^b 24.
[2] This problem is more fully treated in chapter 58.
[3] The same question is treated in chapters 13 and 15.
[4] Reading ἐστὶ καὶ φερόμενος, διαλύεται (W. D. R.); cp. 901^b 17.
[5] Cp. chapter 23.   [6] Cp. 901^b 20.
[7] i. e. the air in the hollow upon which the sound strikes and from which it is refracted, resembles the air in the hollow of the mouth from which the sound first proceeded.
[8] Cp. xix. 2. Reading γεγώνασιν (cp. 901^b 31).

is much the same as when a number of persons throw
stones but each throws a different stone, or at any rate
most of them do so. Neither in the latter case will any 905^a
missile travel far (or at any rate not correspondingly
farther),[1] nor in the former case will the voice reach
farther. For this great voice is that of many, not of one;
so at a short distance it appears correspondingly greater
(just as a number of missiles reaches the same spot), but at
a great distance this is no longer so.

53 Why do those who are nervous have deep voices, but 5
those who are afraid speak shrilly,[2] though a feeling of
shame is a kind of fear?[3] Or are the two conditions really
very different? For those who feel shame blush (and
nervousness is a kind of shame),[4] whereas those who are
afraid turn pale. It is clear then that in those who are
afraid the heat fails in the upper part of the body, so that 10
the breath, being weak, sets only a little air in motion;
and that which is small in bulk travels quickly, and in the
voice quickness is shrillness. But in those who feel shame
the heat in the region of the breast travels upwards, as
is shown by the fact that they blush. Now a strong
force[5] sets a great mass of air in motion, and a great
mass travels slowly, and in the voice slowness is deepness. 15

54 What is the cause of hesitation of speech?[6] Is it due
to the chilling of the region in which the sound is produced, and to a condition resembling apoplexy in that part
of the body?[7] This is why those who hesitate, if warmed
with wine and deriving thence a continuity of speech,
are better able to connect their words together.

[1] i. e. in the rare event of two persons helping to hurl the same
stone.
[2] The same problem is treated in chapter 32.
[3] And ἀγωνία is a kind of shame, see below. For the difference
between φόβος and ἀγωνία see 869^a 1 ff., ^b 7 ff., and note on *ib.* ^a 2.
[4] It is impossible in English to find separate words to express αἰδώς
and αἰσχύνη. αἰσχύνη is 'shame', but αἰδώς is a more complicated
feeling which includes 'shame', 'awe', 'honour', and a 'sense of
wounded honour'; here it seems to denote a combination of 'shame'
and 'awe' or 'dread'.
[5] Such as that exerted by heat.
[6] The same problem is treated somewhat differently in chapter 60.
[7] Cp. 903^b 8–10 and note.

20   Why is it that of all animals man alone is apt to become **55** hesitating in speech?[1] Is it because he alone possesses the power of uttering words, while the other animals only have voices? Now those who hesitate in their speech use their voice, but they cannot connect their words together.

Why is the voice shriller in winter and in those who **56** 25 are sober, and deeper in summer and in those who are drunken? Is it because the quicker a voice is the shriller it is, and it is quicker when it proceeds from one who is in a state of tension? The bodies of those who are sober are in a more solid condition than those of the drunken, and bodies are in a more solid condition in winter than in summer; for heat and warmth have a dissolvent effect upon the body.

30   **57**

Why does the voice come to perfection later in man than in any other creature capable of sound?[2] Is it because there are many variations and kinds of sounds in the human voice? For the other animals can express few or no letters;[3] and that which is most elaborate and contains a large number of variations takes a long time to perfect.

35   Why is it that the sight cannot pass through hard **58** objects, but the voice can do so?[4] Is it because the course of the sight can only take one direction, namely, a straight line (as is shown by the rays of the sun and the fact that we can only see what is directly opposite us), whereas the voice can take many directions, since we can hear from everywhere? When therefore the sight is prevented from making its way through in a straight line, because there 40 is no continuous passage between the eye and the object, it is impossible to see through the impeding matter. But **905**ᵇ the air and the voice, since they travel everywhere, find their way everywhere and make themselves audible. On the other hand, the sight can penetrate through liquids, but voices cannot be heard through them or hardly at all, although the liquid is rarer than the earth, because the

---

[1] Cp. x. 40.   [2] Cp. 898ᵇ 32.
[3] Cp. 899ᵃ 1; *H.A.* 488ᵃ 32, 536ᵇ 1.
[4] Cp. chapter 49, and xxv. 9.

passages are small and close together and continuous, and 5
so the sight is not prevented from travelling in a straight
line. For the same reason it is possible to see through
glass, although it is dense, but not through a fennel-stalk,
although it contains rarities, because in the former the
pores are continuous, in the latter they are irregular, and
their size is no advantage if they are not straight.[1] The
voice is not audible through water, because the empty 10
air-spaces[2] in it are too small and so cannot admit the
voice or let it pass through, or only with difficulty ; for the
voice is a kind of air. For that which is rarer is not
necessarily more penetrable, unless at the same time the
passages are adapted to that which is passing through. So
also that which is rarer is not necessarily more compressible,
unless its passages are of such a kind as to admit the 15
passage of other bodies. But, it may be urged, that which
is rare is soft and compressible. True, but in some things
compression is impossible owing to the smallness of the
passages—in glass, for example ; for its passages cannot be
contracted, although it may be rarer than a fennel-stalk,
for the reason already mentioned. So too with water 20
and the like. This then is clear, that, although the rare
and the soft are either identical or else of a very similar
nature, yet it does not follow that the rarer a thing is the
more it admits of contraction. The reason in all these
cases is the same.

59 Why is it that the sound produced becomes less if some
of those who produce it are withdrawn,[3] but its character
is unchanged ? Is it because their voice had formed part 25
of a general mingling of sound, and that which is mingled
is not mingled in one part and not in another, but is
mingled throughout ?[4] So when some of those who make

---

[1] Reading with Bonitz (*op. cit.*, p. 412) διορᾶται, ὅτι τῆς μὲν οἱ πόροι κατάλληλοι, τοῦ δὲ παραλλάττοντες, οὐθὲν δ' ὄφελος εἶναι κτλ.

[2] τὰ διάκενα are the same as the πόροι of the rest of the passage.

[3] This must be the meaning of ἐξαιρουμένων, though it is very inadequately expressed in the text. The source of this problem, like that of chapter 52, is evidently a series of questions connected with chorus singing ; and in its original setting the context doubtless made its meaning clearer.

[4] Cp. *M.X.G.* 977^a 10 ἅπαν ἅπαντι μέρος μέμικται ὁμοίως καὶ τὸ ὅλον.

the sound are withdrawn, the volume of sound comes
forth in the same way as before from the various voices, and
must therefore, though smaller, necessarily retain the same
characteristics.

What is the cause of hesitancy in speech?[1] Are those **60**
who hesitate in too great a hurry because of the heat that
30 is in them, and so they stumble and stop? If so, they
resemble those who are angry, for they too become full
of panting, with the result that a large quantity of breath
comes together. Or do they pant owing to the boiling
of the heat, because it is abundant and cannot come forth
before the proper moment[2] of exhalation? Or is the
right explanation the exact contrary, namely, that it is
the chilling rather than the heating of the region in which
35 the sound is produced—a state resembling apoplexy in
that part of the body? That is why those who hesitate,
when warmed with wine and deriving thence a continuity
of speech, are better able to connect their words together.[3]

Why are voices deeper in the winter?[4] Is it because **61**
then the air is thicker and as a consequence its movement
is slower, and therefore the voice is deeper? Or is it
40 because the air passes more slowly through narrow pas-
906^a sages, and the region round the larynx is closed by the cold
and by the phlegm which flows into it?

Why is it that boys, women, eunuchs, and old men have **62**
shrill voices?[5] Is it because the movement of air which
creates a shriller sound is quicker? Now it is more
5 difficult to move a greater amount of the same thing,[6]
and so those who are in the prime of life draw in
the air in greater quantities, and therefore this air, since
it travels more slowly, makes the voice deeper. In boys
and eunuchs the contrary occurs, because they contain less

---

[1] This problem is the same as that of chapter 54, but some alternative solutions are suggested here.

[2] It appears necessary to read τὸν . . . καιρόν.

[3] This last explanation is a verbal repetition of 905ª 16-19.

[4] Cp. chapter 17.

[5] Cp. chapters 4, 16, and 34.

[6] Reading πλεῖον ὂν (W. D. R.) for πλείονος.

air. Old men's voices tremble[1] because they cannot control
them, just as, when invalids and children take hold of 10
a long stick by one end, the other end shakes, because they
have no control over it; this too is the cause of trembling
in old men, namely lack of control. We must suppose also
that trembling of the voice in those who are nervous or
afraid or chilled is due to the same cause. For in one
whose voice is in this state, since most of the heat collects 15
within as a result of the above conditions,[2] the rest,[3] which
is small in quantity, cannot control the voice; consequently
it shakes and trembles. This is the reason why artists
who belong to the class of those who are conscious of
nervousness speak in a low voice at first, until they settle
down to their work; for by keeping the voice low they 20
can control it.

[1] There is an anacoluthon in this sentence, the infinitive τρέμειν
being picked up by διὰ τοῦτο καὶ οἱ πρεσβῖται τρέμουσιν.

[2] The text is disturbed. In the above τοιαύτην, ⟨τοῦ θερμοῦ διὰ⟩ τῶν
τοιούτων has been translated. The Latin version of T. G. has: *cum
enim, qui vocem ita emittit, eius calor pulsus ab affectibus illis intro
se colligat maxima a parte*, &c. The insertion of *calor* here is quite
in accordance with the doctrine that it is heat which sets the voice in
motion (cp. 902ᵇ 37–9); also the theory of περίστασις or ἀντιπερίστασις
τοῦ θερμοῦ is exceedingly common in the *Problems*, see note on 876ᵇ 32.

[3] Reading ⟨τὸ⟩ λοιπὸν (W. D. R.).

BOOK XII

PROBLEMS CONNECTED WITH THINGS OF PLEASANT ODOUR

WHY is it that perfumes produced by burning affect the 1 senses less at a short distance?[1] Is it because the effluvium is pleasanter when mingled with the air in a weak form, 25 as happens in medicinal myrrh? Or can the contrary of this be the explanation, namely, that the fire destroys the odour in the immediate neighbourhood of the flames? For the odour is produced when the perfume evaporates; wherefore near the embers the effluvium has no odour, but it appears purer and thinner the farther away it is.

30 Why is it that the odours of burning perfumes and of 2 flowers are less sweet-scented at a close distance?[2] Is it because particles of earth[3] are given off with the odour, and these, owing to their weight, fall more quickly to the ground, and therefore the odour is pure at a greater distance? Or is the effluvium not at its strongest either quite near to its source or very far from it? For close 35 at hand it has not yet gained strength, while at a distance it has become dissipated. It is said that trees become 3 sweet-scented upon which the rainbow has fallen. Is this true or false?[4] And if it is true, what can be the cause of **906ᵇ** the phenomenon?[5] That it does not happen always and as

[1] The same problem or kindred questions are treated in chapters 2, 4, and 9. The source of these problems is clearly Theophrastus, *de Caus. Plant.* vi. 17. 1; fr. 3 (*de Odoribus*), 12, 13.

[2] Cp. chapters 1, 4, and 9.

[3] For the 'earthy element' in plants, cp. *de Plant.* 822ª 12, ᵇ 2, &c.

[4] λέγεται γάρ, as Prantl (*op. cit.*, p. 350) has shown, does not begin a new problem. Chapter 3 is a digression which raises a side issue, as in the source from which this problem is taken (Theophrastus, *de Caus. Plant.* vi. 17. 7). In several MSS. λέγεται γάρ ... κατασκίψη follows τὸ συμβαῖνον (l. 38), which shows that a difficulty was felt in beginning a new problem with a statement such as λέγεται γάρ, instead of a question; this alteration, however, would give a form of problem which cannot be paralleled elsewhere.

[5] Reading αἰτίαν ⟨ἂν⟩ εἴη (so also Richards).

a universal rule is obvious; for rainbows often occur without
any visible effect on the trees.   When it does happen (for it
does occur sometimes and this has given rise to the saying),
the effect is not produced on every kind of wood.   The cause
can only be attributed to the rainbow *per accidens*, espe- 5
cially if the rainbow does not really occur in nature but
is an effect produced on the eye by refraction.[1]   Now the
phenomenon, as we said, does not occur whatever the
condition of the wood; for shepherds say that sweet odour
is noticeable after the rains which accompany the rainbow
not in green or in dry trees but in burnt wood, and in 10
particular where briers and brambles grow and trees which
have sweet-scented flowers.   The reason of the sweet scent
is the same as in the soil; for where the soil is hot and
burnt through and through, anything which grows from it
is at first sweet-scented. For things which contain but
little moisture, if they are burnt at all, become sweet-
scented; for the heat concocts this moisture.   (So, all the 15
world over, those parts towards the sun have a sweeter
odour than those towards the north; and of the former
those towards the east have a sweeter odour than those
towards the south, for the districts of Syria and Arabia
have more soil, but Libya is sandy and free from moisture.)
For there must not be a large amount of moisture—for 20
much moisture is difficult of concoction—nor must there
be a complete absence of it, or else there will be no
evaporization.   These conditions are fulfilled in newly
burnt wood and wood which naturally has a sweet odour
in itself. This is proved to be true by the flowers, for
it is through them that the wood emits its scent. The
theory that sweet odour is engendered in any trees upon
which the rainbow rests is due to the fact that this cannot 25
happen without the presence of water; for it is when the
wood has been wetted and has then concocted the moisture
by the heat which is in it, that it gives out the vapour
which is being engendered in it.   But [2] there must not be
a large amount of water; for too much water drenches the

---

[1] Cp. *Meteor.* 372[a] 18, 32 ; *de Mundo*, 395[a] 29 ff.
[2] Reading οὐδέ for οὔτε, as suggested by Bekker.

tree and extinguishes the heat previously caused by the
30 burning. Now the rains which follow the rainbow, so far
from being heavy, may almost be called slight. Also if
there is a number of rainbows, the rain is not heavy, but
it falls little and often. It is therefore natural under these
circumstances that men notice nothing unusual except
the rainbow and attribute to it the cause of the sweet
odour.

35 Why is it that flowers and burnt perfumes smell sweeter **4**
at a distance,[1] whereas close at hand they have rather the
smell either of vegetation or of smoke? Is it because
scent is a form of heat and sweet-scented things are hot?
907ᵃ Now heat is light, and so, the further the perfumes penetrate, the more does their scent become purified from other
concomitant odours produced by their leaves and by smoke,
which is a watery steam; at a short distance, on the other
hand, the mingled odours[2] are simultaneously perceptible
in the plants in which they are present.

5 Why do things always emit a stronger odour when they **5**
are in motion?[3] Is it because they fill a larger space of
air than when they are at rest? The result is that the
odour is thus transmitted more quickly to our perception.

Why is it that we perceive odours less in the winter, **6**
especially in frosty weather? Is it because the air is more
10 free from motion when it is cold? The motion therefore
set up by the body which produces the odour cannot have
such a far-reaching effect owing to the difficulty of im-
parting motion to the effluvium and to the air in which
it is present.

Why do perfumes have a more pungent odour when **7**
they are burnt on ashes than on the fire?[4] And why is
their odour stronger and more persistent when they are
15 burnt on ashes? Is it because their odour is less thoroughly concocted on ashes, and therefore greater in bulk?

---

[1] Cp. chapters 1, 2, and 9.
[2] i.e. the odour of the leaves and of the 'smoke' as well as the scent.
[3] Cp. xiii. 12.   [4] Cp. below, chapter 11.

Now fire by quickly concocting their natural force alters their odour; for concoction involves alteration in that which is concocted.

8   Why do those roses in which the centres are rough 20 smell sweeter than those in which they are smooth? Is it because those roses smell sweetest which partake most of the natural characteristics of the rose? Now the rose is naturally 'spiky', and so it smells sweeter when its characteristics are more a centuated.

9   Why are the odours both of burnt perfumes and of flowers less pleasant at a short distance?[1] Is it because 25 at a short distance the earthy element is transmitted with the scent, and so mixing with it lessens its strength, whereas the odour travels to a distance? It is for this reason too that flowers when rubbed lose their scent.[2]

10   Are scents smoke [or air][3] or vapour? For it makes a difference, in that the former is produced by fire, the 30 latter without it. And is something transmitted from the sense to the objects producing the scent or vice versa, causing a continuous motion in the adjoining air? Also, if any effluvium is given off by these objects, one would expect them to become less; yet we see that those things which have the strongest scent last the longest.

11   Why have perfumes a more pungent odour when they 35 are burnt on ashes than on fire?[4] Is it because their odour is less thoroughly concocted on ashes and is therefore greater in bulk? Consequently a large quantity of the earthy element is vaporized in the process and becomes smoke; but the fire burns up the earthy element before it can escape, and so the odour is purer and reaches the senses untainted by the smoke. This is also the reason 907^b why flowers when rubbed smell less sweet; for the rubbing

<hr>

[1] Cp. chapters 1, 2, and 4.
[2] Because rubbing brings out the earthy element, which prevails over the scent, cp. 907^b 1-3, 33-4.
[3] ἢ ἀήρ, which has probably crept into the text owing to the mention of ἀήρ in l. 33, should be omitted, since only two alternatives are offered in the next sentence.
[4] Cp. chapter 7.

imparts motion to the earthy element and the slow heat[1] does not destroy it.

Why is it that sweet-smelling seeds and plants promote 12 the flow of urine?[2] Is it because they contain heat and 5 are easily concocted,[3] and such things have this effect? For the heat which is in them causes quick digestion[4] and their odour has no corporeal existence; for evil-smelling plants, such as garlic, by reason of their heat promote the flow of urine, but their wasting effect is a still more marked characteristic. But sweet-smelling seeds contain heat, because odour is in general engendered by heat; 10 while evil-smelling things are unconcocted. Now anything which is to promote the flow of urine must be not only hot but also easily concocted, in order that it may accompany the liquids in their downward course and effect their digestion.

Why is it that wines mixed with water have a less strong 13 odour[5] than when they are unmixed? Is it because wine 15 mixed with water is weaker than unmixed wine? Now the weaker is more easily changed by any force acting upon it than the stronger.[6] So wine mixed in the water is more easily affected than unmixed wine. Now it is characteristic of that which is easily affected[7] to yield[8] to something else or to receive something which does not belong to it; unmixed wine, therefore, has a strong odour, but wine mixed with water is odourless.

[1] i.e. that produced by friction.
[2] This problem is partly identical with i. 48 and is repeated in xx. 16.
[3] Reading εὔπεπτα, cp. 865ᵃ 20, 924ᵇ 19: the reading λεπτά is probably due to λεπτύνει in the next line.
[4] See note on 865ᵃ 21.
[5] Reading ἧττον for θᾶττον.
[6] Reading ⟨θᾶττον⟩ ἐξίσταται in order to have a comparative to govern the genitive τοῦ ἰσχυροτέρου.
[7] Reading εὐπετεστέρου.   [8] Reading ὑπεῖξαι (W. D. R.).

BOOK XIII

PROBLEMS CONNECTED WITH THINGS OF UNPLEASANT ODOUR

1 WHY is it that urine acquires a more unpleasant odour the longer it remains in the body, whereas ordure becomes less unpleasant to the smell? Is it because the latter becomes drier the longer it remains in the body (and what is dry is less liable to putrefaction), but urine thickens, and 25 the fresher it is the more like it is to the original liquid drunk?

2 Why is it that things of unpleasant odour do not seem to have an odour to those who have eaten them? Is it because, owing to the fact that the scent penetrates to the mouth through the palate, the sense of smell soon becomes satiated and so it no longer perceives the odour inside the 30 mouth to the same extent—for at first every one perceives the odour, but, when they are in actual contact with it, they no longer do so, as though it had become part of themselves—and the similar odour from without is over-powered by the odour within?

3 Why have flowers an unpleasant odour when they are rubbed? Is it because the earthy element, which is in the flower, mingles with the odour?[1]

4 Why is it that no living creature is pleasant to the smell 35 except the panther[2]—which is pleasing even to the animals, for they are said to find pleasure in its odour—and when they decay they are unpleasant to the smell, but many plants when they decay and wither become still more pleasant to the smell? Is it because the cause of evil odour is an unconcocted condition of excretion? For this reason 908^{a} the perspiration of some people is sometimes unpleasant,

---

[1] Cp. 907^{a} 27, ^{b} 1 ff.
[2] Cp. Theophrastus, *de Caus. Plant.* vi. 5. 2.

particularly in those whose perspiration is not usually unpleasant, as the result of disease.[1]   Also the exhalations and
eructations of those who are in an unconcocted state are
unpleasant. The same cause must be ascribed for evil
odour in the flesh and in that which is analogous to it (by
5 which I mean that which in other animals corresponds to
flesh) ; for here too there is sometimes unconcocted excretion. This then when it putrefies is a cause of evil odour
in living creatures and in decaying bodies. For this reason
too the fat and the bony parts and the hair have no evil
odour, because the fat and bones are already concocted,
10 while the hair contains no moisture. Now plants contain
no excretion.[2] Or is there excretion in them also, but,
because plants are naturally dry and hot, is the moisture
in them more easily concocted and not of a thick consistency ? This can be illustrated from the soil, which is
pleasant to the smell in hot regions, such as Syria and
Arabia, and from the fact that the plants which come from
15 there are sweet-smelling, because they are dry and hot;
and such plants are not liable to decay. But animals are
not dry and hot,[3] and so their excretions are unconcocted
and malodorous, and likewise their[4] exhalations, and when
they decay the moisture putrefies. This does not happen
in plants, because they contain no excretions.

20   Why are things of unpleasant odour more unpleasant **5**
when they are hot than when they are cool ? Is it because
odour is a vapour and an effluvium ? A vapour, then, and
an effluvium is caused by heat ; for a movement takes place,
and heat is the source of the movement. Cold, on the
contrary, is a source of stagnation and contraction and
25 downward movement;[5] but heat and all odours have an
upward tendency, because they are in the air, and the
organ which perceives them is above and not below ; for
odour penetrates to the brain and so causes perception.

---

[1] The Teubner text misprints τοιοῦ τοι ἐκτῶν for τοιοῦτοι ἐκ τῶν.
[2] This is the Aristotelian view, cp. *P. A.* 650^a 22, *de Plantis,* 817^b 19.
[3] τοιαῦτά ἐστι καὶ θερμά appears to be a mixture of two readings,
(1) ξηρά ἐστι καὶ θερμαί, (2) τοιαῦτά (= ξηρὰ καὶ θερμά) ἐστι.
[4] Reading with Richards καὶ ⟨αἱ⟩ διαφύσεις.
[5] Reading φοροῦν, neuter of the participle of φορέω.

6 Why, if one eats garlic, does the urine smell of it, whereas this does not happen when other things are eaten which have a strong odour? Is it because, as some of the followers of Heraclitus say,[1] vaporization takes place 30 in the body just as in the universe, and then, when the process of cooling succeeds, moisture is formed in the universe and urine in the body, so the vaporization from the food, when it is formed by intermixture, causes the odour (for it is odour after it has undergone change)?[2] If so, ought not all the foods too which have a strong odour 35 to produce this effect, which we know they do not? Furthermore, concretions from vapour do not resume their original form—which would result in wine, for example, being produced from the vapour of wine instead of water, as actually happens—and so this part of their theory is also untrue. The truth is that garlic, alone of foods which **908ᵇ** have an odour which is strong and also promotes the flow of urine, has the quality of inflating the lower part of the belly; all other such foods (radishes, for example) engender[3] breath higher up or else do not promote the flow of urine. But garlic[4] has these three qualities: it promotes the flow of urine, it engenders breath, and it does so in the lower 5 part of the body. The region round the privy parts and the bladder feels the effect of such foods owing to its nearness[5] and because it is liable to admit breath; that this is so is shown by the distension of the privy parts. It is clear therefore that the excretion of garlic is more liable than that of any other such food to reach the bladder with the breath, and this excretion mingling with the urine 10 imparts its odour to it.

7 Why is it that the mouths of those who have eaten nothing, but are fasting, have a stronger odour, 'the smell of fasting', as it is called, but when they eat the odour

---

[1] For other applications of the Heraclitean doctrine of ἀναθυμίασις cp. below 934ᵇ 33 ff., *de Anima*, 405ᵃ 25, 26.

[2] Reading μεταβάλῃ.   [3] Omitting καὶ before τὰ πνεύματα.

[4] κάτω cannot stand here; it is in its proper place in the next line. The Latin version of T. G. has *allium vero tria nimirum haec facit*, and we must read τούτῳ (= σκορόδῳ) which the context demands.

[5] i. e. to the lower part of the stomach.

ceases, when one would expect it to increase? Is it because, as the stomach becomes empty, the air becomes hotter from the absence of motion and causes the breath and the excre-
15 tions of phlegm to putrefy? That the air becomes hotter is proved by the fact that fasting also induces an increase of thirst. When food is taken, the odour ceases because it is less than that of the food; for the heat in the food overcomes the internal heat, so that it cannot undergo any process of change.[1]

20 Why has the armpit a more unpleasant odour than any **8** other part of the body? Is it because it is least exposed to the air?[2] Such parts have a particularly unpleasant odour because putrefaction takes place in them owing to the stagnation of fat. Or is it because the armpit is not moved and exercised?

Why is it that those who have a rank odour are still **9** more unpleasant when they anoint themselves with un-
25 guents? Is it because this kind of thing happens in many instances; for example, if something acid and something sweet are mixed, the resulting whole is sweeter? Now any one who perspires has an unpleasant odour, and unguents are productive of heat and therefore induce perspiration.

Why is it that the odour of the breath of those who **10** 30 are bent and deformed is more unpleasant and oppressive?[3] Is it because the region round the lungs is contracted and bent out of an upright position, so that it does not give a free passage to the air, but the moisture and the breath, which tends to be enclosed within, putrefies?

Why is it that most unguents are unpleasant when they **11** mingle with perspiration, but others have a sweeter or at
35 any rate not a more unpleasant odour? Do those which change as a result of movement or friction deteriorate in odour, whereas those which do not are improved? There

---

[1] i. e. produce putrefaction which engenders the 'smell of fasting'.
[2] Cp. 867^a 4-7.
[3] This is quoted by Apollonius, *de Mirab.* 37, as from the *Physical Problems* of Aristotle.

are some such perfumes, just as there are some flowers
from which scents are made, which deteriorate when rubbed 909^a
or heated or dried, white violets, for example; but others
remain the same, for instance roses.   The unguents too
made from flowers of the former class change, while those
made from the latter do not; and so rose-perfume is least
liable to change.   Also unguents have a more unpleasant
odour on those whose perspiration is malodorous, through 5
mingling with their opposite, just as honey when mixed
with salt becomes not sweeter but less sweet.

12   Why do objects always produce a stronger odour when
they are in motion?[1]   Is it because they fill up the air?
The result is that the odour is thus transmitted more 10
quickly to our perception.

[1] This chapter is an almost verbal repetition of xii. 5.

BOOK XIV

PROBLEMS CONNECTED WITH THE EFFECT OF LOCALITY ON TEMPERAMENT

WHY are those who live under conditions of excessive **1** cold or heat brutish in character and aspect? Is the cause the same in both cases? For the best mixture of conditions benefits the mind as well as the body, but excesses of all kinds cause disturbance, and, as they distort the body, so do they pervert the mental temperament.

Why is it that in Pontus corn, if exposed to the cold, **2** keeps intact for many years?[1] Is it because the extraneous moisture is evaporated together with the heat, as happens in grapes? For some things are evaporated by the cold and others with the heat.

Why do burning fevers occur more frequently in the **3** coldest season? Is it because the cold imprisons the heat[2] within? In the summer the contrary occurs, the interior of the body being cooler than the exterior. Burning fever is the inflammation in which,[3] the exterior of the body being cold, the interior is in a condition of excessive heat.

Why are the Ethiopians and the Egyptians bandy-**4** legged? Is it because the bodies of living creatures become distorted by heat, like logs of wood when they become dry? The condition of their hair too supports this theory; for it is curlier than that of other nations, and curliness is as it were crookedness of the hair.

---

[1] Cp. Theophr. *de Caus. Plant.* iv. 16. 2.

[2] For ἀντιπερίστασις τοῦ θερμοῦ see 867[b] 32 and note.

[3] The text, as it stands, does not give any good sense, but the meaning is quite clear from a comparison with 862[b] 31 ff., which expressly states that burning fever comes from within and is due to the collection of heat inside the body. The simplest emendation is to read with Sylburg πυρετὸς ⟨ἐν ᾧ⟩ τῶν κτλ.

5   Why is it that in damp regions copulation is more likely to lead to the birth of female offspring ?[1] Is it because a large amount of moisture thickens more slowly, and in damp regions the semen is moister owing to the presence of more moisture in the temperament ?

6   Why is it that in marshy districts sores on the head are quickly cured, but those on the legs only with difficulty ?[2] Is it because the moisture, since it contains an earthy element, is heavy, and heavy things are carried downwards ? Thus the upper parts of the body are easily concocted, because the impurities are carried downwards; but the lower parts become full of abundant excretion which easily putrefies.

7   Why is it that those who live in airy regions grow old slowly, but those who inhabit hollow and marshy districts age quickly ? Is it because old age is a process of putrefaction, and that which is at rest putrefies, but that which is in motion is either quite free from, or at any rate less liable to, putrefaction, as we see in water ? In lofty regions, therefore, owing to the free access of the breezes, the air is in motion, but in hollow districts it stagnates. Furthermore, in the former, owing to its movement, the air is always pure and constantly renewed, but in marshy districts it is stagnant.

8   Why are the inhabitants of warm regions cowardly, and those who dwell in cold districts courageous ?[3] Is it because there is a natural tendency which counteracts the effects of locality and season, since if both had the same effect mankind would inevitably be soon destroyed by heat or cold ?[4] Now those who are hot by nature are courageous, and those who are cold are cowardly. But the effect of hot regions upon those who dwell in them is that they are cooled, while cold regions engender a natural state of heat in their inhabitants. Both races are large of stature—those

---

[1] Cp. *G. A.* 766^b 34, where the same view is stated.
[2] The same problem occurs in i. 18.   [3] Cp. chapter 16.
[4] For this use of καίειν for the effects of both extreme heat and extreme cold cp. *Meteor.* 382^b 8 καίειν λέγεται . . . τὸ ψυχρόν.

who live in cold regions because of the innate heat in them, and those who inhabit hot districts owing to the heat in which they live; for increase of stature occurs both in those who are hot and as a result of heat, whereas cold has a contracting effect. Since then those who live in cold districts

20 have a powerful principle of growth in themselves, and those who live in hot regions encounter no external cold which prevents their growth, both naturally admit of considerable increase in stature. But this is less true of those who live in our latitudes, because the principle of growth in them is less strong, and those who live in cold regions feel the contracting effect of cold.

25 Why are those who live in hot regions longer-lived? Is **9** it because their natural condition is drier, and that which is drier is less liable to putrefaction and more lasting, and death is as it were a kind of putrefaction? Or is it because death is due to the chilling of the interior heat,[1] and every-

30 thing is chilled by a surrounding medium which is colder than itself? Now in warm regions the surrounding air is hot, but in cold regions it is cold and so more quickly and effectively destroys the interior heat of the body.

Why are those who live in hot regions longer-lived? **10**

35 Is it because they preserve their heat and moisture better? For death is the corruption of these.[2]

Why is it that we become drowsier in marshy districts? **11** Is it because there we are more cooled, and cooling, being

40 a kind of rest,[3] induces sleep, and sleep occurs during rest?

910[a]   Why is it that those who live on board ship, though **12** they spend their time on the water, have a healthier colour than those who live in marshes? Is the weather and the free access of the breezes the cause? Now water makes men pale when it putrefies, a process which is due to the absence of movement; that is why those who live in marshy regions are rather pale.

---

[1] Cp. *de Iuv. et Sen.* 469[b] 18; *de Vit. et Mort.* 478[b] 32.
[2] A condensed form of the previous chapter.
[3] i.e. cold is ἡσυχία, just as heat is κίνησις.

13 Why is suffocating heat very frequently experienced in 5
wintry regions, much more so than in warm districts ?[1] Is
it because of the moisture in the air ? For as a result of
the same heat applied to it water becomes hotter than air,
and therefore damper air [2] becomes hotter than dry air.[3]
Or perhaps the air is not really hotter [4] in these regions,
but only seems so by contrast with the general coolness, as 10
the sun emerging from a cloud seems hotter in contrast with
its effect when it is behind a cloud.

14 Why do those who live in southerly climes tend to have
black eyes ? Is blueness of the eyes due to excess of
internal heat, whereas blackness is due to its absence, as
Empedocles affirms ? Just, therefore, as those who dwell 15
in the north have blue eyes, because the internal heat is
prevented from escaping owing to the external cold ; so in
those who dwell in southerly climes the moisture cannot
escape owing to the surrounding heat, but the heat escapes
because there is nothing to bar its exit, and the moisture 20
left behind causes blackness; for when light departs that
which is left behind is dark. Or does the pigmentation of
the eye assimilate itself to the colour of the rest of the
body ? If so, the eyes of those who live towards the north
are blue, because they are themselves white (for blue is
akin to white) ; and those who dwell in the south being 25
black, their eyes also are black.

15 Why are those who live in warm regions wiser than
those who dwell in cold districts ?[5] Is it for the same
reason as that for which the old are wiser than the young ?
For those who live in cold regions are much hotter, because
their nature recoils owing to the coldness of the region in
which they live, so that they are very like the drunken and
are not of an inquisitive turn of mind, but are courageous [6] 30
and sanguine ; but those who live in hot regions are sober
because they are cool. Now everywhere those who feel

---

[1] Cp. 938ᵃ 37 ff.
[2] Reading ὁ ἀὴρ ⟨ὁ⟩ ὑγρότερος (W. D. R.).
[3] Reading ξηροῦ for θερμοῦ (W. D. R.).
[4] Reading θερμότερος for ξηρότερος (W. D. R.) ; T. G. renders *calidior*.
[5] Cp. *Pol.* 1327ᵇ 23 ff.   [6] Cp. 909ᵇ 10 ff. ; 910ᵃ 37 ff.

fear make more attempt to inquire into things than do the
self-confident, and therefore they discover more. Or is it
because the race of those who live in warm regions is more
ancient, the inhabitants of the cold regions having perished
35 in the Flood,[1] so that the latter stand in the same relation
to the former as do the young to the old?

Why are the inhabitants of warm regions cowardly, and 16
those who dwell in cold regions courageous?[2] Is it because
human beings have a natural tendency which counteracts
910ᵇ the effect of locality and season (for, if both had the same
tendency, they would soon be destroyed)? Now those who
are hot by nature are courageous and those who are cold
are cowardly. The effect of hot regions upon their inhabitants is to cool them (for, their bodies having rarities,
5 the heat escapes out of them), but those who live in a cold
climate become heated in their nature, because their flesh is
densified by the external cold, and when it is in this
condition the heat collects internally.

　[1] For references to the Flood in Aristotle see *Pol.* 1269ᵃ 4 ff.,
Meteor. 352ᵇ 16 ff. Synesius is perhaps referring to this passage
when he says (*Encom. Calvit.* 22) περὶ ὧν παροιμίων Ἀριστοτέλης φησὶν
ὅτι παλαιᾶς φιλοσοφίας (v.l. ἱστορίας) ἐν ταῖς μεγίσταις φθοραῖς ἀπολομένης
ἐγκαταλείμματα περισωθέντα διὰ συντομίαν καὶ δεξιότητα. The doctrine of
the Flood is also found in Theophrastus, cp. J. Bernays, *Theophrastos'
Schrift über Frömmigkeit*, p. 50. Plato refers to the Flood in *Tim.*
22 A, C, 23 A, B, *Crit.* 109 D, 111 E; for other classical references see
J. B. Mayor's note on Juvenal i. 83.
　[2] This problem is partly identical with chapter 8.

BOOK XV

PROBLEMS CONNECTED WITH
MATHEMATICAL THEORY

1   WHY is it that of all the lines which divide a rectilinear figure into two parts that drawn from angle to angle alone bears the name of diameter ?[1] Is it because the diameter, as its name implies, divides the figure of which it is the diameter into two parts without destroying it ? The line therefore which divides it at its joints[2] (by which I mean 15 the angles) will be the diameter; for it does not destroy the figure but divides it, like those who divide up implements of war for distribution. But a division which cuts through a composite figure in the lines which form it destroys the figure; for a rectilinear figure is constructed on angles.

2   Why is the diameter so called ?[3] Is it because it is the only line which divides a rectilinear figure into two parts, as though one should call it the 'dichameter' ?[4] And why[5] 20 is it the only one that bears this name of all the lines which divide a rectilinear figure into two parts ? Is it because it is the only line which divides the figure at the points where its limbs bend,[6] whereas all other lines divide it in its sides ?

3   Why do all men, barbarians and Greeks alike, count up to 10 and not up to any other number, saying for example, 2, 3, 4, 5 and then repeating them, 'one-five', 'two-five', 25

---

[1] διάμετρος has the meanings both of diameter and diagonal.

[2] The rectilinear figure is conceived as something organic, its sides being members which are jointed together at the angles; this is more clearly brought out in ll. 21, 22 below.

[3] A repetition in a shorter form of chapter 1.

[4] i.e. 'that which measures into two parts'. All the MSS. here read διάμετρος, but the emendation to διχάμετρος is certainly correct.

[5] Reading with Bekker διὰ τί for διότι.

[6] Cp. above, ll. 14, 15 and note.

just as they say eleven, twelve ? [1]   Or why do they not stop
at some point beyond ten and repeat from there ?   For
every number is made up of one, two, &c., combined with
a preceding number,[2] and thus a different number is formed ;
but the counting always proceeds in fixed sets of ten.   For
it is clearly not the result of chance that all men [3] invariably
30 count in tens ; and that which is invariable and universal
is not the result of chance, but is in the nature of things.
Is it because ten is a perfect number ?   For it combines
every kind of number, odd and even, square [4] and cube,
length and surface, prime and composite.   Or is it because
ten is the original number, since one, two, three, and four
35 together make ten ? [5]   Or is it because the bodies which
move in the heavens are nine in number ? [6]   Or is it
because in ten proportions four cubic numbers result,[7] from
which numbers the Pythagoreans [8] declare that the whole
universe is constituted ?   Or is it because all men have ten
fingers, and so, as though possessing counters that indicate
911^a the numbers proper to man, they count all other things by
this quantity ?   One race among the Thracians alone of all
men count in fours, because their memory, like that of
children, cannot extend farther and they do not use a large
number of anything.

⟨Why is it that the shapes of the heavenly bodies always 4
5 appear to us the same ?   Is it⟩ [9] because the earth is a
centre ?   For the shapes which appear to us are always

---

[1] The Greek ἕνδεκα, δώδεκα, 'one-ten', two-ten', bring out the point
better than the English 'eleven', 'twelve'.

[2] e. g. thirty-one, thirty-two, &c.

[3] Reading with Bekker ποιοῦντες ⟨πάντες⟩ φαίνονται.

[4] Omitting the commas after ἄρτιον and τετράγωνον.

[5] i. e. ten, not one, is the unit, which for convenience has been
divided into four fractions 1, 2, 3, and 4, which added together
make 10.

[6] i. e. there are nine planets (including the sun and moon), which
with the addition of the earth make 10.

[7] e. g. in ten proportions obtained by continuous multiplication of
1 by 2 four cubes occur: $1 (1^3)$, 2, 4, $8 (2^3)$, 16, 32, 64 (4^3), 128, 256,
512 (8^3).

[8] Diels, *Vorsokr.* 1^3, 350. 1.

[9] This problem is not translated in T. G.'s Latin version and the
text is clearly unsatisfactory.   The statement of the problem is derived
by Bussemaker from another ancient version.

similar. This does not seem [1] to be so unless one views them
from the centre, but they would sometimes appear triangular,
sometimes irregular foursided figures, and sometimes take
other forms.[2]   Now the earth would appear to us to be the
centre of the universe, if we could view it from the heavenly
bodies. For the earth being spherical, the centre of the universe and of the earth will be the same.   But we dwell on the 10
surface of the earth, so that it is not from the centre but at
the distance of half the diameter that the heavenly bodies
appear to have the shapes that they do appear to have.
What reason then is there why the appearance of their
shapes should not remain the same when the distance is
increased ?

5   Why is it that, although the sun moves with uniform
motion, yet the increase and decrease of the shadows is not
the same in any equal period of time ? [3]   Is it because the 15
angles to the objects seen, that is the angles made by
the rays [4] of the sun and subtending equal arcs, are equal ?
Now if these are equal, so also are the angles which the
rays when produced [5] make in the triangle formed by
the first ray [6] and the object seen and the shadow.   If
the angles are equal, the line which is farther from the 20
object seen must be greater than that which is less far ;
for we know that this is so.   Let the circumference,
therefore, be divided into any number of equal parts, and
let the object seen be Θ.   When therefore the sun at A
falling on Θ [7] makes the shadow $\Theta\Lambda$,[8] the ray must fall on
Λ.[9]   But when the sun comes to B, the ray from B will 25

[1] Reading with Bussemaker ⟨οὐ⟩ δοκεῖ.
[2] No sense is to be made of the text as it stands ; in particular
there is nothing for τούτου (l. 9) to refer to.   It seems probable that
something has fallen out owing to *homoeoteleuton*, e. g. ἐδόκει ⟨ἂν. τοῦ
δὲ κόσμου ἂν ἐδόκει⟩ ἡ γῆ.
[3] Putting the comma before, and not after, ἐν τῷ ἴσῳ χρόνῳ.
[4] Retaining the MS. reading ὑπὸ τῶν ἀκτίνων.
[5] Reading εἰ δ᾽ αὗται, καὶ ⟨ἃς⟩ ἐκβαλλόμεναι ποιοῦσιν ⟨αἱ⟩ ἀκτῖνες.
T. G. renders *quodsi illi aequales sunt, eductos quoque inde aequales
esse necesse est.*
[6] i.e. the ray from the sun when it is at A to Δ, the top of the
object Θ.
[7] Reading προσβαλὼν τῷ Θ (W. D. R.), cp. 911ᵇ 37.
[8] Reading with Bussemaker ΘΛ for ΘΑ.
[9] Reading with Bussemaker Λ for A.

fall within $\Theta\varLambda$,[1] and similarly again when the sun comes to
$\varGamma$; otherwise one straight line will touch another straight
line at two points. Since therefore AB is equal to $B\varGamma$, the
angles which subtend them[2] at $\varDelta$ will also be equal, for
they are situated about the centre. But if the angles on
this side[3] of $\varDelta$ are equal, so also are the corresponding
30 angles in the triangle; for they are at the apices of the
first pair of angles.[4] So while the angle is divided into two
equal parts,[5] the line $\varLambda E$ will be greater than the line EZ
within $\varLambda\Theta$.[6] So too with the other angles formed by the
rays from the circumference. At the same time it is clear

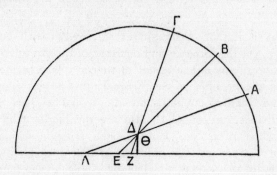

that the shadow must be shortest at midday and that then
35 its increases are least. For the sun is most over our head
at midday, and stifling heat occurs both for the reason just
mentioned[7] and because there is no wind; for wind is
caused when the sun dissipates the air near the earth. If
911ᵇ therefore it does so simultaneously in both hemispheres,
midnight and midday would naturally be windless.

¹ Reading with Bussemaker $\Theta\varLambda$ for ΘA.
² Reading ὑπὸ ταύταις.
³ Reading with Bussemaker τῇδε for τῇ.
⁴ i. e. the angle $\varLambda\varDelta E$ equals the angle $E\varDelta Z$, these angles being at the
apices of the triangles $A\varDelta B$ and $B\varDelta\varGamma$.
⁵ i. e. the angle $\varLambda\varDelta Z$ is divided into two equal parts $\varLambda\varDelta E$ and
$E\varDelta Z$.
⁶ Reading with Bussemaker ἡ $\varLambda E$ τῆς EZ ἐν τῇ $\varLambda\Theta$. The fact that
$\varLambda E$ is greater than EZ proves the main point of the problem, viz. that
the decrease of the shadows is not uniform in an equal period of time.
⁷ i. e. because the sun is directly overhead.

6 Why does the sun penetrating through quadrilaterals form not rectilinear shapes but circles, as for instance when it passes through wicker-work ? Is it because the projec- 5 tion of the vision is in the form of a cone,[1] and the base of a cone is a circle, so that the rays of the sun always appear circular on whatever object they fall ? For the figure also formed by the sun must be contained by straight lines, if the rays are straight ; for when they fall in a straight line on to a straight line, they form a figure contained by straight lines. And this is what happens with the rays ; for they 10 fall on the straight line of the wicker-work, at the point where they shine through, and are themselves [2] straight, so that their projection is a straight line. But because the parts [3] of the vision which are cut off towards the extremities of the straight lines are weak, the parts of the figure 15 about the angles are not seen ; but what there is of straight line in the cone describes a straight line, while the rest does not, but the sight falls on part of the figure without perceiving it. For there are many things to which the sight penetrates without our seeing them, objects, for instance, which are in darkness. A similar phenomenon is the fact that a quadrilateral figure appears polygonal, and at a greater distance circular. Now since the projection of sight is in the form of 20 a cone, when the figure is removed to a distance the parts of the vision which are cut off towards the angles, because they are weak and few, do not see anything when the distance is increased ; but the parts of the vision which fall upon the centre of the figure, being numerous and strong, are more persistent. When, therefore, the figure is near at hand, they 25 can [4] see the parts in the angles ; but, when the distance is greater,[5] they cannot do so. For this reason too a curved line removed to a distance appears straight, and the moon on the eighth day seems to be contained by straight lines, if the vision falls upon the line which encloses it and not on its breadth. For when the circumference is near, the sight 30

---

[1] Cp. above, 872ª 37.
[2] Reading αὐταὶ with Bekker.
[3] Omitting ἀπὸ after ἀποσχιζομένας, cp. below, l. 22.
[4] Reading δύνανται (Sylb.).
[5] Reading πλείονος δ'αὐτοῦ (W. D. R.).

can discern how much nearer one part of the circumference is than another; but when it is distant, the sight does not perceive it clearly, and it seems to be equally distant; and so it appears to be straight.

35　　Why, though the moon is spherical, do we see it straight **7** when it is half-full? Is it because our vision and the circumference of the circles which the sun makes when it falls upon the moon are in the same plane? Whenever 912^a this happens, the sun appears as a straight line; for, since that which casts its vision on a sphere must see a circle, and the moon is spherical, and the sun looks down upon it, there must be a circle which is caused by the sun. When therefore this is opposite to us, the whole is visible and the 5 moon appears to be full; but when it changes owing to the altered position of the sun, its circumference becomes on a plane with our sight and so it appears straight, and the rest appears circular, because a hemisphere is opposite our vision, and this has the appearance of a semicircle; for the 10 moon is always facing our vision, but when the sun sheds its rays we do not see it. And after the eighth day it begins to fill out from the middle, because the sun as it passes on makes the circle incline more towards us; and the circle being thus presented to view resembles the section of a cone. It assumes a crescent-like appearance when the sun changes its position; for when the circle of the sun 15 reaches the extreme points, which make the moon seem half-full, the circumference of the circle appears; for it is no longer in a straight line with the vision, but passes beyond it. When this happens and the circle passes through the same points, it must necessarily appear to have a crescent shape; for a part of the circle is directly on a 20 plane with the eye (a part of the circle, that is, which was formerly opposite to us),[1] so that part of the brightness is cut off.[2] Then the extremities too remain in the same position, so that the moon must have a crescent shape to a greater or less extent according to the sun's movement;

---

[1] Putting a comma after ὄντος.
[2] Reading ἀποτέμνεταί ⟨τι⟩.

for when the sun changes its position, the circle upon
which it looks also turns, remaining on the same points;
for it might assume an infinite number of inclinations, since 25
an infinite number of the largest circles can be described
through the same points.

8   Why is it that the sun and moon, which are round, have
the appearance of being flat? Is it because all things[1] of
which the distance is uncertain seem to be equidistant, when
they are more or less distant? And so in a single body 30
composed of parts, provided that it is uniform in colour,
the parts must necessarily appear equidistant, and the equidistant must appear to be uniform and flat.

9   Why does the sun make long shadows as it rises and sets,
and shorter when it is high in the heavens, and shortest 35
of all at midday? Is it because, as it rises, it will at first
make a shadow parallel to the earth and cast it to an
infinite distance,[2] and then make a long shadow, which

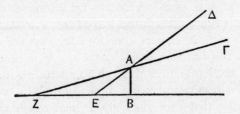

grows ever less because the straight line from the higher
point falls within that from the lower point. Let *AB* be
the gnomon,[3] and *Γ* and *Δ* two positions of the sun. The 40
ray from *Γ*, the line *ΓZ*, will fall outside the line *ΔE*;[4] and **912^b**
the shadow *BE* is formed when the sun is higher in the
heavens, and *BZ* when it is lower,[5] and it will be shortest
when[6] the sun is at its highest and over our head.

[1] Reading πάντα.
[2] Reading ὑπερτενεῖ, and omitting ἄνισον as the corruption of a gloss
ἀνίσχων.
[3] i.e. the pole or pillar used for casting a shadow, or the index of
a sun-dial.
[4] Reading ΔE for ΓE.
[5] Reading κατωτέρω (W. D. R.) for κατωτάτω.
[6] Reading ὅταν ἀνωτάτω ᾖ (Ruelle).

Why are the shadows thrown by the moon longer than **10**
5 those thrown by the sun, though both are thrown by the
same perpendicular object? Is it because the sun is higher
than the moon, and so the ray from the higher point must
fall within that from the lower point? Let $A\varDelta$ be the

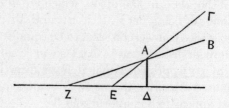

gnomon, B the moon, and $\varGamma$ the sun. The ray from the
moon is BZ, so that the shadow will be $\varDelta Z$; but the ray
from the sun is $\varGamma E$, and its shadow therefore will necessarily
10 be less, viz. $\varDelta E$.

Why is it that during eclipses of the sun, if one views **11**
them through a sieve or a leaf—for example, that of a
plane-tree or any other broad-leaved tree—or through the
two hands with the fingers interlaced, the rays are crescent-
shaped in the direction of the earth?[1] Is it because, just
as, when the light shines through an aperture with regular
15 angles, the result is a round figure, namely a cone[2] (the
reason being that two cones are formed, one between the
sun and the aperture and the other between the aperture
and the ground, and their apices meet), so, when under
these conditions part is cut off from the orb in the sky,[3]
there will be a crescent on the other side of the aperture
from the illuminant, that is, in the direction of the earth
20 (for the rays proceed from that part of the circumference
which is a crescent)?[4] Now as it were small[5] apertures are

---

[1] i. e. on the lower side of the medium through which they shine.
[2] Cp. 911[b] 5.
[3] The Latin version of T. G. renders *ergo cum pars orbi superiori
detrahitur*, and something like the following is probably the right
reading, ὅταν οὖν ἐχόντων οὕτως ⟨τοῦ⟩ ἄνωθεν κύκλου ἀποτέμνηταί ⟨τι⟩,
ἔσται μηνίσκος κτλ.   [4] Placing a full stop after ἀκτῖνες.
[5] αἱ δέ is certainly corrupt, and we should probably read μικραὶ δέ,
which is indicated by the Latin version of T. G., *pro foraminum
exiguitate*, and which is implied by the contrast of ἡ διὰ μεγάλων ὀπῶν.

formed between the fingers and in a sieve, and so the phenomenon can be more clearly demonstrated than when the rays pass through wide apertures. Such crescents are not formed by the moon, whether in eclipse or waxing or waning, because the rays from its extremities are not clear-cut, but it sheds its light from the middle, and the middle 25 portion of the crescent is but small.

12   Why does the parhelion not occur either when the sun is in mid-heaven or above the sun or below it, but only at the side of it? Is it because the parhelion is produced when our visual ray to the sun is refracted, and this station- 30 ary condition of the air, on the occasion of which the vision is refracted, cannot occur either near the sun or far away from it? For, if it is near, the sun will dissolve it, whereas, if it is far away, the sight will not be refracted; for, if it is strained to a distance, it is weak when refracted from a small refractor.[1] (So too a halo does not form.) If then a refractor forms opposite the sun and near to it, the sun 35 will dissolve it, whereas if it be far away, the incidence of the sight upon it will be too weak. If, however, it forms at the side of the sun, it is possible for the refractor to be at such a distance that neither does the sun dissolve it nor does the sight ascend weakened[2] by passing under the earth. It does not form below the sun because, being near the earth, 40 it would be dissolved by the sun; whereas, if it were above the sun when the sun is in mid-heaven, the sight would be **913^a** distracted. And it cannot form at all even at the side of the sun when it is in mid-heaven, because, if the sight is directed too far under the earth, very little of it will reach the refractor, so that, when it is refracted, it will be very[3] weak.

13   Why does the extremity of the shadow caused by the 5 sun seem to tremble? For it is not due to the fact that the

[1] i. e. the stationary air. Sight and light are identified here as else-where frequently in the *Problems*, the sight being said to travel up to the object seen and back again to the eye.

[2] Reading ἀσθενῆ for ἀθρόαν, which gives exactly the opposite of the sense required, cp. below, 913^a 2-4.

[3] Reading πάνυ with Ruelle.

sun is travelling along; for it is impossible for it to move
in contrary directions, and it is of such motion that trembling consists. (Moreover it is uncertain why a shadow
changes its position, as also why the sun itself moves.) Is
it due to the movement of the so-called motes in the air?
10 These can be seen in the rays which enter through a
window; for they move even when there is no wind. These
then being constantly carried from the shadow into the light
and from the light into the shadow, the common boundary
between the light and the shadow is seen to move similarly.
For changing[1] from side to side of it, these motes cause as
it were shadow in one place and light in another; so that
15 the shadow appears to move, though it is not really it but
the motes which move in this way.[2]

---

[1] Reading μεταβάλλοντα for μεταβάλλονται.
[2] Reading ἐκεῖνα for ἐκεῖναι with Bussemaker.

BOOK XVI

PROBLEMS CONNECTED WITH INANIMATE THINGS

1 WHY is it that the bases of bubbles in water are white, and if they are placed in the sun they do not make any 20 shadow, but, while the rest of the bubble casts a shadow, the base does not do so but is surrounded on all sides by sunlight ? And, what is still more wonderful, even if a piece of wood is placed on the water in the sunlight, ⟨there is no continuous shadow but⟩ [1] it is cut off by the water at that point. [2] Is no shadow really formed ? Is the shadow dissolved by the sun ? If then a shadow is to be defined as anything 25 which is not visible to the sun, the whole mass of the object all round must be visible to the sun; but the impossibility of this has been demonstrated in the treatises on optics, [3] for even the largest optical system cannot see the whole circumference of the smallest visible object.

2 Why are bubbles hemispherical ? Is it because the radii between the centre and the outer air extend in every direction upwards to the same distance and thus necessarily 30 produce a hemispherical form ? The corresponding hemisphere below is cut off by the watery surface in which the central point is situated.

3 Why is it that in magnitudes of uneven weight, [4] if you set the lighter part of them in motion, the object thrown

---

[1] The text here makes no sense, and it is clear from T. G., who renders *nec si lignum per aquam in sole apposueris, umbra ligni continua exsultabit sed*, &c., that something has fallen out.

[2] ταῦτα gives no possible sense, and ταύτῃ (= ' on the surface of the water ') has been translated.

[3] There is no evidence that Aristotle wrote a work on Optics (cp. Bonitz, *Index*, 104ᵃ 61 ff.) ; so we must suppose a general reference here to works on Optics, cp. 959ᵇ 2 οἱ περὶ τὰ ὀπτικά.

[4] The example of the loaded dice indicates that we should read βάρος for βάθος.

35 revolves in a circle, as happens, for example, with loaded
dice if you throw them with the unweighted side turned
towards you ?[1] Is it because the heavier part cannot travel
at the same speed as the lighter when hurled with the same
force ? Now the object must travel as a single whole, but
913ᵇ cannot move alike in all its parts ; therefore if the parts were
moved with equal speed they would move in the same line,
while since one part[2] travels more quickly than the other, the
object necessarily revolves as it moves ; for it is only in
this manner that the parts[3] which are always opposite one
5 another can follow unequal paths in the same time.

Why is it that objects which fall to the earth and rebound **4**
describe similar angles to the earth's surface on either side
of the point at which they touch the surface ?[4] Is it because
all things naturally tend to travel at right angles to the
earth ? Objects, therefore, which fall upon the ground at
10 right angles, striking the surface perpendicularly and dia-
metrically, when they rebound, form angles of that size,[5]
because the diameter divides the angle at the surface into
equal parts. But objects which fall obliquely, since they do
not strike the ground perpendicularly but at a point above
the perpendicular, when they are thrust back by that against
15 which they strike, travel in the opposite direction. This in
the case of round objects is due to the fact that,[6] striking
against it[7] in their course, they revolve in an opposite
direction to that in which they are thrust back, whether
their central point is at rest or changes its position. In the
case of rectilinear objects it is due to the fact that their
perpendicular is thrown backwards after being brought
forward ;[8] just as happens to those whose legs are sheared

---

[1] This problem is partly identical with chapter 12 below.
[2] i. e. the lighter.   [3] Reading τὰ (W. D. R.) for ταῦτα.
[4] Cp. chapter 13.   [5] i. e. right angles.
[6] ὅτε of the Teubner text is a misprint for ὅτι.
[7] ἐν αὐτῷ is perhaps corrupt.
[8] Reading διὰ τὸ τὴν κάθετον αὐτῶν εἰς τοὔμπροσθεν προσενεχθεῖσαν
ἐκκρούεσθαι. T. G. renders *rectis vero compacta lineis, quod per-
pendiculum eorum in partem priorem adductum retorquetur*. The
corruption of προσενεχθεῖσαν may have been due to a desire to provide
a principal verb, which is unnecessary, since συμβαίνει·φέρεσθαι is to
be supplied from ll. 14–15.

away from under them or whose scrotum is pulled down- 20
wards, for such persons always fall in a contrary direction
and backwards, because their perpendicular is raised above
the ground[1] and then thrust forward. For clearly the
opposite of perpendicularity will be to fall backwards and
downwards, and objects carried downwards would be
heavier. That, therefore, which in these persons involves 25
a fall, becomes movement in rebounding objects. Neither
round nor rectilinear objects therefore rebound at right
angles, because the perpendicular divides the objects in
motion into two parts depthways, and there cannot be
several perpendiculars to the same plane surface cutting
one another,[2] which will happen if a perpendicular is formed 30
at the moment of their impact at the point where the object
in motion strikes the plane surface,[3] so that the original
perpendicular along[4] which it travelled must necessarily be
cut by the new perpendicular. Now since the object will
be borne back, but will not be borne back at a right angle,
it remains that the angle on either side of the point of
impact with the plane surface must be an acute angle; for 35
the right angle forms the division between the opposite
angles.

5   Why is it that a cylinder, when it is set in motion, travels
straight and describes straight lines with the circles in
which it terminates, whereas a cone revolves in a circle, its
apex remaining still, and describes a circle with the circle in 914[a]
which it terminates? Both move with a circular motion,
but the cylinder describes straight lines on the plane surface,
while the cone describes circles because the circles which
compose the cone are unequal and the greater circle
always moves more quickly than the less about the same 5

---

[1] Omitting ἰσάζειν αὐτὰ and reading ἐκπίπτουσιν διὰ τὸ τὴν κάθετον
μετέωρόν τε κτλ. (W. D. R.).
[2] Reading αὐτάς for αὐτάς (so too Bussemaker).
[3] The text as it stands will not translate, since the repetition of
συμβήσεται gives two principal verbs. Cᵃ omits ὑπ' αὐτῆς ...
τέμνεσθαι; but better sense is gained by omitting διχοτομεῖσθαι ...
συμβήσεται, its insertion being probably due to a gloss on the words
immediately following.
[4] Reading ἐφ' ἧς (Bussemaker).

centre. Now since all the circles composing the cone move
at different rates, it results that the outermost circles travel
over most space and describe the longest line in the
same time (hence they must move in a circle); for all the
circles are described by the same straight line,[1] and when
10 the straight line revolves the various points on it do not
describe an equal line in the same time, but can travel along
an equal line only if they proceed in a straight direction.
But in the cylinders, since all the circles are equal and
about the same centre, the result is [2] that, since they touch
the plane surface at all the points on them at the same
time, as they roll they travel at a uniform speed (because
15 cylinders [3] are uniform throughout), and reach the plane
surface again simultaneously when each has completed its
own circuit; thus the straight lines described on the plane
surface are also equal, for the circles describe them by
contact, since they both are equal and travel at the same
speed. Now the lines described by the same line travelling in a straight direction [4] are straight, and so the
20 cylinder would travel [5] straight along them; for it makes
no difference whether you drag the cylinder over the plane
surface at the line where it first [6] touched the plane surface,
or whether you roll it over it; [7] for the result will always
be that an equal and similar line made up of points on the
cylinder will touch the plane surface, both when the cylinder
is dragged and when it is rolled along.

25   Why is it that the section of a rolled book, which is flat,[8] 6
if you cut it parallel to the base becomes straight when

---

[1] i.e. the line from the apex of the cone to the point of contact of
the plane surface and the base of the cone.

[2] The sense here is clear and is that of the Latin version of T. G.,
*Evenit ut et simul suis omnibus punctis planum contingendo parili
celeritate volvantur.* Hence συμβαίνει ἅμα τοῦ ἐπιπέδου τὰ ἐν αὐτοῖς
πάνθ' ἁπτομένους σημεῖα φέρεσθαι is read.

[3] Bonitz, *op. cit.*, p. 412, reads κύκλους for κυλίνδρους; but τοὺς
κύκλους is already the subject of the sentence and would not be
repeated, and τοὺς κυλίνδρους clearly refers to cylinders in general.

[4] i. e. when drawn along instead of being rolled.

[5] Reading ἂν φέροιτο for ἀναφέροιτο.

[6] Reading ᾗ πρώτῃ for ᾗ ἡ πρώτη (so too Bussemaker).

[7] Reading αὐτῷ (Bonitz) for αὐτό.

[8] Omitting καὶ εὐθεῖα with Cᵃ.

unrolled, but if it is cut obliquely becomes crooked?[1] Is it due to the fact that, since the circles in the first section are in the same plane, the result is that the oblique section is not parallel but is partly[2] more and partly less distant from the first section, so that, when the roll is unfolded, the circles, which are in the same plane and have their origin in the same plane,[3] assume, when unrolled, the line which they themselves form? For the resulting line is formed from the circles which are in the same plane, so that the line, being on a plane, is also straight. But the line[4] of the oblique section when it is unrolled, not being parallel to the first section, but partly more and partly less distant from it (this being the position of the section relative to it), will not be on a plane and therefore not straight either; for part of a straight line cannot be in one plane and part in another.

7   Why is it that magnitudes always appear less when **914[b]** divided up than when taken as a whole? Is it because, though things which are divided always possess number, in size they are smaller than that which is single and undivided? For that which is great is said to be great owing to its continuity and because it is of a certain size, but the number of its parts[5] is always greater than the number of any undivided magnitude. So it is only natural that the whole should appear greater than the parts into which it is divided; for, though the whole and its parts are identical, the whole, being continuous, possesses more of the quality of magnitude, while the parts have more of the quality of number.

8   Of the phenomena which occur in the water-clock the cause seems to be in general that ascribed by Anaxagoras;[6]

---

[1] The problem might be stated in other words thus: 'Why does a roll which is made up of sections of parchment unroll absolutely straight if all sections are cut square, while it will not do so if any section is cut obliquely?'

[2] Reading ἀλλὰ τῇ μὲν (W. D. R.).

[3] Reading a comma instead of a full stop after ἐπιπέδῳ.

[4] Reading ἡ δὲ for ἥ τε.

[5] Reading ὁ δὲ ἀριθμὸς ⟨τῶν μερῶν⟩ πᾶς κτλ., to complete the sense; T. G. renders numerus vero partium omnis.

[6] Diels, Vorsokr.³ i, p. 390, 28 ff.; cp. Phys. 213ᵃ 27. The present

for the air which is cut off within it is the cause of the water not entering when the tube has been closed. The air, however, by itself is not the cause; for if one plunges the water-clock obliquely into the water, having first blocked up the tube, the water will enter. So Anaxagoras does not adequately

15 explain how the air is the cause; though, as has been said, it certainly is the cause. Now air, whether impelled along or travelling of itself without any compelling force, naturally travels in a straight line like the other[1] elements. When therefore the water-clock is plunged obliquely into the water, the air preserving its straight course is driven out

20 by the water through the holes opposite to those which are in the water, and, as it goes out, the water flows in. But if the water-clock is plunged upright into the water, the air not being able to pass straight up, because the upper parts are closed, remains round the first holes; for it cannot contract[2] into itself.[3] The fact that the air can keep out

25 the water by its immobility can be illustrated by an experiment with the water-clock itself. For if you fill the bulb itself of the water-clock with water, having stopped up the tube, and invert it with the tube downwards, the water does not flow along the tube to the outlet. And when the outlet is opened, it does not immediately flow out along the tube

30 but only after a moment's interval, since it is not already at the outlet of the tube but passes along it afterwards, when it is opened. But when the water-clock is full and in an upright position, the water passes through the strainer[4] as soon as ever the tube is opened, because it is in contact with the strainer, whereas it is not in contact with the

35 extremities of the tube. The water does not, therefore, flow into the water-clock, for the reason already mentioned, but

passage is the *locus classicus* on the construction of the *clepsydra*, or water-clock, in its simplest form as used in the law courts to regulate the length of speeches. It appears to have been a hollow globe terminating above in a narrow neck or tube (αὐλός) with a stopper and with several holes at the bottom, through which the water escaped when the vessel was filled and the stopper removed.

[1] Reading τἆλλα.
[2] Reading σάττεσθαι (Bonitz).
[3] Reading αὑτὸν (so also Diels); T. G. renders *in sese contrahi non possit.*
[4] i. e. the holes at the bottom of the bulb of the water-clock.

flows out when the tube is opened because the air in it being set in motion up and down causes considerable movement [1] in the water inside the water-clock. The water then, being thrust downwards and having itself also a tendency in that direction, naturally flows out, forcing its way through the air outside the water-clock, which is set in motion and is equal in **915^{a}** force to the air which impels it but weaker than it in its power of resistance, because the interior air, since it passes through the tube, which is narrow, flows more quickly and violently and forces the water on. The reason why the water does not flow when the tube is closed is that the water on 5 entering into the water-clock drives the air forcibly out of it. (That this is so is shown by the breath and noise engendered in it as the water enters.[2]) And driving the air forcibly along it rushes into the tube itself, and [3] like wedges [4] of wood or bronze driven in by cleavage, remains in position without anything else to hold it together, until 10 it is expelled from the opposite direction, as pegs [5] which are broken in wood are knocked out. This occurs when the tube is opened for the reasons already mentioned. If [6] this is the reason, it is only natural that it [7] should not flow out or make its way forth, since the air forcibly prevents it [8] and becomes inflated. (The noise which is made shows that 15 the water is drawn up by the air, and this is a common phenomenon.) All the water then, being drawn up and being in itself [9] continuous, remains in the same position under the pressure of the air, until it is thrust away again by it; and, since the first part of the water remains in the same position, the rest of the water is dependent from it in

---

[1] Reading κίνησιν for κένωσιν; T. G. renders *motum excitat pleniorem.*

[2] Reading ἐρυγμὸς εἰσιόντος τοῦ ὕδατος; T. G. renders *spiritus ructusque quos ingrediente humore intus excitari sentimus.*

[3] Reading βίᾳ ⟨δ'⟩ ὠθοῦν συνεισπίπτει εἰς τὸν αὐλὸν αὐτὸν ⟨καὶ⟩ καθάπερ.

[4] Reading ἐμπιεστὰ with Yᵃ.

[5] Reading, with Diels, ἐπιούρους.

[6] Reading εἰ with all the best MSS., and placing a comma after ταῦτα.

[7] Reading αὐτὸ (Bussemaker).

[8] Reading ἢ ἐξι⟨έναι κωλύ⟩οντος (with Diels) βίᾳ τοῦ ἀέρος.

[9] Diels reads αὐτῷ (*sc.* τῷ ἀέρι).

one continuous mass.   It is only natural that this should be
20 so ; for it is the property of the same thing to move something from its own place and to hold it when it has moved
it,[1] and to do so for a longer time, if that which holds and
that which is held are of equal force, or if that which holds [2]
is stronger, as occurs in the present case ; for air has greater
force than water.

25   Why is it that the parts of plants and of animals which **9**
have no functional importance are all round—in plants, for
instance, the stem and the shoots, and in animals the legs,
thighs, arms, and chest—and no whole or part is triangular
or multi-angular ?   Is it due, as Archytas[3] used to say, to
30 the fact that in natural movement the proportion of equality
is always present (for he holds that all things move in a
proportion), and that this is the only proportion which can
return to itself, and so it forms circles and rotundities
wherever it occurs ?

Why do extremities always take rounded forms ?   Is it **10**
because nature makes everything as excellent and as
35 beautiful as the available material permits, and a rounded
form is the most beautiful, being as uniform as possible ?

Why does a circular object[4] when it is thrown at first **11**
describe a straight line, but, as it ceases to move, describe
a spiral, until it falls ?   Does it describe a straight line at
first, because the air on either side of it alike keeps it
915^b upright ?   The inclination then to either side being equal,
the line also which it describes must be of such a nature
that it divides the space on either side of it equally,
and such a line is a straight line.   But when it inclines
to one side, because the air on either side of it is not
even, it no longer describes an equal line with its inner
5 and with its outer edge, but is forced to describe a circular
line.

---

[1] Reading ὡς ἐκίνησεν (Bussemaker) for ὡς ἐκείνης.
[2] Reading τὸ ἴσχον (so too Bussemaker).
[3] The Pythagorean philosopher.
[4] The writer has no doubt a flat-edged discus in mind as the
circular object.

12　Why is it that in magnitudes of uneven weight,[1] if you
set the [2] lighter part of them in motion, the object thrown
revolves in a circle, as happens for example with loaded
dice if you throw them with the unweighted side towards
you?[3] Is it because the heavier part cannot travel at the 10
same speed as the lighter when hurled with the same force?
Now since it must necessarily move, but cannot do so in the
same manner, that is in a straight line, it must take an
inward direction and revolve; just as, if part of the object
had as a whole remained motionless owing to a weight in
the centre, the part next to the person setting the object
in motion would have moved so as to occupy the position
of the part away from him, while the farther side would 15
have moved towards him. But when the whole object
moves and, as it travels, has a weight in the middle, it must
necessarily behave in the same manner.[4]

13　Why is it that objects which are travelling along, when
they come into collision with anything, rebound in a direction opposite to that in which they are naturally travelling,
and at similar angles?[5] Is it because they move not only
with the impetus which accords with their own nature but 20
also with that which is due to the agent which throws them?
Their own impetus then ceases when they reach their own
proper position (for everything comes to rest when it reaches
the position to which it is naturally carried), but, owing to
the extraneous impetus, it is forced to continue to move,
not, however, in a forward direction, because it is prevented 25
from doing so, but either sideways or in a direct line
backwards.[6] Now every object rebounds at similar angles,
because it is travelling to the point to which it is carried by
the impetus which was imparted by the person who threw
it; and at that point it must be travelling at an acute angle
or at a right angle. Since then the repelling object stops
the movement in a straight line, it stops alike the moving

[1] Reading βάρος for βάθος; see note on 913ᵃ 34.
[2] Reading ⟨τὸ⟩ κουφότερον with Richards; cp. 913ᵃ 35, 915ᵇ 9 f.
[3] This problem is partly identical with chapter 3 above.
[4] i. e. revolve.　　　　　　　　　　　[5] Cp. chapter 4.
[6] We should probably read ὄπισθεν ⟨W. D. R.⟩ for ὀρθόν.

30 object and its impetus. As then in a mirror the image
appears at the end of the line along which the sight travels,
so the opposite occurs in moving objects, for they are
repelled at an angle of the same magnitude as the angle at
the apex [1] (for it must be observed that both the angle and
the impetus are changed), and in these circumstances it is
35 clear that moving objects must rebound at similar angles.

[1] Let *A* be the point from which the
object is thrown, and *BC* a wall against
which it strikes at the point *D*. The
angle which it forms, *ADC*, will be ἡ κατὰ
κορυφὴν γωνία. The object will rebound
to *E* forming the angle *BDE* which will
equal the angle *ADC*. Thus the object
rebounds 'at a similar angle'. The above
is a case where the object strikes the wall
at an acute angle; if it strikes it at right
angles the similar angles will be right
angles.

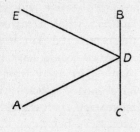

BOOK XVII

PROBLEMS CONNECTED WITH ANIMATE THINGS

1 WHY do those who are unsymmetrical appear larger when set side by side with other men [1] than by themselves? Is it because that which is symmetrical is one, and symmetry more than anything else gives unity to a thing, and that 916^a which is one tends to be indivisible, and the indivisible is smaller, whereas asymmetry by causing diversity creates a multiplicity? When things therefore are seen by themselves, their dimensions are less likely to be noticed; but this is not so when they are seen side by side with one another. That then which is indivisible appears to be one, 5 and the impression which it makes on the beholder is one because of its symmetry. But that which is unsymmetrical makes a greater impression, as though it were many, and appears greater because, though in reality only one, it seems to be many; for it partakes of the nature of magnitude, because it is continuous, and of number, because of the inequality of its parts; and so being increased in both 10 these respects, it naturally appears great by the side of that which is simple and one.

2 Why do animals and plants grow more in length than otherwise? Is it because length increases three times over, width twice, and depth once? For length is the first and original dimension, and so it increases both of itself, and 15 secondly in combination with width, and thirdly in combina-

---

[1] ἀλλήλους, if retained here, must be used not in its fullest reciprocal sense, but more generally of 'other men', i.e. members of the same species but not ἀσύμμετροι. If this involves too much straining of the meaning of ἀλλήλους, the simplest change is to ἄλλους. It is quite clear from 916^a 11 that the unsymmetrical are contrasted not with one another but with the symmetrical (there called τὸ ἁπλοῦν καὶ ἕν). The Latin version implies the reading συμμέτρους, which is perhaps right, the reading ἀλλήλους having arisen either from παρ' ἄλληλα of 916^a 5, or from a gloss on ἀσυμμέτρους copied by mistake for συμμέτρους.

tion with depth. But width implies an increase in two
dimensions only, in itself and at the same time in depth.[1]

In what sense must we understand the terms ' prior ' and **3**
' posterior '? As those who lived in the time of Troy are
' prior ' to us, so are those who lived before them ' prior ' to
20 them and so on *ad infinitum* ? Or since there is a beginning
and a middle and an end of the universe, and when a man,
as he becomes old, reaches the limit and turns again towards
the beginning,[2] that[3] which is nearer to the beginning is
earlier, what prevents our being nearer to the beginning
than to the end, in which case we should be ' prior ' ? Just
25 as the course[4] of the firmament and of each of the stars is
a circle, why should not also the coming into being and the
decay of perishable things be of such a kind that the same
things[5] again come into being and decay? This agrees
with the saying that ' human life is a circle '.[6] To demand
that those who are coming into being should always be
numerically identical is foolish, but one would more readily
30 accept the theory of the identity of the species. And so we
should ourselves be ' prior ', and one might suppose the
arrangement of the series to be such that it returns back in
a circle to the point from which it began and thus secures
continuity and identity of composition. For Alcmaeon[7]
declares that men perish because they cannot link together
35 the beginning to the end[8]—a clever saying, if one supposes
that he uses it metaphorically and the literal meaning is not
insisted upon. If then human life is a circle, and a circle
has neither beginning nor end, we should not be ' prior ' to
those who lived in the time of Troy nor they ' prior ' to us
by being nearer to the beginning.

---

[1] Reading βάθει for μεγέθει with Bonitz, *op. cit.*, p. 412.
[2] i. e. the point where existence and non-existence meet.
[3] Omitting δέ.   [4] Reading, with Richards, ἡ φορά.
[5] Reading ταὐτὰ for ταῦτα.
[6] Cp. *Phys.* 223ᵇ 24 ; Herodot. i. 107 ; Tac. *Ann.* iii. 55.
[7] Alcmaeon of Croton, cp. *Met.* 986ᵃ 27 and Ross's note; *H. A.*
492ᵃ 14, 581ᵃ 16 ; and Diels, *Vorsokr.*³, p. 135, 10.
[8] i. e. when a man reaches the end of life, personal identity is lost
and the new life starts with a new personality.

BOOK XVIII

PROBLEMS CONNECTED WITH LITERARY STUDY

1 WHY is it that some people, if they begin to read, are 916ᵇ overcome by sleep even against their will, whereas others wishing to be overcome by sleep are kept awake by taking up a book?[1] Is it because in those in whom movements of breath take place owing to the coldness of their nature 5 or of melancholic humours, which by their coldness engender an unconcocted excretion of breath—in such people, the intelligence, when it is set in motion and does not think of anything with concentrated attention, is checked by the second movement,[2] which has a cooling effect, and this causes a tendency to sleep? But when they fix the intelligence firmly upon something, as happens in reading, they 10 are impelled by the heating movement, which is unchecked by anything, and so they cannot go to sleep. In those who are in a natural condition, however, when the intelligence, which is very powerful, stands at a single point and does not keep changing from one subject to another, every function in that region[3] (whose inactivity involves sleep) is at a standstill;[4] 15 and when the intelligence stands still and is as it were weary, being situated in the head, it weighs it down and produces sleep. But as long as the mind moves naturally, it does not go to sleep; for it is then that it is most alive, and wakefulness rather[5] than sleeping is the cause of life.

---

[1] A comparison with the parallel passage in chapter 7, which clearly deals with the same problem and is partly identical with the present chapter, shows that τοὺς δὲ βουλομένους ποιεῖ ἐγρηγορέναι must be read here; cp. 917ᵃ 19 and note (so too Bussemaker).

[2] i. e. the unconcocted excretion of breath.

[3] i. e. the head.

[4] Reading ἵσταται as in 917ᵃ 30.

[5] Reading with Bonitz, op. cit., 413, ⟨μᾶλλον⟩ αἴτιόν ἐστιν; but αἴτιον is possibly itself corrupt and some such word as ἰδιαίτερον, 'more characteristic of', seems to be required.

Why are contentious disputations useful as a mental **2** exercise? Is it because they involve frequent victories and 20 defeats? They therefore quickly instil a spirit of rivalry; for, when men are victorious, they are induced by their joy to contend yet more, and, when they are defeated, they continue the struggle in hopes of turning defeat into victory. Those engaged in struggles of other kinds act in the same way, and so when fighting and getting the worst of it often refuse to come to terms.

25 Why is it that in rhetorical displays men prefer examples [1] **3** and fables [2] rather than enthymemes? [3] Is it because they like to learn and to learn quickly, and this end is achieved more easily by examples and fables, since these are familiar to them and are of the nature of particulars, [4] whereas enthymemes are proofs based on generalities, with which 30 we are less familiar than with the particular? Further, we attach more credence to any evidence which is supported by several witnesses, and examples and fables resemble evidence, and proofs supported by witnesses are easily obtained. Further, men like to hear of similarities, and examples and fables display similarities. [5]

35 Why do we talk of an orator, or a general, or a business **4** man as being shrewd, but not use the term of a musician or of an actor? Is it because the powers of the two last are exercised apart from any desire of gaining an advantage (for their aim is pleasure), whereas the three first aim at some advantage? For a good orator or general or business **917ᵃ** man is one who can gain some advantage, and shrewdness consists mainly in getting the better of some one else.

Why is the philosopher generally regarded as superior **5** to the orator? [6] Is it because the philosopher treats of the nature of injustice, while the orator says that such and such a person is unjust, and the orator states that such and such

---

[1] Cp. *Rhet.* 1357ᵇ 25–30, *Rhet. ad Alex.* 1429ᵃ 21 ff.
[2] λόγοι here equivalent to μῦθοι, cp. below, l. 35.
[3] Cp. *Rhet.* 1357ᵃ 32 ff., *Rhet. ad Alex.* 1430ᵃ 23 ff.
[4] Cp. *Rhet.* 1357ᵃ 27, 28.   [5] Cp. *Rhet. ad Alex.* 1429ᵃ 25–7.
[6] This problem is repeated in a longer form in xxx. 9.

a person is a tyrant, while the philosopher discusses the nature [1] of tyranny ?   5

6   Why is it that some men spend their time in pursuits which they have chosen, though these are sometimes mean, rather than in more honourable professions ?   Why, for example, should a man who chooses to be a conjurer or an actor or a piper prefer these callings to that of an astronomer or an orator ?   Is it because some men would prefer to undertake the more honourable professions but do not do so because 10 they do not feel confident that they would succeed in them ? Or is it because each man chooses the calling in which he thinks he can excel and devotes himself to that which he chooses, giving up the greater part of each day to it, in order that he may improve his own proficiency [2] in it ? Now when men have chosen a calling from the first and 15 have become accustomed to it, they lose the power of discriminating between the higher and the lower ; for their mind is warped by their bad choice.

7   Why is it that some persons, if they begin to read, are overcome by sleep even against their will, whereas those who wish to go to sleep are made unable to do so if they take up a book ? [3]   Is it because in those in whom 20 movements of breath take place owing to the coldness of their nature or of melancholic humours, which by their coldness engender an unconcocted excretion of breath—in these when the intelligence is set in motion and does not think of anything with concentrated attention, the intelligence is checked by the second movement,[4] and so they undergo a great mental change and go to sleep (for the 25 movement of breath is overcome) ?   But when they fix their intelligence on something, as happens in reading, they are impelled by the movement of breath [5] unchecked by any-

---

[1] Reading, with Richards, ποῖον.

[2] Reading κρατιστεύων (cp. above, l. 12) for κράτιστος ὤν.

[3] The problem of this chapter is obviously the same as that of chapter 1 and we must read τοὺς δὲ βουλομένους οὐ ποιεῖ δύνασθαι (W. D. R.).

[4] Reading τῇ ἑτέρᾳ κινήσει, cp. above, 916ᵇ 8 and note.

[5] The parallel passage (916ᵇ 10) has θερμαντικῆς, but πνευματικῆς can stand here since ἡ πνευματικὴ and ἡ θερμαντικὴ κίνησις both refer to

thing, and so cannot sleep. But in those who are in a
natural condition, when the intelligence is fixed on one
30 thing and does not keep changing from one subject to
another, every function in that region (the inactivity of
which involves sleep) is at a standstill. (Similarly during a
rout,[1] if the leader halts, all the forces under his command
halt also.) For naturally that which is light rises, while the
heavy sinks.[2] As long, therefore, as the mind moves
naturally, it does not go to sleep; for it is then that it is
35 most alive.[3] When the mind stands still and is as it were
weary, the intellect undergoes a change, and the corporeal
elements rise to the head and produce sleep. Reading
might be expected to prevent sleep; but wakefulness is not
due to the fact that we are thinking (for then our mind is
most concentrated) but to the constant change; for the
917ᵇ intellectual activities which cause wakefulness are those in
which the mind searches and finds difficulties rather than
those in which it pursues continual contemplation; for the
former cause lack of concentration, while the latter do not.

Why is it that in contentious disputes no trifling can ever **8**
occur? Is it because such reasoning is apparent syllogism,
5 and syllogism involves only a brief discussion; and, if it be
prolonged, after a time the false reasoning is detected and
the disputant can withdraw the premisses which he has
granted?

Why do we feel more pleasure in listening to narratives **9**
in which the attention is concentrated on a single point than
in hearing those which are concerned with many subjects?
10 Is it because we pay more attention to and feel more pleasure
in listening to things which are more easily comprehended,
and that which is definite is more easily comprehended

---

the same thing, viz. the movement of breath when it is unaffected by
natural cold or melancholic humours.
   Cp. *Post. An.* 100ᵃ 12.
  [2] This sentence seems out of place here and would make better
sense if it were inserted after ποιεῖ τὸν ὕπνον, l. 36.
  [3] οὕτω γὰρ ἔχει gives no sense and is obviously corrupt. As the
parallel passage 916ᵇ 17 has ζῇ γὰρ τότε μάλιστα, we should here read
οὕτω γὰρ ζῇ μάλιστα or something similar.

than that which is indefinite ?   Now a single thing is definite,
but a plurality partakes of the nature of the infinite.

10   Why do we like to hear of events which are neither very
old nor quite new ?   Is it because we discredit events which
occurred long before our time and take no pleasure in 15
events which we discredit, while we can still as it were
perceive very recent events and so take no pleasure in
hearing about them ?

BOOK XIX

PROBLEMS CONNECTED WITH MUSIC

WHY do those who are grieving[1] and those who are 1
enjoying themselves alike have the flute played to them?
20 Is it in order that the distress of the former may be lessened
and the pleasure of the latter increased?

Why is it that, when the same person uses the same vocal 2
power, the sound travels farther when he is singing or
shouting with others than when he does so by himself?[2]
Is it because the doing of anything with a number of other
people—compressing, for instance, or pushing something—
does not produce an effect in simple proportion to the
25 number of persons; but, just as a line two feet long
describes a circle[3] which is not double but quadruple that
described by a line a foot long, so collective actions have
greater force in proportion to their number than when they
are carried out separately?[4] When, therefore, a number of
persons sing together, the force of their voice unites, and
impels the air simultaneously, so that it travels many times
as far; for the voice produced by all is the multiple of each
single voice.

30 Why does the voice waver most when singing *parhypate*[5] 3
and to no less a degree than when singing *nete* and the
higher notes, although the interval is greater? Is it because

---

[1] The reference is to the use of the flute at funerals.

[2] Cp. xi. 52.

[3] Vollgraff is no doubt right in thus interpreting γράφειν in its usual
sense in geometry.

[4] i.e. multiplication takes place and not mere addition.

[5] The following is the usual scheme employed by Peripatetic writers
(see Jan, *Musici Scriptores*, p. 81):

hypate parhypate lichanos mese paramese trite paranete nete
  e   *f*   *g*   *a*   *b*   *c'*   *d'*   *e'*.

There seems no reason why, in a diatonic scale, *parhypate* should be
specially difficult to sing. Bojesen and Stumpf therefore suppose that
the reference is to an enharmonic scale, in which the interval from
hypate to *parhypate* is a quarter-tone, which would actually be hard to
take.

the interval [1] is more difficult to sing and is a primary element? [2]   Now the difficulty is due to the straining and pressure of the voice; and these require an effort, and things which require an effort are more likely to fail.

4   But why is *parhypate* difficult to sing, but *hypate* easy, 35 although there is only a quarter-tone between them? [3]   Is it because *hypate* is accompanied by relaxation of the voice and also because after tension it is easy to slacken? [4]   It is probably for the same reason that what a man says with violence,[5] he says with this note or *paranete*.[6]   [For one must . . . with a consciousness of the character which one is representing and under conditions most akin to it according to one's purpose.] [7]   [But what is the first condition of 918^a concordant music?] [8]

5   Why do men take greater pleasure in listening to those who are singing such music as they already know than music which they do not know? [9]   Is it because, when they recognize what is being sung, it is more obvious that the 5 singer is as it were achieving [10] his aims, and this is pleasant to contemplate?   Or is it because it is less [11] pleasant to learn?   And the reason of this is that in the one case there is acquisition of knowledge, in the other the use and recognition of it.   Further, that which is familiar is always pleasanter than the unfamiliar.

6   Why does recitation with a musical accompaniment have 10 a tragic effect when introduced into singing?   Is it owing

[1] Stumpf has been followed here in taking ταύτην and αὕτη to refer to the quarter-tone.
[2] i. e. the quarter-tone is the smallest interval in the musical scale.
[3] The meaning seems to be: 'Why is it easier to sing the same interval downwards than upwards?'
[4] Reading with Jan ἀναχαλᾶν for ἄνω βάλλειν.
[5] Reading with Bussemaker and Stumpf βίαν for μίαν.   The interpretation here adopted is that of Stumpf.
[6] We should, with Stumpf, expect *paramese* rather than *paranete* here.
[7] This sentence (which is incomplete, since there is no infinitive after δεῖ) appears to be out of place here.
[8] This sentence appears to be the statement of another problem, the solution of which is lacking.
[9] Cp. below, chapter 40.   [10] Omitting ὁ; cp. ^a 24.
[11] Reading with Richards ἢ ὅτι ⟨ἧττον⟩ ἡδύ.

to the resulting contrast? For the contrast gives an expression of feeling and implies extremity of calamity or grief, whereas uniformity is less mournful.

Why did the ancients, when they gave the scale seven **7** notes, leave in *hypate* and not *nete*?[1] Is this a false statement, since they left in both and omitted *trite*, or is the truer answer that the lower note contains the sound of the higher note,[2] so that *hypate* gives the impression of the octave above better than (*nete* for the high note needs[3] more force, while the low note is easier to utter)?

Why does the low note[4] contain[5] the sound of the high **8** note?[6] Is it because the low note is greater and resembles an obtuse angle, while the high note resembles an acute angle?[7]

Why do we listen with greater pleasure to a solo when a **9** man sings it to the accompaniment of a flute or lyre?[8] Yet the same tune is sung note for note[9] with or without

---

[1] Cp. below, chapter 47. For the scheme of eight notes used by the Peripatetic writers, see note on 917ᵇ 30. Two stages can be traced in the earlier evolution of the seven-stringed lyre (see Jan, *op. cit.*, p. 81).
(*a*) The earliest form was:

hypate	parhypate	lichanos	mese	paramese or trite	paranete	nete
e	*f*	*g*	*a*	*b*	*c'*	*d'*

(*b*) After the time of Terpander *trite* (= *b*) was omitted (cp. below, 920ª 15–17), and *nete* was made equivalent to *e'*:

hypate	parhypate	lichanos	mese	paramese or trite	paranete	nete
e	*f*	*g*	*a*	*c'*	*d'*	*e'*

The Peripatetic, being familiar with the eight-note scale which was evolved from the seven-note scale, inverts the order in which the two systems came into being. The question arises why *nete* (= *e'*) was omitted as in system (*a*) above. The answer, having system (*b*) in mind, asks whether it is not a truer statement of the case to say that *nete* (= *d'*) was retained and *trite* (= *b*) rejected.
[2] The phrase ἰσχύει τὸν τῆς ὀξυτέρας φθόγγον gives no meaning since ἰσχύει is a neuter verb and cannot govern an accusative. If it is retained, we must read something like ἰσχύει ⟨πλέον⟩ τοῦ τῆς ὀξυτέρας φθόγγου. A better alternative is to read ἴσχει, with Eichtal and Reinach (*Rev. Ét. Grec.* v. (1892) p. 33), who compare 918ª 40 ἢ ὅτι τὸ βαρὺ μέγα ἐστίν, ὥστε κρατερόν; καὶ ἔνεστιν ἐν τῷ μεγάλῳ τὸ μικρόν.
[3] Some verb must be supplied to complete the sense: ἐπεὶ ⟨δεῖται⟩ τὸ ὀξὺ δυνάμεως (Wagener) is more probable than the insertion of σημεῖον by the Teubner editors. ἐπεὶ ... φθέγξασθαι seems, however, quite irrelevant here.   [4] i. e. *hypate*.
[5] Reading ἴσχει, as above, for ἰσχύει.   [6] i. e. *nete*.
[7] Cp. *de. An.* 420ᵇ 1 ff.   [8] Cp. below, chapter 43.
[9] Reading πρόσχορδα (Jan); cp. Plato, *Laws*, xii. 812 D.

accompaniment. This creates a problem, for if it gave more delight to hear more of the same thing,[1] we ought to sing to the accompaniment of a large number of flute-players and this 25 ought to be even more pleasant. Is it because the singer is more obviously achieving his aim when he is accompanied y a flute or lyre ? And the accompaniment of a number of flute-players or lyres does not add to the pleasure, because it drowns the singing.

10   Why, if the human voice is more pleasant than an instrument,[2] is the voice of a man singing without words—as, for 30 example, when making meaningless warblings[3]—not so pleasant as a flute or lyre ? Or is it true that even in the case of an instrument we get less pleasure if it is not expressive of meaning ? The instrument, however, has an advantage even in its actual effect ; for while the human voice is pleasanter, instruments strike the note better than the human mouth, wherefore they are pleasanter to hear than meaningless warblings.

11   Why is the voice higher when it echoes back ?[4]   Is it 35 because it is smaller,[5] having become weaker ?[6]

12   Why does the lower of two strings sounded together always give the tune ? For if one omits *paranete*, when one should sound it with *mese*, the tune is given none the less ; but if one omits *mese*, when one should sound both, the tune is lost.[7] Is it because the low note is large and 40 therefore strong, and the less is contained in the greater ?[8] So too if *hypate* is stopped down in the centre,[9] two *netes* are produced.   918ᵇ

---

[1] Reading εἰ γὰρ ἑτέρπε (Jan) μᾶλλον τὸ αὐτὸ πλέον ⟨ὄν⟩, ἔδει κτλ.
[2] Putting a comma after φωνή instead of after ᾄδοντος.
[3] For the meaning of τερετίζειν see *An. Post.* 83ᵃ 33.
[4] For ἀπηχεῖν cp. 899ᵃ 24.   [5] Reading with Vollgraff ἐλάττων.
[6] Cp. above xi. 6 and 20. Lord Rayleigh (*Theory of Sound*, ii. p. 152) notes that echoes returned from such reflecting bodies as a group of trees are sometimes raised an octave.
[7] Reading ἂν γὰρ ἐάσῃ τὴν παρανήτην, δέον συμψῆλαι τῇ μέσῃ, γίνεται τὸ μέλος οὐδὲν ἧττον· ἐὰν δὲ τὴν μέσην, δέον ἄμφω ψῆλαι οὐ γίνεται. This is the reading of Monro, except that he reads παραμέσην, for which Fétis and Gevaert read παρανήτην. The Teubner editors wrongly report Monro as reading ψιλά.
[8] Cp. 918ᵃ 20.
[9] i. e. by striking the string on either side of the central point. The

Why is it that the low note in the octave gives the effect **13** of unison with the high, but not vice versa ?[1] Is it because, if possible, the sound of both notes is in both notes, but, failing that, in the low note, since it is greater ?

Why does the accord in the octave escape notice, and **14** why does there appear to be a simple unison, as for example in the Phoenician lyre and in the human voice ?[2] For the upper and lower notes[3] do not give the same sound but are analogous[4] to one another at the octave. Is it because their sound appears to be practically the same owing to the analogy, and analogy is equality in sounds, and equality is of the one ?[5] The same deception occurs also in the pipes.

Why were ' nomes ' not composed in antistrophes like **15** all other songs, that is, choric songs ? Is it because the ' nomes ' were assigned to virtuosi, and as these were already able to imitate different characters and sustain their parts, the songs composed for them became long and elaborate ? Like the words, therefore, the music conformed to the imitation, becoming constantly different; for it was more essential for the music to be imitative than the words.[6] (For this reason too dithyrambs, since they have become imitative, no longer have antistrophes, as they had formerly.) The reason is that in the old days free citizens themselves formed the choruses; it was difficult, therefore, for a large number

fact that *hypate* can be made to produce two *netes* is a proof that the less is contained in the greater.

[1] i.e. a note contains as a harmonic or upper partial the note an octave higher than itself, whereas it does not contain the note an octave lower than itself. Our author seems to have had some knowledge of 'undertones', i.e. harmonics which work downwards instead of upwards, so far as the octave is concerned.

[2] e.g. a man and a boy, when they think they are singing the same tune, are really singing an octave apart.

[3] Reading with Eichtal and Reinach ἐν τοῖς ὀξ⟨έσιν καὶ τοῖς βαρ⟩έσιν ὄντα.   [4] Reading ἀνὰ λόγον.

[5] Reading διὰ τὸ ἀνάλογον, ⟨τὸ δὲ ἀνάλογον⟩ ἰσότης ἐπὶ φθόγγων, τὸ δὲ ἴσον τοῦ ἑνός. This is clearly the text rendered by T. G., who translates 'an modus proportionis facit ut sonus quasi idem esse appareat? proportio enim in sonis aequalitas est, aequale autem omne ad unitatem referendum est'.

'This is certainly true of the only 'nome' of which the words have come down to us, the *Persae* of Timotheus, which resembles the meaningless libretto of an inferior opera and must have depended for its effect on the music and the mimetic powers of the performer.

to sing together like virtuosi, so they sang in one mode.[1]
For it is easier for a single person to make many changes
than for a large chorus, and for a professional than for
those who are preserving the character of the music. And
so they made the music more simple for them. Now the
antistrophic song is simple; for there is one rhythm[2] and 25
one unit of metre. For the same reason songs executed
from the stage are not antistrophic, but those sung by the
chorus are so; for the actor is a virtuoso and an imitator,
but the chorus is less imitative.

16 Why is 'antiphonal'[3] accompaniment[4] more pleasing 30
than 'symphonic' accompaniment?[5] Is it because in the
former the consonance is more obvious than when the
accompaniment of the singing is 'symphonic'? For of
the two notes played by the instrument one must be in
unison with the note sung, and so two notes contending
against one drown the other note.[6]

17 Why is it that singing in fifths[7] does not give the effect
of 'antiphony'?[8] Is it because one 'symphonic' note is

---

[1] ἐναρμόνια Yᵃ, ἐν ἁρμονίᾳ Cᵃ Xᵃ AP. Chabanon's conjecture ἐν μιᾷ
ἁρμονίᾳ has been adopted; the corruption can be explained by suppos-
ing that μιᾷ was written αʹ.

[2] Reading with Jan εἰς ῥυθμός. The MS. reading ἀριθμὸς can be
explained as a misunderstanding of αʹ (= εἰς) ῥυθμός.

[3] ἀντίφωνος can be applied in general to any reproduction of a tune
in a different part of the scale; but it is frequently used in these
problems in the technical sense of the accord in the octave, the only
interval in the view of the Greeks which could be used consecutively in
singing. σύμφωνος is used either (1) of any consonance (cp. the use
of συμφωνεῖν in l. 31, and ἡ διὰ πασῶν συμφωνία (l. 40), and chapter 39,
where τὸ σύμφωνον includes all consonances, (2) in the technical sense
as applied to musical accompaniment when two notes are played by
an instrument, one of which is the same as that of the voice (ὁμόφωνος),
the other consonant with the voice, i.e. a fourth or a fifth higher.
ὁμοφωνία (= unison) occurs when two identical notes are used simultaneously.

[4] That harmonized musical accompaniment is here intended is
shown by the words of ll. 31–2 ὅταν πρὸς συμφωνίαν ᾄδῃ (cp. D. B.
Monro, *J. of P.* I, pt. ii, pp. 87–8).

[5] Cp. chapters 35 and 39.

[6] i.e. one of the notes played on the instrument is identical with
that uttered by the singer; these two notes drown the third note,
i.e. the second note played on the instrument.

[7] T. G. appears to render διὰ πέντε ⟨καὶ διὰ τεσσάρων⟩.

[8] 'Antiphonal' is here used in its wider sense of reproducing the
same tune in a different part of the scale.

35 not the same as the other 'symphonic' note,[1] as are the notes which are an octave apart? For in the accord[2] in the octave the deep note in the lower part of the scale is analogous to the high note in the upper part; it is, therefore, as it were at once the same and different. But this does not occur in fifths and fourths, so that the sound of the 'antiphonal' note does not appear, for it is not identical.

40 Why is it that the accord in the octave alone is used in 18 919ᵃ singing?[3] For in 'magadizing'[4] this and no other accord is used. Is it because it alone is made up of 'antiphonal' notes, and with 'antiphonal' notes, if but one be sung, the same effect is produced as if both were sung? For the one note in a way contains the sounds of both, so that, when one 5 is sung, the concordant note[5] at this interval is also sung; and when they sing both,[6] or when one note is sung and the other played on the flute, they both as it were sing one note. Therefore the accord in the octave alone is sung, because the 'antiphonal' notes have the sound of one note.

But why does the power of producing the effect of a single 19 10 note belong only to 'antiphonal' notes? Is it because they alone are equidistant from *mese*?[7] The presence then of this mean creates a certain similarity in their sounds, and the ear seems to tell us that it is the same note and that they are both extremes.

Why is it that, if, after tuning the other strings, one alters 20 *mese* and uses the instrument, the ear is offended and an 15 unmusical effect is produced not only when *mese* is used,

---

[1] Reading with Jan ἡ σύμφωνος τῇ συμφώνῳ.

[2] Reading ἐκεῖ with Vollgraff for ἐκείνη. The meaning clearly is that there is the same succession of corresponding notes in the scale as sung by a man's voice and by a boy's.

[3] Cp. below, chapter 39ᵇ.

[4] The μάγαδις was a large stringed instrument containing at least two octaves (Athenaeus, xiv. 36; Anacreon, fr. 18; Xen. *Anab.* vii. 3. 32); hence μαγαδίζειν comes to mean the singing of a succession of notes by different voices in octaves.

[5] Reading with Jan ἡ σύμφωνος for ἡ συμφωνία.

[6] Punctuating καὶ ἄμφω ᾄδοντες, ἢ τῆς μὲν ᾀδομένης, τῆς δὲ αὐλουμένης, ὥσπερ κτλ.

[7] This is untrue, and the whole problem is singularly inept and clearly inserted by a writer who knew nothing of music.

but in the rest of the piece as well, whereas, if *lichanos* or
any other string is altered, it only seems to make a difference
when that particular string is used?[1]   Surely this is only
natural; for in all good music *mese* occurs frequently, and
all good composers have frequent recourse to *mese*, and, if 20
they leave it, they soon return to it, as they do to no other
note.   Similarly in language, if certain connecting particles
are removed, such as τε and καί, the language is no longer
Greek; whereas the omission of some particles does not
offend the ear, because certain particles must be frequently 25
used, if there is to be language, but others not.   So *mese*
is as it were a conjunction among sounds, and more so than
the other[2] notes, because its sound occurs more often.

21   Why is it that of singers those who are singing low notes
are more conspicuous if they sing out of tune than those 30
who are singing high?   So too those who make mistakes
in time in the lower notes[3] are more conspicuous.   Is it
because the period of time occupied by the low note is
longer, and this longer period is more perceptible (for,[4]
lasting for a greater time, it creates a deeper sense-
impression), whereas a quick,[5] high note escapes notice 35
owing to its swiftness?

22   Why does a large choir keep better time than a small
one?[6]   Is it because they look more to one man, their leader,
and dance[7] more slowly and so more easily achieve unity?
For mistakes occur more frequently in quick singing.

23   Why is *hypate* double *nete*?[8]   Is it because in the first 919[b]
place, when half the string is struck and when the whole

---

[1] Cp. below, chapter 36.
[2] Reading with Ruelle and Stumpf ἄλλων for καλῶν. μάλιστα τῶν
καλῶν ⟨μελῶν⟩ is, however, possible: 'particularly in good music', cp.
above, l. 19.
[3] Reading with the MSS. βαρυτέρῳ. The generally accepted emendation βραδυτέρῳ spoils the sense; the question of duration being
introduced in the *solution*.
[4] Omitting ἤ before ὅτι with Reinach and Eichthal, and punctuating
αἰσθητός, ὅτι.
[5] Reading ταχὺ with the MSS.   [6] Cp. below, chapter 45.
[7] Reading ὀρχοῦνται with Graf.
[8] Reading with Wagener and Jan τῆς νήτης ἡ ὑπάτη.   The solution

string is struck an accord in the octave is produced? So too with wind instruments,[1] the sound produced through the middle hole and that produced through the whole flute 5 give an accord in the octave. Again, in the reed-pipe an accord in the octave is obtained by doubling the length, and this is how flute-makers produce it. Similarly they obtain a fifth by means of a length in the ratio of 3 to 2.[2] Again, those who construct Pan-pipes stuff wax into the extreme end of the *hypate*-reed, but fill up the *nete*-reed 10 to the middle. Similarly they obtain a fifth by means of a length in the ratio of 3 to 2, and a fourth by means of a length in the ratio of 4 to 3. Further, *hypate* and *nete*[3] on triangular stringed instruments, when they are equally stretched, give an accord in the octave when one is double the other in length.

15 Why, if one strikes *nete*[4] and then stops it down, does 24 *hypate* alone seem to resound?[5] Is it because the vibration produced from *hypate* is very much of the same nature as the sound of *nete*, because it is in accord with it? When it is increased by the addition of its like, it alone is audible, the other sounds being imperceptible owing to their smallness.

20 Why is *mese* ('the middle note') so called in the scale, 25 though there is no middle of eight notes?[6] Is it because in the old days scales had seven notes,[7] and seven has a middle?

shows that *hypate* is double *nete* in length of string. In 920ᵃ 29, where *nete* is said to be double *hypate*, the reference is to frequency of pitch.

[1] τῶν συρίγγων is here used generally of wind instruments, of which particular examples are given, (1) the single flute (σῦριγξ), (2) the reed-pipe (αὐλός), and (3) the Pan-pipes (σύριγγες).

[2] Deleting the square brackets inserted in the Teubner text and putting a full-stop after ἡμιολίῳ. There is no reason why the method of producing a fifth should not be mentioned here as well as in l. 10, since it is a question of a different instrument.

[3] Reading with Bojesen αἱ for οἱ or εἰ of the MSS.

[4] Deleting the second νήτην.

[5] Cp. below, chapter 42. As a matter of fact the striking of *hypate* would set up a sympathetic vibration in *nete* to a much greater extent than vice versa.

[6] A longer version of this problem occurs at chapter 44. For the usual scheme of eight notes used by the Peripatetic writers see note on 917ᵇ 30.

[7] See note on 918ᵃ 14.

26 Why do most men sing high when they sing out of
tune?[1] Is it because it is easier to sing high than low?
Or is it because singing high is worse than singing low,[2]
and a mistake is doing what is worse?   25

27 Why is it that of all things which are perceived by the
senses that which is heard alone possesses moral character?[3]
For music, even if it is unaccompanied by words, yet has
character; whereas a colour and an odour and a savour
have not. Is it because that which is heard alone has
movement, not, however,[4] the movement in us to which the
sound gives rise (for such movement exists also in the other 30
things which affect our senses, for colour also moves our
sight), but we perceive the movement which follows such
and such a sound? This movement resembles moral
character both in the rhythms and in the melodic disposition of the high and low notes, but not in their
commingling; for 'symphony' does possess moral character.
This does not occur in the other objects of sense-perception. 35
Now these movements are connected with action, and
actions are indicative of moral character.

28 Why are the 'nomes' (νόμοι) which are sung so called?
Is it because before men knew the art of writing they used
to sing their laws (νόμοι) in order not to forget them, as
they are still accustomed to do among the Agathyrsi?[5] 920[a]
They, therefore, called the earliest of their subsequent songs
by the same name as their earliest songs.

29 Why do rhythms and tunes, which after all are only voice,
resemble moral characters, whereas savours do not, nor yet
colours and odours?[6] Is it because they are movements, 5
as actions also are? Now efficient action is already moral
and determines character, but savours and colours have no
similar effect.

---

[1] Cp. below, chapter 46.
[2] Cp. 920[a] 23, where a low note is said to be more noble than a high.
[3] Cp. below, chapter 29.
[4] Punctuating with most editors μόνον, οὐχὶ ἦν.
[5] A Scythian tribe (Herod. iv. 100).   [6] Cp. chapter 27.

Why is neither the Hypodorian nor the Hypophrygian **30**
mode suitable for use by the chorus in tragedy?[1] Is it
because they do not admit of antistrophic melody?[2] They
¹⁰ are used, however, from the stage, because they are imitative.[3]

Why were Phrynichus and his contemporaries primarily **31**
musicians? Is it because in those days the lyrical portions
of tragedies were many times longer than the purely
metrical?[4]

Why is the 'diapason' (accord in the octave) so called **32**
and not named after the number of notes a 'diocto', like
¹⁵ the 'diatessaron' (fourth) and the 'diapente' (fifth)? Is it
because the notes were originally seven in number,[5] and
then Terpander took away *trite* and added *nete*, and in his
time it was called 'diapason' and not 'diocto', since it was
really 'diepta'?

Why is it more satisfactory for a singer to pass from **33**
a high to a low note than from a low to a high note? Is it
²⁰ because the former amounts to beginning at the beginning,
for the *mese*, or leader,[6] is the highest note in the tetrachord? But in passing from a low to a high note one
begins not at the beginning but at the end. Or is it because
a low note is nobler and more euphonious after a high
note?

Why are a double fifth[7] and a double fourth not con- **34**
²⁵ cordant, whereas a double octave is?[8] Is it because

---

[1] The same problem is treated at greater length in chapter 48.

[2] Gevaert explains as follows: 'Elles se prêtaient mal à la mélodie
absolue, exprimant un état d'âme permanent. Elles s'appliquaient
uniquement aux chants scéniques ou semi-scéniques coupés en sections
libres; elles affectionnaient en conséquence la mélopée déclamée,
visant à une expression précise.'

[3] Reading with Wagener μιμητικά. For the meaning of the term
cp. 922ᵇ 17–27.

[4] i.e. the choruses were still the principal element (as in Aeschylus'
earliest play, the *Supplices*), and the actor who spoke and did not sing
his lines took only a minor part.

[5] See note on 918ᵃ 14.

[6] Omitting the καὶ inserted by Ruelle after ἡγεμών.

[7] δι' ὀξειῶν is the Pythagorean name for a fifth (cp. Nicomachus,
ch. 9 in Jan's *Mus. Script.*, p. 252).

[8] This problem is more fully and clearly treated in chapter 41.

neither a double fifth nor a double fourth is in a super-particular ratio,[1] though a fourth and a fifth are so?[2]

35^a   Why is the accord in the octave the most beautiful of all? Is it because its ratios are contained within integral terms,[3] while those of the others are not so contained? For since *nete* is double *hypate*,[4] as *nete* is two, so *hypate* is one; and as *hypate* is two, *nete* is four; and so on. But *nete* is to *mese* in the ratio of $\frac{3}{2}$ to 1 (for a fifth is in this ratio), and that which is in the ratio of $\frac{3}{2}$ to 1[5] is not contained within integral terms; for as the lesser number is one, so[6] the greater number is one with the addition of a half, so that it is no longer a comparison of whole numbers, but fractions are left over. The like happens also with the fourth; for the 'epitrite'[7] of a term is as great as that term[8] and one third as great again. Or is it because the accord which is made up of both the other two[9] is the most perfect, and because it is the measure[10] of the melody?[11]

35^b   Why ⟨is the sound shrillest in the middle of the note? Is it because⟩[12] in any body which is displaced the move-

---

[1] This sentence is obviously incomplete in the MSS. and for the above translation Jan's suggestion δὶς διὰ τεττάρων ⟨ἐπιμόριόν⟩ ἐστιν has been read; cp. 921^b 5. The meaning of ἐπιμόριον (cp. *Met.* Δ. 1021^a 2) is 'that which is $\frac{n+1}{n}$ of something else'; but the author seems to confine his attention to values of n not greater than 3, since only octaves, fourths, and fifths are considered.

[2] A fifth being in the ratio of 3 to 2 and a fourth in the ratio of 4 to 3, a double fifth is $\frac{9}{4}\left(=\frac{4+5}{4}\right)$ to 1, and a double fourth $\frac{16}{9}\left(=\frac{9+7}{9}\right)$ to 1.

[3] Unity is always taken as the second term of the ratio; the author's idea is that for a consonance the first term must either be an integer, as in the octave, or of the form $\frac{n+1}{n}$ (ἐπιμόριον), as in the fourth and fifth.

[4] See note on 919^a 1.

[5] Reading τὸ γὰρ διὰ πέντε ⟨ἡμιόλιον, τὸ δ'⟩ ἡμιόλιον.

[6] Reading with Bekker and Bojesen τοσοῦτόν τε καὶ.

[7] i.e. that which is in the ratio of $\frac{4}{3}$ to 1.

[8] Reading with Bussemaker and Bekker ὅσον τ' ἐκεῖνο καὶ.

[9] i.e. the accord in the octave.

[10] i.e. the melody keeps within the compass of the octave.

[11] Putting a question mark after μελῳδίας, where the problem evidently ends, as it does in Gaza's version.

[12] It has been generally recognized that the latter portion of this

ment is most violent in the middle and quieter at the
920ᵇ beginning and end, and when the movement is most violent
the sound of that which is displaced is shriller ? For this
reason also strings which are tightly stretched give a shriller
note, for their movement is quicker.[1] Now if a sound is the
displacement of air or of something else,[2] a sound which is
5 in the middle of its course must be shrillest. If this were
not so, there would be no displacement of anything.

Why is it that if *mese* is altered, the sound of the other **36**
strings also is spoilt,[3] but if on the other hand *mese* is left
alone and one of the other strings altered, the note which
10 is altered[4] alone is spoilt ?[5] Is it because for all strings
'being in tune' means standing in a certain relation to
mese,[6] and the tension[7] of each is already determined by
mese? If, therefore, that which is the cause of their being
in tune and which holds them together is taken away, their
proper relationship appears to be no longer maintained.
But if one string is out of tune but *mese* is not altered,
15 naturally the defect lies in that string only ;[8] for all the
others are in tune.

Why is it that, though height in a voice is in accordance **37**
with smallness and lowness in accordance with largeness
(for a low note is slow owing to its largeness, and a high
note quick owing to its smallness), yet more effort is required
to sing a high than a low note, and few can sing the top
20 notes, and the 'Orthian songs'[9] and high music are hard to
sing owing to the strain which they involve ? Yet it requires
less effort to set in motion that which is small than that which
is large, and this ought to be true also of the air. Is it

chapter belongs to another problem. Reinach and Eichtal's suggested statement of the problem has been adopted in the translation :
διὰ ⟨τί ἡ φωνὴ ἀνὰ μέσον ὀξυτάτη ; ἢ ὅτι⟩ παντὸς κτλ.

[1] Cp. 899ᵃ 13.   [2] Placing a comma after φορά.

[3] Reading with Stark φθειρόμεναι.

[4] Reading with Sylburg ⟨ἡ⟩ κινηθεῖσα.

[5] Reading with Stark φθείρεται. The problem is the same as that
of chapter 20.

[6] Omitting the comma after the first ἁπάσαις and δὲ after τὸ, and
deleting the second ἁπάσαις.

[7] Reading τάσις for τάξις (so also Ruelle).

[8] Reading ἐκλείπει μόνον with Bojesen.

[9] Reading οἱ νόμοι ⟨οἱ⟩ ὄρθιοι. Orthian songs were of a stirring,
martial kind.

because the possession[1] of a naturally high voice and the singing of high notes are not the same thing, but naturally high voices are always due to weakness because of the inability to set more than a little air in motion, and the little air thus set in motion is carried quickly along? But height 25 of note in singing is a sign of strength; for that which is carried violently along is carried swiftly.[2] Hence persons in robust health[3] can sing high. And it requires an effort to sing the high notes, but the low notes are easier.[4]

38 Why do all men delight in rhythm and melody and concords in general? Is it because we naturally rejoice in natural movements?[5] This is shown by the fact that 30 children rejoice in them as soon as they are born. Now we delight in the various types of melody for their moral character,[6] but we delight in rhythm because it contains a familiar and ordered number and moves in a regular manner; for ordered movement is naturally more akin to us than disordered, and is therefore more in accordance 35 with nature. This is shown by the fact that by working and eating and drinking in an ordered manner we preserve and improve our nature and strength, whereas if we do these things irregularly we destroy and derange our nature; for diseases are disturbances of the natural order[7] of the 921[a] body. Thirdly, we delight in concord because it is the mingling of contraries which stand in proportion to one another. Proportion, then, is order, which, as we have said,[8] is naturally pleasant. Now that which is mingled is always more pleasant than that which is unmingled, especially if, being perceived by the senses, it contains equally the force of both extremes; and in a concord the 5 proportion has this characteristic.[9]

---

[1] Reading ⟨τὸ⟩ ὀξύφωνον.
[2] Omitting διὸ τὸ ὀξὺ δυνάμεως σημεῖον as a repetition from the preceding line.
[3] Reading εὐεκτικοί (W. D. R.).
[4] κάτω is clearly due to a gloss on τὰ βαρέα and has displaced another word. For the above translation ῥᾷον (Jan) has been read.
[5] Cp. *Pol.* viii. 1340ª 3, 4.
[6] Reading ἦθος with most editors.
[7] Omitting οὐ with most editors.   [8] 920[b] 33, 34.
[9] Reading δύναμιν ⟨ἔχη· τοῦτο δ'⟩ ἔχει (W. D. R.).

Why is 'antiphony'[1] more pleasant than 'homophony'? **39**
Is it because[2] 'antiphony' is concord in the octave?   For
'antiphony' is produced by young boys[3] and men whose
10 voices are separated in pitch as *nete* is from *hypate*.   Now
any concord is more pleasing than a simple note for the
reasons already stated,[4] and of concords that in the octave
is the most pleasing; whereas 'homophony' produces only
a simple sound.   'Magadizing'[5] is in the concord of the
octave, because, just as in verses the syllables stand to one
15 another in the proportion of equal to equal, or two to one,
or some other proportion, so too the sounds in a concord
stand in a proportion of movement to one another.   In the
other concords the termination of one of the two notes is
incomplete since it coincides with the end of only a half of
the other;[6] and so they are not equal in force,[7] and being
unequal they make a different impression[8] on the sense-
20 perception, as happens in a chorus[9] when at the conclusion
some are singing louder than others.[10]   Furthermore, *hypate*
happens to have the same conclusions to the periods in its
sounds as *nete*,[11] for the second stroke which *nete* makes
upon the air is *hypate*.   As, then, these notes, though
25 they do not do the same thing, terminate together, the
result is that they carry out one common task, like those
who are playing a stringed accompaniment to a song; for

---

[1] Reading ἀντίφωνον with Bojesen and most editors, following T. G.'s
version. For the meaning of the terms 'Antiphony' and 'Homophony'
see note on 918ᵇ 30.   [2] Reading ἢ ⟨ὅτι⟩ with most editors.
[3] Omitting καὶ inserted in the Teubner text before νέων.
[4] i. e. in chapter 38.
[5] See note on 919ᵃ 1. Some editors, following T. G., hold that a
new problem begins at this point and read ⟨διὰ τί⟩ μαγαδίζουσιν ἐν τῇ
διὰ πασῶν συμφωνίᾳ; ἢ ⟨ὅτι⟩ κτλ. The rest of the chapter, however,
seems to follow naturally on the remarks about the superiority of the
concord in the octave.
[6] i. e. in the fifth, the length of the two notes being as 3 : 2, the
slower terminates when one and a half beats of the faster have taken
place; in the fourth, the length of the two notes being as 4 : 3, the
second beat of the faster terminates when one and a half beats of the
slower have taken place.
[7] Placing a comma instead of a full-stop after εἰσίν.
[8] Reading διάφοροι with Reinach and Eichtal.
[9] Deleting the comma after χοροῖς.
[10] Reading ἄλλων ⟨ἄλλων⟩ φθεγγομένων or ἄλλοις ⟨ἄλλων⟩ φθεγγομένοις
(W. D. R.).
[11] Reading συμβαίνει ⟨τῇ νεάτῃ⟩ τὴν αὐτὴν from T. G.'s version.

these, though they do not play the same other notes as the singer, yet, if they finish on the same note, give more pleasure by their conclusion than they give pain by the differences which occur earlier in the piece, because after diversity the unity due to the accord in the octave is very pleasing.[1] Now 'magadizing' is made up of contrary notes,[2] and for this reason it is carried out in the accord in the 30 octave.

40 Why do men take greater pleasure in listening to those who are singing tunes which they already know than if they do not know them?[3] Is it because it is more obvious that the singer is as it were achieving his aim when they recognize what is being sung, and when they recognize it 35 the contemplation of it is pleasant? Or is it because the listener is in sympathy with one who sings what he himself knows? For he sings with him; and every one enjoys singing when he is under no compulsion to sing.

41 Why are a double fifth[4] and a double fourth not concor- **921ᵇ** dant, whereas a double octave is?[5] Is it because a fifth is in the ratio of 3 to 2, and a fourth in that of 4 to 3? Now in a series of three numbers[6] in a ratio of 3 to 2[7] or 4 to 3, the two extreme numbers will have no ratio to one another; 5 for neither will they be in a superparticular ratio[8] nor will one be a multiple of the other. But, since the octave is in a ratio of 2 to 1,[9] if it be doubled the extreme numbers would be in a fourfold ratio. So, since a concord is a compound of sounds which are in a proper ratio[10] to one another, and sounds which are at an interval of two octaves 10 from one another are in a ratio to one another (while double fourths and double fifths are not), the sounds con-

---

[1] Reading τῷ ἐκ διαφόρων τὸ κοινὸν ἥδιστον κτλ.
[2] i. e. high and low.
[3] Cp. above, chapter 5.
[4] For δι' ὀξειῶν see note on 920ᵃ 24.
[5] This chapter is a longer version of chapter 34.
[6] Reading with the MSS. τριῶν.
[7] This phrase clearly means a series consisting of n, $n \times \frac{3}{2}$, $n \times (\frac{3}{2})^2$.
[8] For the meaning of ἐπιμόριος see note on 920ᵃ 26.
[9] Putting a comma instead of a full-stop after λόγῳ.
[10] Reading εὐλόγως with Stumpf; cp. de Sensu, 439ᵇ 31 ff.

stituting the double octave would give a concord (while the others would not) for the reasons given above.

Why is it that, if one strikes *nete* and then stops it 42 ₁₅ down, *hypate* seems to respond?[1] Is it because *nete*, as it ceases and dies down, becomes *hypate*? (This can be illustrated by the fact that it is possible to sing *nete* from *hypate*; for the similarity can be taken from *hypate* as being a response to *nete*.[2]) And since an echo is a response to a note[3], and when *nete* ceases a sound[4] is set in motion ₂₀ which is the same as the note of *hypate*, it is only natural owing to the similarity that *nete* should seem to set *hypate* in motion. For we know that *nete* is not[5] in motion, because it is stopped down, and seeing that *hypate* itself is not stopped down and hearing its note we think that it is *hypate* which is giving forth a sound. (This kind of ₂₅ illusion is quite common, where we cannot perceive the exact truth either by reasoning or by the senses.) Again, it would be nothing extraordinary if, after *nete* is struck when it is very tightly stretched, the bridge were set in motion; and it would not be strange if, when the bridge moved, all the strings were set in motion with it and made ₃₀ a sound. Now the sound of *nete* is alien to the other notes both in its end and in its beginning, but is the same as *hypate* in its end.[6] This having been added to the movement of *hypate* itself, it would not be strange that the sound should seem to be entirely that of *hypate*; and it will be louder than the combined sound of the other notes, because the latter, being as it were impelled by *nete*, ₃₅ give only a soft sound, whereas *nete*, being the most violent of notes, sounds with its full force; and so naturally its second sound would be louder than that of the others, especially if only a slight movement has taken place in them.[7]

---

[1] Cp. chapter 24.

[2] Reading ὡς γὰρ οὔσης ἀντῳδῆς ⟨τῆς⟩ νεάτης (W. D. R.).

[3] Reading ἐπεὶ δὲ καὶ ἠχὼ ἀντῳδή τίς ἐστι [ἀφή ἐστιν] φωνῆς, καὶ τῆς νεάτης ληγούσης ἦχος (W. D. R.).

[4] Reading κινεῖται for κινεῖ with Vollgraff.

[5] Reading with Jan ἴσμεν ⟨ὅτι⟩ οὐ.

[6] Cp. 921ᵃ 23.

[7] Reading with Sylburg ἄλλως τε καὶ βραχείας κινήσεως αὐταῖς γεγενημένης. T. G. clearly renders ἄλλως τε καί.

43 Why do we listen [1] with greater pleasure to a solo sung 922ᵃ
to a flute than to one sung to a lyre? [2] Is it because
anything becomes still more pleasant when mingled with
what is more pleasant? [3] Now the flute is more pleasant
than the lyre, so that singing would be more pleasant when
it mingles with the flute than with the lyre. Further, [4] that
which is mingled is more pleasant than that which is unmingled, if there is a simultaneous perception of both the 5
elements. For wine is pleasanter than 'oxymel', [5] because
natural mixtures are more thoroughly mingled than those
which we make ourselves. For there is also wine which is
mingled of bitter and sweet savours, as is shown by the
so-called vinous pomegranates. Singing, then, and the
flute mingle with one another owing to their similarity, 10
for they are both produced by breath. But the sound of
the lyre, since it is not produced by breath (which is what
makes the sound of the flute less noticeable), [6] mingles less
well with the voice and, causing a contrast in the perception, has a less sweetening effect, as has been said of savours.
Furthermore, the flute by its own sound and by its likeness
to the voice covers up many of the mistakes of the singer; 15
but the sounds of the lyre, which are isolated and mingle
less well with the voice, since they are themselves observed,
and exist, on their own account, [7] show up the mistakes of
the singing as well, providing as it were a standard for
criticizing it. And when there are many mistakes in the
singing, the combined effect of the singing and the accom- 20
paniment must necessarily be worse.

44 Why is *mese* [8] ('the middle note') so called, though
there is no middle of eight notes? [9] Is it because in the

---

[1] Reading with Xᵃ μονῳδίας ἀκούομεν ἐάν κτλ.

[2] The sense of the solution requires ἢ ⟨ἐὰν πρὸς⟩ λύραν. This is not
the same problem as that of chapter 9, although in the MSS. the
questions are identical.

[3] Reading πᾶν τῷ ἡδίονι μιχθὲν ἥδιον ἔτι ἐστίν.

[4] Putting a full-stop after εἴη and reading with Bojesen ἔτι for ἐπεί.

[5] An artificial drink made of honey and vinegar.

[6] So that it mingles better with the voice. Reading ᾗ (Egger for ἢ)
ἧττον αἰσθητὸν ὁ τῶν αὐλῶν.   [7] Reading αὐτοὶ (W. D. R.) for αὐτοῖς.

[8] Omitting τῶν μὲν ὀκτώ: the MSS. have τῶν μὲν ἑπτά, which gives
just the wrong sense and is due to a false gloss.

[9] This problem is a longer version of chapter 25.

old days the scales had seven notes,[1] and seven has a
middle? Again, since of the points which fall between
two extremes the middle alone forms a kind of starting-
25 point,[2] that which lies between the points which verge
towards either end in an extended space, being also a
starting-point [3]—*that* will be the true middle. And since
nete and *hypate* are the extremes of the scale [4] and the
other sounds lie between them, of which the one which is
called *mese* alone is the beginning of the second tetrachord,[5] the name *mese* ('middle note') is amply justified;
for of the points lying between certain extremities, as has
been shown, the middle alone forms a beginning.

30 Why does a large chorus keep the rhythm better than a 45
small one?[6] Is it because they look more to one man,
their leader, and dance [7] more slowly, and so more easily
achieve unity? For mistakes occur more frequently in
35 quick singing. Now a large chorus attends to its leader,
and no one by differing from the rest would render himself
conspicuous by making himself heard above the rest: in a
small chorus, on the other hand, individuals can make
themselves more conspicuous; they, therefore, vie with
one another instead of looking to their leader.

Why do most men sing high when they sing out of 46
922ᵇ tune?[8] Is it because it is easier to sing a high note than a
low note? They have at all events a tendency to sing
high and so make mistakes in what they sing.

Why did the ancients, when they made the scales consist 47
of seven strings, leave in *hypate* but not *nete*?[9] Or should
5 we say that they omitted not *nete* but what is now called
paramese and the interval of a tone?[10] They treated

---

[1] See note on 918ᵃ 14.   Cp. *Phys.* 262ᵃ 25.

[3] Reading ἔτι ἐπειδὴ ... ἀρχή τίς ἐστιν, [ἔστιν] ⟨τὸ⟩ τῶν ⟨ἐπὶ⟩ θάτερον
... διαστήματι (MSS.) ἀνὰ μέσον, ὃν ἀρχή, τοῦτ᾿ ἔσται μέσον (W. D. R.).
Very possibly, however, ἔστιν ... ἀρχή is a gloss.

[4] Reading μὲν for μέσον with Usener.

[5] i. e. in the old scale of seven notes.

[6] This is a longer version of the problem of chapter 22.

[7] Reading ὀρχοῦνται as suggested by E. Graf in 919ᵃ 38.

[8] Cp. above, chapter 26.

[9] Cp. above, chapter 7 and the note on 918ᵃ 14.

[10] i. e. the disjunctive.

mese,[1] then, as the lower note of the upper 'pycnon';[2]
whence came the name *mese*, because[3] it was the end of
the upper tetrachord and the beginning of the lower, and
was in pitch in an intermediate relation between the
extreme notes.

48 Why do the choruses in tragedy not sing either in the 10
Hypodorian or in the Hypophrygian mode? Is it because
these modes have very little of the kind of tune[4] which is
specially necessary to a chorus? Now the Hypophrygian
mode has a character of action (hence in the *Geryone*[5] the
march-forth and arming are composed in this mode); and
the Hypodorian is magnificent and steadfast, and so is the 15
most suitable of all the modes to accompaniment by the
lyre. Now both these are unsuited to the chorus and more
proper for the characters on the stage; for the latter
imitate heroes, and among the ancients the leaders alone
were heroes, and the people, of whom the chorus consists,
were mere men. So a woeful and quiet character and type 20
of music are suited to the chorus, for they are more human.
These characteristics belong to the other modes, but least
to the Phrygian[6] among them—for it is exciting and orgi-
astic—and most to the Mixolydian.[7] In accordance with this
mode, then, we adopt a passive attitude, and the weak are
more passive than the strong; and so this mode is appropriate to choruses. When we use the Hypodorian and
Hypophrygian modes, on the other hand, we are active, 25
and action is not fitting for choruses; for the chorus is in

---

[1] Reading with Jan μέσῃ τῇ ἐσχάτῃ.

[2] 'Pycnon' is a term used for the range covered by the three lower
notes of the tetrachord when that range is less than that which is
included between the two upper notes ; cp. Aristoxenus, i. 24.

[3] Reading with Bojesen προσηγόρευσαν [ἢ], ὅτι and putting a full-stop
at the end of the sentence.

[4] Reading ὅτι ⟨τὸ⟩ μέλος.

[5] A tragedy attributed to Nicomachus (Nauck², p. 762).

[6] The MSS. here read ὑποφρυγιστί, which cannot stand here, since
the Hypophrygian mode has already been shown to have the character
of action (πρακτικός), which Aristotle in the *Politics* (1341[b] 34) con-
trasts with ἐνθουσιαστικός. The Phrygian mode is characterized in
the *Politics* (1342[b] 3) as ὀργιαστικός and is therefore appropriate here.

[7] Inserting with Bojesen μάλιστα δὲ ἡ μιξολυδιστί from T.G. The
Mixolydian mode was mournful (*Pol.* 1340[a] 42 ff.) and is therefore
appropriate here.

attendance and takes no active part, for it simply shows goodwill towards those with whom it is present.

Why is it that of the sounds which form a consonance **49** the lower is more suited to melody?[1] Is it because 30 melody is in its own nature soft and tranquil, but becomes harsh and full of movement by the admixture of rhythm? Now since the low note is soft and tranquil, and the high note full of movement, of the notes which maintain the same melody the lower would rather be more melodious[2] in the same melody; for melody in itself,[3] as has been shown, is soft.

35 Why is it that the sounds produced from two jars of the **50** same size and quality, one empty and the other half-full, give an accord in the octave? Is it because the sound[4] produced from the half-full jar is double[5] that produced from the empty jar? This surely is just what happens in the pipes. For the quicker the movement, the higher **923ᵃ** seems the note, and in larger spaces the air collects more slowly, and in double the space in double the time, and proportionately in the other spaces. A wine-skin too which is double the size of another, gives an accord in the octave with one which is half its size.

---

[1] Reading with Bojesen μελικώτερον; cp. 918ᵃ 37. The meaning seems to be that where there is an independent accompaniment, it should be above, not below, the singing voice. This appears to have been the Greek practice.

[2] Reading μελικώτερος; see last note.   [3] Reading αὐτὸ with Cᵃ.

[4] Omitting καὶ after γίνεται with Bojesen.

[5] διπλασία here means 'twice as rapid'.

BOOK XX

PROBLEMS CONCERNING SHRUBS AND VEGETABLES

5

1 WHY is it that celery can endure salt water, but the leek cannot? Is it because the roots of the latter are weak, but those of the former are strong, and that which is stronger is less liable to be affected?

2 What is the reason of the saying:

> Mint should neither be eaten nor planted in season of warfare?[1]

Is it because mint has a cooling effect upon the body, as is 10 shown by the corruption which it causes in the semen? This is opposed to courage and spirit, being the same in kind.

3 Why is it that some plants, though they have blossom, have no fruit, such as the cucumber and the pumpkin and the pomegranate? Or have they fruit, the blossom being the fruit? For example the part which blossoms is a fruit- 15 case, and the cucumber is a fruit-case.

4 Why is it that some plants are edible only after they have been boiled, while others can be eaten raw? Do the juices of such plants as are not at first edible become sweeter when the plants have been warmed by heat, whilst in others the juices are originally sweet, and these can be 20 eaten raw?

5 Why is it that some plants are boiled, others roasted? Is it because the moister plants do not require so much moistening,[2] while the drier plants must not be further dried? Now anything which is boiled becomes moister

---

[1] See Leutsch, *Paroemiogr.* ii. 530.
[2] Reading οὐ τοσοῦτον ⟨ὑγρανθῆναι⟩. The Latin version of T. G. renders 'an quod humidiora non eatenus humectari ... oportet'.

and softer, and that which is less moist becomes dry if
exposed to the fire.

25   Why are some plants edible and others inedible? Is it **6**
owing to their juices? For plants which in their raw state
have unconcocted juices and, when heated, do not undergo
change, are inedible. Now those of which the juice is
edible but somewhat strong are used as condiments; for
plants which have a strong savour in a small compass serve
toflavour those of which the savour is distributed over a
large bulk.

30   Why is it that some plants live only until they have **7**
produced seeds and having borne seeds dry up—grass, for
instance, and the so-called herbs—while others do not, but
bear seeds time after time? And of those which live only
until they have produced seed why are the majority annuals,
while horse-parsley produces its fruit in the second year and
35 having done so dries up? Is it because all things flourish
until their seed [1] reaches its prime (for man too continues
to grow until the age of thirty, sometimes in height [2] and
sometimes in bulk), but when they can no longer produce
seed, as in the case of man, they begin to dry up and grow
923ᵇ old—in some cases slowly and in proportion? [3] The reason
why some forms of life are long-lived and others short-
lived is to be the subject of another treatise. [4] But since
the perfection of the seed is the limit in all cases, it neces-
5. sarily follows that the short-lived bear fruit only once or
only a few times, and the long-lived many times; so that
the weakest bear [5] only once and so necessarily dry up;
and those of them which can bear seed in a year are
annuals, whilst others, like horse-parsley, do so in the second
year, both plants and trees alike. [6]

---

[1] Reading καὶ for κατὰ (Platt). Some MSS. read καὶ κατὰ.
[2] Reading μήκει (Bonitz) for πλήθει.
[3] i. e. in proportion to their length of life.
[4] Apparently a direct reference to *de Longit. et Brev. Vitae* 464ᵇ 19 ff.
[5] Reading ἐνεγκεῖν (Bonitz) for ἐνέγκοι.
[6] The Latin version here translates a longer text: 'alia postero ut
equapium. Quae vero praevalida surgunt, haec annis plusculis post
fructificare incipiunt, diuque vitam agere possunt, fructificareque
saepius, ut arbores'. This gives a much fuller sense and the Greek

8   Why is it that if one digs down to the roots of celery 10 and surrounds them with barley-husks, and puts earth over these and then waters the plants, the roots become very large?[1] Is it because the barley-husks, being hot and spongy, hold the nourishment in a mass so that it does not rise upwards, but, being hot, causes concoction, and so considerable growth takes place?   15

9   Why is it that if one buries gourds or pumpkins in the ground when they are still small, they become large?[2] Is it because the wind and the sun dry everything up and prevent growth, and make everything smaller in bulk but closer in texture? (As can be seen in the difference between trees growing in windy and sunny[3] localities and 20 those in hollow and moist places, the latter being large and spongy in texture, the former small and dense.) Now the burying of things in the earth is the contrary of this and produces a contrary result. (A similar difference occurs in fruits placed in vessels; if pumpkins are placed in hollow fennel-stalks or boxes, and pomegranates or apples 25 in earthenware jars, the apples become large and spongy,[4] but the pumpkins become small and hard because they grow against a resisting surface.) The reason then is that the nutriment is increased, because it is not dispersed by the wind or dried up; for the covering of earth prevents it from being thus affected.

10   Why are the seeds of pungent plants more pungent than 30 the roots and the leaves? Is it because everything is derived

---

text as we have it probably has a lacuna between τῷ ὑστέρῳ ἔτει and ὥσπερ τὰ δένδρα.

[1] The source of this problem is Theophrastus, *de Caus. Plant.* v. 6, 3.

[2] Cp. Theophrastus, *op. cit.* v. 6, 4.

[3] Reading εἰλώδεσι for ἐλώδεσιν; Theophrastus has εὐείλοις.

[4] The text here is unsatisfactory and perhaps beyond emendation. For the above translation the following text has been read : τὰ μὲν μεγάλα σομφὰ δέ, οἱ δὲ μικροὶ στερροὶ δέ, αὐξανόμενοι εἰς ἀντίτυπον. The omission of μή before εἰς ἀντίτυπον may be justified since (1) the negative should be οὐ not μή, and (2) μή gives no sense. The phrase εἰς ἀντίτυπον seems to imply a reference to the well-known practice in ancient and modern times of enclosing growing gourds in some narrow receptacle in order to shape them for use as receptacles for liquid (cp. Theophrastus, *Hist. Plant.* vii. 3, 5). The contrast then is between gourds placed in a fennel-stalk or some other narrow receptacle and apples stored in a large earthenware vessel.

from the seed and distributed to the other parts from it, as it were pre-existing in it, as some contend, including the juices and odours, since the odours always become distinctive as soon as the seeds are formed? If, therefore, the
35 pungency in the rest of the plant is derived from the seed, it is only natural that it should be present in the greatest degree in the seed.[1]

Why are thin radishes more pungent? Is it because the **11** larger radishes are more concocted owing to the lapse of time?

924[a]   Why is it that the caper-plant will not grow easily in **12** tilled ground [2]—for the experiment has often been made of transplanting the roots or sowing the seed (for in some places it is more profitable than roses)—but grows best
5 among the tombs because the ground is most untrodden? As regards this and similar questions the principle must be accepted that all things do not come into being and grow from the same matter, but some things originally come into being and grow from the corruption of other things —for instance lice and the hair on the body when its
10 nutriment is corrupted and when the body is itself[3] in a state of deterioration. As therefore in the body certain products are engendered from the excrement of nutriment (which means that concoction is incomplete), and since, when nature cannot prevail over the excrement, the commonest excretions are absorbed into the bladder and bowels, while from others living organisms
15 are engendered[4] (and so these attain the greatest growth in old age and disease [5]), so in the earth some products are engendered and grow from the concoction of nutriment, others from excretions and matter that is in a condition which is the opposite of concoction. Now tillage concocts

---

[1] Reading αὐτῷ (= τῷ σπέρματι) for αὐτό.
[2] Cp. Theophrastus, *op. cit.* i. 3, 6; iii. 2, 1.
[3] Reading αὐτοῦ for ἀεὶ τό. Richards reads τοῦ for τό.
[4] This passage is directly referred to in *Meteor*. iii. 381[b] 9-13, where the question of the formation of living organisms in the body is said to be treated ἐν τοῖς ἑτέροις, which Alexander Aphrodisiensis interprets as ἐν τοῖς προβλήμασι.
[5] Because then nature has the least power of resistance.

the nutriment and makes it productive, and from this the cultivated fruits are formed. The products, therefore, of this cultivation are called cultivated because they are benefited by art, undergoing as it were a kind of training. Plants, on the other hand, which cannot be so benefited 20 or are formed from an opposite condition, are 'wild' and will not grow in a highly tilled soil. For tillage spoils them by trying to train them ; for they are engendered from corruption. It is to this class that the caper-plant belongs.

13   Why is it that, when radishes are in their prime in the winter, if one cuts off the leaves and heaps earth round 25 them and treads it in so as to keep out the water, they grow to an extraordinary size in the summer ?[1] Is it because the heaping up of the earth round them secures them from becoming corrupted by preventing the water from rotting them, and the nutriment, which the plant used to send into the shoot, enters into the radish, so 30 that it must either itself increase in size or send out lateral shoots and grow other roots, as do onions ? For onions, if they are not pulled up each year but are left in the ground during the winter, become multiplied. Now onions are among the plants which send out shoots laterally ; but the radish does not do so, and must therefore increase in bulk, because it absorbs all the nutriment.   35

14   Why is it that if one plants pumpkins or gourds near a well and, when they are ripe, lets them down into the well and covers them over, they remain green for a whole year ?[2] Is it because the vapour from the water cools them and prevents them from drying up and keeps them in good condition, and the covering of them up fosters the breath which has formed in them ? Their conservation is due to the fact that 924ᵇ they still receive nutriment, because their roots are left undisturbed ; for even if one removes the shoots, when they have borne fruit, and after cutting them away heaps earth round the roots and treads it down, the plant will produce early 5

[1] The source of this problem is Theophrastus, *de Caus. Plant.* v. 6, 2–3.
[2] The source of this problem is Theophrastus, *op. cit.* v. 6, 5–6.

pumpkins, because the roots can survive; for the pumpkin-plant[1] is not a biennial. Plants treated in this way[2] will bear fruit more quickly than seedlings, because the root, the most important part of their organism, is already present in their growth, whereas in seedlings the roots must grow first. Furthermore,[3] the heaping of earth round
10 the root engenders warmth, so that it is preserved and sends up a shoot more quickly. So too if one sows gourd-seeds during the winter in small wicker baskets and waters them with hot water and carries them out into the sun and places them by the fire, very early gourds will be produced if one plants them out in the ground, as they are, in the baskets, when the proper season arrives.

15 Why are plants watered at dawn or at night or in the **15** evening? Is it in order that the sun may not consume the water? Or is it because, when the water is warm, it corrupts the plants which are watered with it?

Why is it that sweet-smelling seeds and plants promote **16** the flow of urine?[4] Is it because they contain heat and are easily concocted, and such things have this effect? For
20 the heat which is in them causes quick digestion,[5] and their odour has no corporeal existence; for evil-smelling plants, such as garlic, owing to their heat, promote the flow of urine, but their wasting effect is a more marked character-istic. But sweet-smelling seeds contain heat, because odour is entirely engendered by the presence of some heat; but evil-smelling things are unconcocted. Now anything which
25 is to promote the flow of urine must be not only hot but also easily concocted, so that it may accompany the liquids in their downward course and effect their digestion.

Why is it that vegetables which are produced from older **17** seeds (for example, two or three years old) produce more

---

[1] Reading ἐστι with C^a.   [2] Reading οὗτοι for αὐτοί.
[3] ἐν ᾗ is clearly corrupt, as it has no antecedent. It is clear, how-ever, that the right reading is ἔτι δὲ ἡ περίσαξις ἀλέαν ποιεῖ, ὥστε σώζεσθαι καὶ θᾶττον ἀνιέναι βλαστόν, cp. Theophrastus, *l. c.*, ἔτι δὲ ἡ περίσαξις ἀλέαν παρέχουσα θᾶττον ἀνιέναι ποιεῖ βλαστόν.
[4] This problem occurs also at xii. 12, and is partly identical with
i. 48.   [5] Cp. 865^a 21 and note.

stalk than those grown from fresh seeds?[1]   Is it because,
just as in animals that which is at its prime produces 30
semen most readily, so too very old seeds lose their vigour
by evaporation, and those which are produced from fresh
seeds are too weak because they still contain excrement
which is alien to them, but those which are of moderate age
are strongest, because the moisture has left them, and so
they produce seed more readily?   And the production of
seed is the same process as the production of stalk, since
the seed comes from the stalk.

18   Why does rue grow best and most abundantly if it is 35
grafted on to a fig-tree?[2]   Now it is grafted inside the bark
and plastered with clay.   Is it because the roots of the rue
require heat and warmth (and this is why they are benefited
by being surrounded with ashes), and the fig-tree contains
heat?   That this is so is shown by the fact that its sap is 925ᵃ
the most pungent of all and by the amount of smoke which
it produces when burnt.[3]   It therefore possesses the same
kind of heat and moisture as ashes, so that if ashes benefit
rue, it must necessarily flourish greatly when grafted on
the fig-tree, since, whereas ashes give off no fluid, the
flow of liquid from the fig-tree is continuous, its moisture
being never exhausted.   5

19   Why do some plants always produce empty stalks?
Are they among those plants which have to produce something other than stalk?[4]

20   Why is it that in Attica, while all other fruits are very
sweet, thyme is very bitter, yet thyme is a kind of fruit?
Is it because the soil there is thin and dry,[5] so that the 10
plants which grow there do not contain much moisture?

---

[1] Cp. Theophrastus, *op. cit.* iv. 3, 5-6.
[2] Cp. Theophrastus, *op. cit.* v. 6, 10.
[3] Cp. Theophrastus, *Hist. Plant.* v. 9, 5.
[4] The Latin version of T. G. apparently translates a different text
here, since it renders: 'an illis quarum natura imbecillior est, has
rarum inanemque emittere caulem necesse est?'
[5] There is clearly a lacuna here.   The margin of Xᵃ notes ἴσως λείπει·
ἢ ὅτι ἀγρὸς ἐκεῖνος λεπτός τε καὶ ξηρός ἐστι.   The Latin version of T. G.
also translates this reading, and it has been adopted in the above
translation.

In plants, then, which are naturally sweet, owing to the moderate quantity of moisture which they contain, when the sun has absorbed the greater part of it the remainder is easily concocted; for it is difficult for a large amount, but easy for a moderate amount, to be ripened. Fruits, there-
15 fore, which are naturally sweet become more so; but in those which are naturally dry and not sweet, the natural moisture fails, because it is scanty, and is very far from being sweet. For the sun absorbs the sweetest and lightest part of it; and these fruits have no superfluous moisture, as have other fruits.

Why do pennyroyal and narcissi and onions bloom if 21
20 hung up at the time of the summer solstice? Is it because there is unconcocted nutriment in them, which[1] in winter does not become concocted owing to the cold, but at the summer solstice owing to the season becomes concocted, and so the growth takes place? This growth, however, because there is no influx of moisture, quickly dies down; for if they have not some source of nutriment or influx of
25 moisture, they dry up. A similar phenomenon occurs in Scythia, where, owing to the presence of abundant snow, the corn remains a long time in the earth and then suddenly shoots up.

Why does the onion alone make the eyes smart to such 22 an excessive degree (hence it is said to derive its name because it makes one cover up the pupil),[2] whereas marjoram and other pungent plants do not have this effect? For the
30 nasturtium, though it is more stinging, does not cause tears to the same extent if placed near the eyes, whereas the onion has this effect both when so placed and when eaten. Is it because many differences attach to each of the pungent plants, which give each its peculiar property? The nasturtium then, because it is hotter, is so dry that it
35 prevails over the liquefaction which it causes; for it causes tears when it is eaten, but it does not cause tears when

---

[1] Reading ἤ for ᾗ in l. 21.
[2] i. e. κρόμμυον is popularly derived from κόρη, the pupil, and μύειν, to close.

placed near the eyes, because it does not give off any thin vapour, being too dry and hot to do so. But marjoram and such warm plants are dry, though only slightly so ; and **925^b** that which is to cause tears must be stinging and moist and viscous. This is why olive oil causes tears, though its sting is weak ; for it penetrates owing to its viscosity and tenuity and causes pain, and the pain causes melting. Now the 5 onion has such properties that its moisture and the vapour which it gives off are hot and tenuous and viscous ; and so, when it is placed near the eye, it causes tears, because the vapour which it gives off is of such a character and carries with it a thin moisture ; and, when it is eaten, the exhalation penetrates and produces the same effect.[1] Garlic, on the 10 other hand, is hot and pungent and contains moisture, but is not viscous ; and so does not cause tears.

23 Why is it that myrtle-berries which have been compressed in the hand seem to us sweeter than those which have not been so compressed ? Is it for the same reason as makes 15 dried grapes sweeter than fresh clusters and undried grapes ? For dried grapes are, it appears, flavoured by the juice, which is naturally sweet (for they are even externally saturated by it), but the grapes which are still in the cluster are not so flavoured. So too myrtle-berries, which are naturally sweet and have their sweetness within, like grapes 20 when they are compressed, become saturated by the sweetness which is within them and are clearly sweeter externally.

24 Why is it that, the smaller myrtle-berries are, the more they tend to have no stones, and the same is true also of dates and clusters of grapes, in which[2] the small grapes have no stones at all or only smaller stones ? Is it because, 25 being less perfect, they have less distinctly formed stones ? For the purpose of the stone is to contain the seed. Now the berries are smaller, because they are mere offshoots and imperfect, and they are less sweet than those which have

---

[1] There is clearly a lacuna here. Sylb. supplies ταὐτὸ ποιεῖν δύναται from T. G.
[2] Omitting δ'.

proper stones; for they are less concocted, and concoction is a process which produces perfection.

30   Why is it that in some fruits the parts which are near the **25** root are more bitter (for example in the cucumber), but in others the parts towards the upper extremity (for example in acorns)? Is it because in the former the nutriment in that part is unconcocted, because there is a continual influx along the root; while the latter are naturally dry, and so, when the sweetness is drawn off from the extremity and 35 has become concocted, they are henceforward dry and the bitterness is left behind like salt? Now as anything becomes dry, it becomes more bitter, just as olives and acorns become bitter as they grow old.

926^a   Why do some plants sprout when they are not in the **26** earth, but either cut off or placed in store, lily-stalks, for example, and garlic and onions?[1] Is it because they all have nutriment within themselves and not in any definite place outside the plant?[2] [It is therefore their superabun- 5 dance of nutriment which makes them sprout, as is clear from the fact that squills and purse-tassels do the same.] Now each of them grows not merely because it contains nutriment, but only when that nutriment is concocted and distributed; it therefore contains nutriment before, but it only grows when the season comes at which this process takes place owing to the concoction caused by the season,[3] as happens also to crocodiles' eggs. The growth, however, 10 is not continuous, because there is no influx of more nutriment.

Why is it that garlic and onions grow better according **27** as they are drier when planted, whilst other plants grow worse under such conditions? Is it because all plants of this kind are exceedingly full of moisture? If, then, they are planted in this condition, they enjoy equable conditions.

---

[1] See below, chapter 28.
[2] οὐθὲν φυτόν is obviously corrupt. For the above translation ἔξωθεν τοῦ φυτοῦ has been read. The two following sentences ἡ περιουσία . . . ποιοῦσιν, which occur again in chapter 28, are omitted by the best MSS.
[3] Reading πεττούσης ⟨τῆς⟩ ὥρας.

A further reason is that they are less likely to rot if they are dried before being planted.

15

28　Why is it that garlic and onions alone among plants sprout when they are stored away?[1] Is it because they are full of moisture and nutriment? It is abundance of nutriment, then, which makes them sprout, as is clear from the fact that squills and purse-tassels do the same. But they grow only when the proper season for each of them comes.

20

29　Why is it that plants which are watered with cold water are sweeter than those watered with warm water? Is it because the warm water when it becomes enclosed in the plant is saltier (just as that which is saltier is hotter, and that which is sweet is the opposite, that is, in a sense, cold)? Now the nutriment of vegetables is liquid, and it is this which gives them their juices.

25

30　Why is it that garlic has a stronger odour when it has run to stalk than when it is young? Is it because, when it is young, there is still a large quantity of alien moisture in it which deprives it of its strength? When, however, the plant has ripened, the alien moisture having been already excreted, it then has its own proper odour; and this is naturally pungent.[2] Similarly, all other fruits when they are young are more watery. This is the reason why young onions are less pungent.

30

31　Why is it that, if myrtle-branches are not embalmed,[3] the berries rather than the leaves drop off, whereas, if they are embalmed with seaweed, the leaves drop off but the berries do not? Is it what naturally happens if the branches are not embalmed, for the berries naturally drop off when they become ripe? This does not occur when the branches are stored away, but the moisture in the seaweed only prevents the moisture in the berries from undergoing change. The leaves, on the other hand, drop off as the branches become dry, and the seaweed, which is salty, has a drying effect

35

926ᵇ

---

[1] Cp. above, chapter 26.
[2] δριμεία is omitted by a misprint after φύσει in Bekker's text.
[3] Apparently for use as chaplets.

upon them. The leaves thus undergo different processes
when they remain on the tree and when they are stored
away.

Why do melons[1] grow best in marshy plains which are 32
5 humid, for example, round Orchomenus and in Egypt,
which appears to be a well-watered country? Now
marshy districts are full of water and melons themselves are
somewhat moist; and this is why those grown in gardens
are poor. Is it because they have to be planted deep
10 owing to the hardness of the ground? For clayey, flat
ground becomes very hard, and plants grow best which are
deeply planted. Or is it because the ground must be dry,
because the plant itself is naturally moist? For thus being
pulled in opposite directions it will attain the mean. Now
ground which is somewhat marshy but deep contains
nutriment owing to the depth of the soil and the locality,
15 but not in an excessive quantity, because the ground dries
up again.

Why is it that rue and certain unguents give the per- 33
spiration an evil odour?[2] Is it because things which have
a heavy and pungent odour, mixing with the excretory
fluids, make the odour of these still more unpleasant?

20 Why is rue said to be a remedy against the evil eye?[3] 34
Is it because men think they are victims of the evil eye
when they eat greedily or when they expect some enmity
and are suspicious of the food set before them? For
instance, when they take anything for themselves from the
same course, they offer some one else a portion, adding the
25 words, 'so that you may not cast the evil eye upon me'.
All therefore will take with alarm of what is offered them,
whether liquid or solid, of those foods, the constriction or
vomiting forth of which causes the solids to be carried upwards and ejected or the flatulence from the liquid to give

---

[1] Reading οἱ σίκυοι ⟨οἱ⟩ πέπονες (Richards).
[2] Repeated from ii. 13, where see note on 867^b 9.
[3] The belief in the evil eye was evidently as widespread in the
Mediterranean lands in ancient times as it is to-day ; see Otto Jahn,
Berichte d. Sächsischen Gesellschaft, 1855, pp. 28 ff., and A. Michaelis,
J. H. S., 1885, p. 312.

rise to pain and writhing. Rue, therefore, being eaten beforehand, since it is naturally warming, rarefies the organ which receives the food and the whole body, with the result 30 that it drives out[1] the flatulence[2] enclosed within it.

35 Why is it that marjoram, being thrown into the must, makes the wine sweet, and two cupfuls are thrown into a jar of wine? Is it because it takes away the elements which cause harshness by absorbing into itself by its dryness 35 the watery and sedimentary parts? That it is these which cause harshness is shown by the fact that wines are less soft if water is added or if they have been allowed to stand a long time on the lees. Also when they make raisin wine,[3] they expose the grapes for a long time to the sun, which draws out the watery element and concocts the 927^a remainder. Now marjoram produces the same result, for it is dry and hot, and so naturally has a lasting effect.

36 Why do black myrtle-trees have thicker foliage than white? Is it because they are a wilder species? That they are so is proved by the fact that they grow in the untilled 5 ground[4] and undergo very little modification as a result of cultivation. Now wild plants invariably have denser foliage; for, because their fruit is less concocted, the nutriment is diverted into the foliage.

---

[1] Reading ἐξωθεῖν: all MSS. read ἔξωθεν.
[2] The Teubner text misprints πνεῦμα as πεῦμα.
[3] Reading γλυκύν (sc. οἶνον) for γλυκύ, see Bonitz, *Index*, 157ª 17.
[4] Reading ἀργοῖς (Bussemaker) for ἀγροῖς.

BOOK XXI

PROBLEMS CONCERNING BARLEY-MEAL, BARLEY-CAKE, AND THE LIKE

WHY is it that barley-gruel and wheaten-flour become 1
whiter if oil is poured on to them, though oil is reddish in
colour? Is it because oil naturally foams when it is mixed
with liquid, and foaming causes whiteness? Now mixing is
carried out by pounding and motion, and is most complete
15 in the case of corporeal substances. This process occurs in
foods which are boiled, and so makes them whiter.

Why is it that foods made from wheat suit our bodies 2
best and are more nourishing than those made from barley?[1]
Is it because wheat contains a moderate amount of stickiness,
and food ought to have this quality, since it ought to cling
20 and adhere to the body, and its stickiness causes it to do
so? But barley[2] is less cohesive, and so cakes in which
the barley is well kneaded are more nourishing than those
in which it is not kneaded.

Why is it that of wheaten-flour that which is ground first 3
is whiter, but of barley-meal that which is ground last?[3]
Is it because barley, being dry, breaks into pieces, whereas
25 wheat is soft and crushes? Now in both it is the inner part
which is whitest.

Why do loaves appear whiter when they are cold than 4
when they are hot? Is it somehow for the same reason
that stale oil is whiter than fresh? For the cause of the
30 blackness is the water which in both cases is present in

---

[1] Cp. Hippocr., *de Diaeta*, ii. § 40.

[2] Reading ἀλλὰ ⟨ἡ κριθὴ⟩ ψαθυρώτερον. γλισχρός and ψαθυρός are
regularly contrasted (cp. ll. ^b7 ff.), hence it is impossible for ψαθυρώτερον to refer to ἡ ἐκ τοῦ πυροῦ τροφή, which has already been stated to
be γλισχρόν. The Latin version of T. G. renders *hordeum vero
rigidius est,* and evidently read ἡ κριθή, though ψαθυρώτερον is
incorrectly translated.

[3] A longer version of this problem occurs in chapter 7.

larger quantities when they are fresh; but after a time, owing to evaporation, the water remaining near the surface becomes less. Now it is either the passage of time or the heat of the sun which causes evaporation from the oil; and from loaves the heat goes forth as they cool and has entirely departed when they are cold, whereas it is still present when they are warm.

5   Why do loaves which contain no salt weigh heavier than 35 those which are salted, the other ingredients being exactly the same? The contrary would be expected, since salt is added, and salt is heavier than water. Is it because the salt causes drying to take place? This is why things which are preserved with salt remain uncorrupted; for the moisture in them is taken up and dried up by the salt, and 927[b] it is the moisture in things that is corrupted by heat. So too in bread the moisture is taken up by the salt and evaporates outside. Stale bread therefore is lighter than hot bread, since it is colder. Now in loaves which do not contain salt this moisture is present in greater quantities 5 and makes them heavier.

6   Why is it that loaves which have become cold, if they are moistened and placed in contact with one another, do not cohere, whereas hot loaves do so? Is it because the cold loaves give off with the vapour the sticky moisture which is in them, and, because this has gone forth, do not cohere (for the water with which they were wetted is too un- 10 cohesive); but the hot loaves contain a certain amount of stickiness, and so, when they are moistened and the vapour comes forth, the heat, owing to its rarity, is given off, but the sticky matter, which comes out with it and mingles with the moisture, causes the loaves to adhere together?[1]

7   Why is it that of wheaten-flour that which is ground first[2] 15 is whiter, but of barley-meal that which is ground last? Is it because barley, being dry, breaks into pieces, and this happens most when it is ground for a very long time, but

---

[1] Reading προσέχεσθαι ἑαυτοῖς (so too Bussemaker).
[2] Reading τὰ πρῶτα for τὰ ἄλφιτα, cp. chapter 3 ([a] 23) which is a shorter version of the same problem.

the flour which is inside the wheat is soft and fine and is
20 crushed out at first? Now in both cases it is the inner part
which is whitest.

Why is it that barley-cake becomes more indigestible the **8**
more it is kneaded, whereas wheaten-bread becomes easier
to digest? Is it because dough becomes less by being much
kneaded (and this is the nature of that which is sticky), but
the moisture has been expelled from every part of the loaf
25 by the fire, so that, when the moisture has been entirely
expelled, the loaf becomes more uncohesive the more it is
kneaded, because in the kneading it is divided up into
smaller particles? Now that which is uncohesive is more
easily concocted. Barley-cake, on the other hand, the more
it is kneaded becomes more sticky, as the liquid mingles in
it; and that which is sticky is not easily divided up, and
30 such foods are not easily concocted; for that which is to be
concocted must be split up into small parts.

Why does barley-cake become less when it is kneaded, **9**
whereas dough becomes more? Is it because barley-meal
when moistened and kneaded unites owing to the binding
quality of the moisture, because it is of even texture and
35 granulated, but wheaten-flour rises, because it is very
dense? For that which is dense grows hot when kneaded
and, when it is hot and inflated, it rises, as does the flesh.

But why does dough increase more when it is heated than **10**
928[a] barley-cake does?[1] Is it because dough contains moisture
which is not separated in such a way that it can escape
when warmed, owing to the kneading? When therefore
it is warmed, breath is engendered, and more breath is
necessarily engendered from a greater amount of moisture.

5 Why is it that although honey is more adhesive than **11**
water, wheaten-flour is more uncohesive, when it is boiled
or baked, if it is mixed with honey-water than with water?
Is it because water becomes stiff and solid under the influence
of the heat, whereas the honey becomes solid but also has

---

[1] Cp. chapter 23.

a drying effect, and so makes the food more uncohesive
(for this quality is produced by dryness)?   10

12   Why do twice-baked loaves, when they are cool, not
become hard?   Is it because wheat has in it a certain sweet
and sticky juice, which is as it were its 'soul'?   This can
be illustrated by the fact that when it is dried it becomes
quite empty, but, when it is wetted, it expands.[1]   This juice, 15
therefore, being present also in wheaten-flour, especially in
that of the purest quality, when the flour is made into dough
and the dough is kneaded the same thing[2] happens, as is
proved by the fact that when it is boiled it becomes more
digestible.[3]   When, therefore, the bread is baked for the
first time, the thin and light part of the moisture[4] is
evaporated from the bread, and the part of the flour which 20
most resembles chaff is burnt out.   But when the dough is
taken out and kneaded again, the smoothest part of the
flour and the[5] stickiest part of the moisture being left
mingle more with one another, owing to the fact that they
have become smoother and stickier, and owing to the effect
of the heat; for their mixing resembles the process of 25
dyeing, so that the dough, when subsequently kneaded, is
like boiled flour.   For when this[6] dough is kneaded and
the lightest flour and the stickiest moisture are left, the
bread, when it has been exposed to the fire, becomes
glutinous and does not dry up; for that which is sticky
cannot be separated, and that which is dense does not of 30
itself give up any moisture.[7]   Twice-baked bread then
undergoes this same process for the reasons mentioned
above, and, always containing moisture, does not become
hard.

13   Why is it that we can go on partaking of some kinds
both of solid and of liquid food for a long period—for

---

[1] Reading ἐκφυσᾶται, since ἐκφύεται does not offer any contrast to
κενοῦται.

[2] Reading ταὐτό for αὐτό.

[3] The point here is not clear, unless boiling, like kneading (cp.
chapter 8), gets rid of τὸ γλίσχρόν and causes ψαθυρότης.

[4] Omitting δέ.

[5] Reading καὶ ⟨τὸ⟩ τοῦ ὑγροῦ.   [6] Reading ἐκείνου.

[7] Reading προίεται ὑγρόν.   ταὐτὸ οὖν τοῦτο καὶ δίπυρος κτλ.

35 instance, food made from barley-meal and wheaten-flour,
and dry wines, and water—whereas we cannot partake
continually of others, though they are pleasanter to the
taste? Is it because some of the foods which we take tend
to float on the stomach and are highly nutritious,[1] so that
when one has discharged them,[2] though their first nutri-
928ᵇ ment has been consumed, a considerable force still remains
in the body, concocted for the first bodily process but
unconcocted for its final purpose and for the succeeding
process? Now most of the pleasing foods belong to this
class; for the fatty and sweet and rich foods seem pleasantest
5 to our taste, and these, however they differ from one another,
are all foods which are nutritious, and not difficult of concoction, and apt to float on the stomach; their force is
therefore lasting, if one takes one's fill of them, and the
perception of them does not quickly pass away;[3] for the
feeling of satiety does not only continue while they are in
the stomach but also when their nutriment has been dis-
10 tributed to other parts of the body. Or is this not the
only reason, and is there a further reason, namely, that
some foods are naturally suited and akin to us? For our
bodies accept all such foods more readily because they are
natural, while they accept less readily those which are
unnatural. And different foods suit different temperaments; for example, honey is the natural food of bees, so
15 that they take no other, though they are physically weak;
so that what they consume must be small in amount, but
must be to their strength as what men eat is to theirs. And
so any pleasing foods which are of this kind seem pleasing
because they are present in small quantities in our nature,
20 but they only appear so for a short time, and then soon
cause a feeling of satiety. But we always need the natural
foods, so that we feel less satiety from foods continually
taken other than those which are most pleasing in themselves.[4]

---

[1] Cp. *de Sensu*, 442ª 10–12.

[2] κενωθῶσι is apparently an 'impersonal' third person plural, which
in this problem alternates with the first person plural.

[3] Reading ἐκλιπεῖν (Bussemaker) for ἐκλιπῇ, and placing a comma
after πληρωθῇ.

[4] δι' αὐτὰ οὐ τῶν ἡδίστων is apparently equivalent to οὐ τῶν δι' αὐτὰ
ἡδίστων.

14   Why is it that the same things seem pleasant when we are becoming accustomed to them and not pleasant if we partake of them too continuously, though being accustomed ₂₅ to anything is doing it often and continuously? Is it because custom engenders a receptive habit but does not bring satiety, whereas taking anything continuously fills up the desire, just as a vessel[1] is filled; for desire is a kind of void?[2] Now habits, when exercised, increase and grow, but vessels when they are filled full do not become any bigger. Hence custom, being an exercise, increases the ₃₀ receptive habit; but that which is continuously taken fills up and satisfies the desire, and, when this is satisfied, we no longer receive any more, and nothing can increase the desire for the reasons already stated regarding the filling of vessels. Furthermore, custom is not pleasant through constantly giving pleasure (for such things too cause pain through ₃₅ continual practice), but because we enter upon the beginning of the process with pleasure and can continue doing the same thing longer than if we were unaccustomed to it. In the same way then as custom, which is pleasant, causes pain, so too do all other pleasant things; for things which happen and foods which are taken continuously, both alike cause pain. The reason is that the powers of acceptance **929ᵃ** and action which we possess in ourselves[3] are not unlimited but limited, and when they have reached their full capacity (and this is continually visible to an increasing extent) the receptive powers are satisfied, and the powers for action can no longer function.   5

15   Why does dough become white when it is kneaded, while barley-cake becomes blacker? Is it because the surface of the barley-meal becomes drier, and it is the[4] heat in the moisture which causes the whiteness? Or is it because, through exposure to the heat, the surface of barley-meal attracts the moisture, since it consists of larger particles?   10

---

[1] Reading ἀγγεῖον for αἴτιον (Bonitz).
[2] Reading κενὸν for καὶ (Bonitz).   [3] Reading αὐτοῖς (Bonitz).
[4] Reading τὸ δὲ ἐν ὑγρῷ θερμὸν ποιεῖ (Yᵃ omits ὁ before ποιεῖ). The Latin version of T. G. renders 'calor autem humori permistus candorem gignit'.

Why does barley-meal adhere better together when **16** mixed with water than with oil, though oil is more viscous? Yet that which is viscous is more binding, and oil is more viscous than water. Is it because water is thinner and so penetrates into everything and makes the barley-meal **15** soft, and the grains adhere together better and are compressed into one another, even though pressed together without any kneading?

Why does bread which is either not kneaded or very **17** much kneaded break up? Does the unkneaded bread do so because it is not sufficiently bound together? Now it is the kneading that binds the bread; so that unkneaded bread is already on the way to breaking up. Further, it **20** contains much moisture not properly mixed in.[1] Bread which is very much kneaded is dry, because it has very little moisture; for when it is heated, the moisture all escapes. So that in both cases the bread breaks up because much moisture goes forth; for much moisture is actually present in the unkneaded bread, and in the over-kneaded bread much ⟨escapes⟩[2] compared to what remains behind.

25 Why is the admixture of barley-meal and liquid lighter **18** than the two things together when unmixed? Is it because, when they are mixed, air is enclosed in them? Or is it because part of the water is evaporated by the heat in the barley-meal, and so the mixture becomes smaller in bulk? The air, however, if it were also mixed in, would not make **30** the mixture any lighter; for air enclosed in air possesses weight.

Why do milk and sweet wine appear sweeter if drunk **19** with barley-meal? Do they appear sweeter in contrast with anything which is not sweet (for barley-meal is not sweet)? Or is it because the barley-meal continues to hold **35** sweetness, and so the perception of it is prolonged?

Why does the same potion seem less strong if it is drunk **20** with barley-meal? Is it because the barley unites what has

---

[1] Which therefore escapes when the baking takes place.
[2] The text as it stands contradicts διὰ τὸ ὀλίγον ἔχειν ὑγρόν (l. 21), and some such word as ἔξεισι appears to have dropped out.

one quality with what has another, or because the barley-
meal interferes with the potion and destroys it, absorbing
it into itself?

21   Why does gruel take up more water than the wheat from **929^b**
which such gruel is made? Is it because the gruel is a kind
of flour, and flour takes up more water (for its bulk is
greater than that of the wheat, for even the particles of the
wheat are packed closely together)? Now that which is 5
more holds more both for this reason[1] and also because
both flour and gruel contain heat, and heat both attracts
the moisture more and expends it by evaporation.

22   Why does wheaten-flour increase much more in proportion than barley-meal when it is kneaded?[2] Is it because
flour admits a large quantity of water, but barley-meal only
a little? (But why does it admit more, for barley-meal 10
would naturally be expected to do so, because it has been
exposed to heat, whereas the flour has not, and that which
has been exposed to heat is drier?) Or is it because flour
admits of more kneading, the reason being that it is composed of smaller particles? As therefore it is potentially as
it were more manifold by reason of the smallness of its
parts, so much the more water does it take up. For it 15
uses the water as a glue—a metaphor employed by
Empedocles in the *Physics*,[3] when he says 'gluing barley
with water'—and it consumes much water for this reason.

23   Why does dough increase more when it has been heated
than barley-cake does?[4] Is it because it contains moisture
which is not separated in such a way that it can escape
when it is warmed, and this[5] moisture, becoming breath 20
and not being able to escape (as it can in the barley-cake)
owing to the density of the dough (for that which is made
up of smaller particles is dense), makes the dough, therefore,

[1] Reading with Bonitz πλεῖον καὶ ⟨διὰ⟩ τοῦτο.
[2] Cp. chapter 9.
[3] Cp. *Meteor.* 382^a 1 and Diels, *Vorsokr.*³ i, p. 239, 7.
[4] A longer version of chapter 10.
[5] Reading with Bonitz ὁ πνεῦμα γενόμενον καὶ οὐ δυνάμενον κτλ.

rise and causes the mass to be greater? Furthermore, the moisture which it contains is more considerable, and it is from this, when it is heated, that the breath is engendered; and from the greater amount of moisture more breath must 25 necessarily be engendered.

Why is it that, of persons engaged in the preparation of **24** cereals, those who handle barley become pale and are subject to catarrh, while those who handle wheat are healthy?[1] Is it because wheat is more easily concocted than barley, and therefore its emanations are also more easily concocted?

30 Why is it that bread, if one toasts it, becomes harder, **25** whereas, if one warms it, it becomes moister up to a certain point? Is it because, when it is toasted, the moisture goes out of it, and so it becomes harder, whereas, when it is warmed, the moisture having acquired consistency is liquefied again by the fire, and so the bread becomes moister?

35 Why does flour, as it cools, become less closely packed, **26** but barley-meal more so? Is it because things which are made up of small particles contain no vacant spaces, and heavy things, by the pressure which they exert, take up the same space whether they are more or less[2] numerically? Barley-meal then is soft; when it cools, therefore, it becomes less, so that the less is more compressed.[3] But wheaten- 930ᵃ flour already consists of small particles, and so it does not cool in this way,[4] but in such a way as to become lighter and not so as to become more closely packed by compression; for wheaten-flour is naturally heavier than barley-meal.

---

[1] This problem occurs again at xxxviii. 10; cp. also 863ᵃ 35 ff. It is quoted as occurring in the Φυσικὰ Προβλήματα of Aristotle by Apollonius, *Hist. Mirab. 7*.

[2] Reading τὰ πλείω ⟨ἢ⟩ ἐλάττω.

[3] Reading συμπιέζεται πλέον. T. G. renders 'ut quod minus est . . . plus constipet in se'.

[4] Reading διὰ τούτου. T. G. renders 'non ideo resiccatur'.

BOOK XXII

PROBLEMS CONNECTED WITH FRUIT   5

1   WHY is it that the volume of food necessary for repletion is not proportionate[1] in the same persons if they eat fruit at the beginning and at the end of a meal? Is it because fruit is much heavier than solid food? This can be illustrated by the fact that figs, though eaten last, are vomited 10 out last. If, therefore, they are eaten first, owing to their weight they sink downwards and leave ample space above, so that one can easily contain the volume of solid food. If, however, the converse takes place, the solid food when it enters in, because it does not sink downwards, quickly occupies the vacant upper space.

2   Why is it that, although sweet foods are more akin to us than pungent, we are more quickly sated by the former?[2] 15 For the contrary might have been expected, since we might naturally be supposed to be less sated by foods which are akin to us. Is it because the organ whereby we receive nourishment[3] and the body, which is nourished, are not sated equally quickly, but sometimes the stomach is full, in those, for instance, who are thirsty, but the thirst is not less? For we do not cease being thirsty because the stomach is 20 full, but when each part of the body has drawn thence its own particular moisture; and we cease being thirsty only when they have received this in sufficiency. The same thing also occurs when we are hungry.

3   Why are we more quickly sated by sweet than by pungent foods?[4] Is it because we cease desiring sweet things sooner? 25 Or, while it is not generally admitted[5] that we become

---

[1] Reading ἀνάλογος with Cᵃ, Aᵖ, and according to Bekker Yᵃ.
[2] Cp. chapter 3.
[3] Reading τρεφόμεθα with Bonitz for πληρούμεθα.
[4] Cp. chapter 2.
[5] Putting a comma after γλυκέων in l. 27; it is obvious that the sentences introduced by μέν and δέ are parallel and that the general sense is the same as that of ll. 16–22 above.

satiated as the stomach is filled by sweet foods, yet might it
not be said that our desire is more quickly sated by them?
Or is it because desire is simply a want, which occurs when
30 we no longer have any nutriment in us or very little?
Pungent foods then are not nourishing, but contain little
nutriment and a considerable amount of excrement. We
therefore naturally seek to eat them in large quantities, and
yet do not satiate our desire with them,[1] because we still lack
nutriment and they do not contain it. But all sweet foods
35 are nutriment, and the body derives a large amount of nutriment from a small quantity of them. When, therefore, it
derives a large amount of nutriment, it can no longer eat,
because it cannot tolerate more. We are therefore naturally
more quickly satisfied by sweet foods.

930ᵇ Why is it that fruits and meat and the like remain **4**
uncorrupted if placed in skins, when these are tightly
inflated, as also do substances placed in closely covered
vessels?[2] Is it because all things become corrupt through
being in motion, and things which are full are without
motion (for it is impossible for anything to be moved
without there being a void), and these vessels are full?

5 Why does wine seem bitter when drunk after the eating **5**
of rotten fruits? Is it because such rottenness contains
bitterness? That, then, which remains on the tongue,
mingling with the draught and becoming diffused in it,
makes the draught bitter. The fruit by itself, when eaten,
10 seems less bitter, because juice of this kind takes effect at
many different points and is divided up into small particles.

Why should dried fruits be eaten? Is it in order that we **6**
may drink sufficiently? For we ought not only to drink to
satisfy the thirst which is engendered by solid food, but also
when the solid food is finished.

15 Why do roasted nuts deteriorate when they become cool, **7**
and also bread and acorns and many such things, but
improve when they are heated again? Is it because, when

---

[1] Reading αὐτῶν.
[2] A shorter version of this problem occurs in xxv. 17.

they become cold, the juice becomes hard, but, when they are warmed up, it becomes liquid again, and it is the juice which is pleasing?

8   Why is it that, for the proper enjoyment of fruits such as 20 figs and the like, one ought to drink with them either unmixed wine or water, which are the opposites of one another? Is it because fruit is both hot and moist owing to the manner of its growth? For it contains much both of fire and of moisture; and so, owing to the fire, the juice causes as it were a boiling within, such as must makes on 25 the surface (though the others, the hard-shelled fruit, also have this force, but in a less degree), while the large quantity of moisture causes an unconcocted condition. Water then, owing to its coldness, extinguishes the boiling, as wine also usually does by its heat; for it takes away its power, just as one fire extinguishes another if the latter be 30 less. And wine by its heat is better able to concoct the moisture, and by its weight it prevails over the scum formed on the surface by the boiling.

9   Why is it that those dried figs are sweetest which are slit twice, and not those which are slit either many times or not at all? Is it because, if they are slit many times, most of the sweetness escapes and evaporates with the moisture, 35 whereas in those which are entirely closed the watery element is considerable, because it has not been turned into vapour? Those, however, which have been slit, but not many times, do not suffer from either of these disadvantages.

10   Why is it that figs when they are dried¹ in an oven are harder if they are left to cool in the oven than if they are 931^a taken out to cool? Is it because in the oven all the moisture is evaporated by the heat, whereas outside the surrounding air cools the moisture and prevents it from escaping and the moisture retains its consistency rather than evaporates?² 5 Now what is dry is hard, and what is moist is soft.

¹ Reading with Sylburg ξηραινόμενα for ψυχόμενα.
² Reading καὶ συνίσταται μᾶλλον ἢ ἐξατμίζει. μᾶλλον γὰρ ἐξατμίζει does not give the required sense.

Why is it that wine and water seem sweeter when taken 11
with something sour, if, for instance, one munches acorns
or myrtle-berries or something of the kind? Is not this
natural and does it not happen in other things too? For
everything seems to assert its identity more forcibly when
10 compared with its opposite, and here the tastes of the two
opposites are in a way set against one another. Or is it
because, as in objects which are being dyed, the tongue has
already been permeated by the sour matter and opens its
pores, and so the sweetness can penetrate better? For
objects which are being dyed are first of all moistened in
sour liquid, because that which is thus permeated[1] takes
15 the dye better.

Why do sweet things seem to be less sweet when they 12
are hot than when they are cold? Is it because two sensations of the two qualities are present together, and so that
of heat dispels the other? Or is it because that which is
sweet[2] is also hot, and it is therefore a case of 'fire upon
fire', and thus the heat prevents the perception of the
20 sweetness? Or is it because fire takes away the power of
everything, since it causes motion? Things, then, which are
hot are nearer to change, but when they cool they become
stable again.

Why is it that chaff concocts hard fruits and does not 13
corrupt those which are already concocted? Is it because
25 chaff is both hot and absorbent? It, therefore, by its heat
causes concoction, while owing to its absorbent property it
attracts the corrupted impurity, which therefore does not
cause corruption.

Why do figs, which are soft and sweet, destroy the teeth? 14
Do they, owing to their stickiness, penetrate into the gums,
and, because they are soft, insinuate themselves into the
30 spaces between the teeth, and, being hot, quickly cause
decay? Perhaps also, owing to the hardness of the seeds,
the teeth are quickly caused to ache in the process of
chewing them up.

---

[1] Reading τῷ ⟨τὸ⟩ διεργασθέν.
[2] Reading γλυκὺ for γλεῦκος, which is invariably used to mean 'must'.

BOOK XXIII

PROBLEMS CONNECTED WITH SALT WATER
AND THE SEA

1 WHY is it that the waves do not ripple in the deep open 35 sea, but only where it is confined and shallow?[1] Is it because a small amount of liquid, as it is carried along, is more divided up by the wind than a large amount?

2 Why do the waves sometimes begin to move before the winds reach them?[2] Is it because the portion of the sea near the source of the wind being impelled along first has 931ᵇ continually the same effect upon the adjoining part, and so, since the sea is continuous, the same effect is caused in every part of it, as though from one continuous impetus? Now this occurs simultaneously, with the result that the first and the last parts of the sea are set in motion at the same time. This effect is not produced in the air, because it is not a single body (since many hindrances affect 5 it from all sides, which often cut short the first and most vigorous movement); the sea, however, suffers from no such impediments, because it is heavier and less easily disturbed than the air.

3 Why do ships seem to be more heavily loaded in harbour than out at sea, and why do they travel more quickly from 10 the open sea towards the land than from the land towards the open sea? Is it because the greater quantity of water offers more resistance than[3] the less, and the vessel sinks deeper into the latter, because it prevails more over it, for it pushes up the water from below? Now in a harbour the sea is shallow, but deep out at sea; so that a vessel will 15 seem to carry a heavier load in harbour and will move with greater difficulty, because it is sunk deeper into the water,

---

[1] Cp. below, chapter 24.
[2] Cp. below, chapters 12 and 28.   [3] Omitting ἐκ.

which offers less resistance. But in the open sea the contrary happens.

Why is it that if anything (for example an anchor) is **4** thrown into the sea when it is rough, a calm ensues? Is it because the sea is stopped by the descending object, with which a certain amount of air is carried down, and this air, carried in a direct course downwards and drawn thither, draws with it also the lateral force which is disturbing the sea? Now a wave does not move downwards from above but along the surface, and, when it ceases, a calm ensues. Furthermore, the sea, as it closes in upon the space opened by the descending object, makes an eddy, and eddies move in a circle. Now since it is a case of a straight line touching a circle at a point (and waves travel obliquely in a straight line), the result would be that the waves touch the circumference of the eddy only at a point, both for the reasons stated and because the eddy pushes the wave off as soon as it comes into contact with it. The place, then, where the eddy is, being without waves, the result is that there is a calm where the surface is broken, because the air, which descended with the object thrown in, subsequently ascending and thrusting the sea upwards, causes it as it were to bubble; for a bubble consists of moisture thrust up by air from below. Now every bubble is smooth and still. A proof that the above process takes place is given by the fact that the sea at the point where the object is thrown in rises a moment later to a higher level than the surrounding sea.

Why is it that sometimes vessels which are journeying **5** over the sea in fine weather are swallowed up and disappear so completely that no wreckage even is washed up? Is it because, when a cavernous space breaks open in the earth beneath the sea, the ship at the same time follows the rush of air [1] into the sea and into the cavern? And in like manner the sea, being carried everywhere [2] round in a circle, is borne downwards; and this constitutes a whirl-

---

[1] It appears unnecessary to read here ῥεύματος for πνεύματος as suggested by Bonitz.
[2] πάντα φερόμενα should perhaps be read.

pool. And ships in the Straits of Messina suffer the same
fate owing to the flow of water, which causes eddies, and
are swallowed up into the abyss, for the reasons stated
above and also because the sea is deep and the land
cavernous to a great distance. The eddies, therefore, overpower the ships and carry them thither, and so no wreckage 10
is washed up. The flow occurs when, the former wind
having stopped, a contrary wind blows over the sea when
it is running under the impulse of the former wind, and
especially when the contrary wind is the south wind. For
the currents flowing against[1] one another try to thrust one
another aside, as happens in rivers, and eddies are formed.
And the original movement, which is strong, is borne 15
whirling round and round from above. Since then the
currents cannot travel laterally (for they are mutually
repelled), they must be thrust down into the depths, and
so whatever is caught by the eddy must necessarily be
carried down too. Hence they build ships with slanting
ends; for cases have been recorded before now in which
a ship with straight ends has been swallowed up.   20

6   Why is the water whiter in the Black Sea than in the
Aegean? Is it owing to the refraction of the vision from
the sea into the air? For in the region of the Black Sea
the air is thick and white, so that the surface of the sea
appears to be similar, whereas in the Aegean it is blue, 25
because it is clear to a great distance, and so the sea too
reflecting the air appears to be similar. Or is it because
all lakes are more whitish than the sea, and the Black Sea
has the character of a lake because many rivers flow into it?
Now lakes are whiter than the sea, and than rivers; for 30
example, painters picture rivers as pale yellow and the sea
as blue. Or is it because the sight cannot penetrate quickly
through fresh water and is refracted into the air,[2] but is not

---

[1] Reading ἀντιρρέοντα for ἀντιπνέοντα. This change gives better
sense than Bonitz's change of πνεύματα for ῥεύματα.

[2] The text as it stands gives no satisfactory sense, and we must
read: ἢ ὅτι διὰ μὲν τοῦ ποτίμου ⟨οὐ⟩ διέρχεται ταχὺ ἡ ὄψις, καὶ ἀνακλᾶται
πρὸς τὸν ἀέρα, ἀπὸ δὲ τῆς θαλάσσης οὔτ' ἄνω ἀνακλᾶται διὰ τὸ μὴ λεῖον εἶναι
τὸ ὕδωρ, κάτω τε κτλ. This gives agreement with the doctrine of ll. 35–
37 and ᵇ8, and, except for the insertion of the first negative (which

refracted from the sea, because the water is not smooth, but
35 the sight tires of trying to penetrate into the depths, and so
the sea appears black ?   But in seas of a lake-like character,
since the fresh water is on the surface and the salt water
below, the sight does not penetrate, but is refracted towards
the daylight ; and so the surface of the sea appears white.

Why is the sea less cold than drinking water, and salt **7**
932ᵇ water in general than fresh ?   Is it because the sea is denser
and has more body ?   Now such things are less susceptible
to cold, just as they are more easily heated ; for owing to
their density they are better able to retain heat.   Or is it
5 because the sea is of a more fatty composition [1] (and so does
not extinguish fire as well as [2] other kinds of water), and
the more fatty anything is the hotter it is ?   Or is it because
it contains much earth and is therefore drier, and the drier
a thing is the hotter it is ?

Why is the sea more transparent than fresh water, **8**
although it is thicker ? [3]   For fresh water is rarer than salt.
10 Has rarity nothing to do with the question, and is the
reason that in salt water there are direct interstices which
are very numerous and wide?   Fresh water, therefore, has
density owing to the small particles of which it is composed,
whereas salt water contains great voids.   Or is it because
the sea is clearer?   For there is no earth in it,[4] but the
sand, which is heavy, is precipitated ; but fresh water is
15 earthy, and the earth [5] floating in its midst is easily stirred
into mud.

Why is the sea more transparent when the wind is in **9**
the north than when it is in the south?   Is it because the
sea has colour when it is calm ?   For there is something

according to Bekker has the MS. authority of Xᵃ), was obviously the
reading translated by the author of the Latin version, which renders,
' an quia per aquam bibi idoneam visus penetrare facile potest, aerem
versus reflectitur : e mari autem nec sursum reflecti potest, quoniam
levis aqua non est, et deorsum progrediens fatigatur '.

[1] Plutarch, *Quaest. Conviv.* iii. 3, refers to this statement as
Aristotelian.

[2] Omitting the full-stop after φλόγα.

[3] Cp. chapter 38.

[4] Reading ἔνεστι for ἔστι.

[5] Reading αὕτη (= ἡ γῆ, implied in γεώδη).

fatty in the juice of salt water, as is shown by the fact that in hot weather an oily substance is excreted from the sea. When, therefore, the sea is calm and warmer, juice of this [20] kind forms on the surface of the sea owing to its lightness.[1] This is less likely to happen when the wind is in the north, owing to the cold. Now water is more transparent than oil; for oil has colour, but water, presenting itself without colour to the vision, gives a clearer image.

10 Why does one dry more quickly after washing in the sea, [25] although sea water is heavier than fresh?[2] Is it because the sea is thicker and earthy?[3] Since, therefore, it has little moisture in it, it dries more quickly.

11 Why are the waves an indication of wind? Is it because they are a sign of wind in the future? For wind is a [30] massing together of air, which occurs because the air is continually thrust forward.[4] But the wind begins to thrust the air forward when it is not yet blowing continuously but only just beginning. The first breath of wind then as it were dies down before having any effect, but it thrusts forward another breath and drives on another mass of air and then dies away. It is clear therefore, when the wave which is thrust forward is already present, that that which [35] sets it in motion will also come; for it causes this effect when it first begins to blow.

12 Why do the waves break forth before the wind?[5] Is it because the wind does not cease to blow[6] and the sea to be rough at the same time, but the sea ceases later? For[7] it is possible that the wind which set the wave in motion **933[a]**

---

[1] Placing the comma before instead of after διὰ κουφότητα.

[2] Plutarch, *Quaest. Conviv.* iv. 1, refers to this problem as Aristotelian.

[3] This is a contradiction of the doctrine of l. 13 above.

[4] Reading with Bonitz ἀέρος, ἢ διὰ τὸ ἀεὶ προωθεῖσθαι γίνετα..

[5] Cp. chapters 2 and 28.   [6] Omitting τὸ before πνέον.

[7] As the text stands there are two principal verbs in the sentence ἢ ὅτι ... αἰσθητόν, namely, παύεται and ἐνδέχεται, and there is no connexion between them. This suggested solution of the problem is obviously the same as that offered in a shorter form in chapter 28 (934[b] 5 ff.) ἢ διότι καὶ τελευτᾷ ὕστερον; τὸ γὰρ πρότερον πνεῦμα ὡσανεὶ προδιαλύεται τοῦ ὠσθέντος κύματος. We must therefore read ἀλλ' ὕστερον ἡ θάλαττα; ἐνδέχεται γὰρ κτλ.

perishes before it becomes perceptible ; and so the wave is not really prior to the wind, but the former is noticeable, while the latter is not. Or do the winds not blow every-where at the same time, but at first only in the quarter from which they arise ? Now as soon as they begin to blow, 5 they set in motion the sea which is near them, and this sets in motion the adjoining sea ; and thus it would be possible for the wave to break forth before the wind reaches it. For the movement is due to the sea and not to wind, being a movement of the sea which travels more quickly than that of the air.[1]

Why is it easier to swim in the sea than in a river ? Is it **13** 10 because the swimmer always leans on the water as he swims, and we receive more support from that which is of a more corporeal nature,[2] and sea water is more corporeal than river water, for it is thicker and able to offer more resistance to pressure ?

Why can one remain longer in the sea than in a river ? **14** 15 Is it because river water is rare and therefore penetrates more into the body and chokes one ?

Why is sea water combustible, while fresh water is not ?[3] **15** Or does fresh water also burn, while the reason why sea water has less power to extinguish fire is because it is of a more fatty composition ?[4] (And that it is so is proved by 20 the fact that an oil is given off from sea water.[5]) Or are the interstices in sea water[6] less able to adapt themselves to fire because they are too wide, and all the more so owing to the presence also of salt ? As, therefore, that which is dry has less power to quench than that which is moist, so that which is drier is proportionately more capable of being 25 burnt, one thing being more so than another, since the drier

---

[1] Reading with Bonitz ἡ κίνησις, ἡ θάττων τοῦ ἀέρος, ἡ τῆς θαλάττης, which is equivalent to ἡ κίνησις ἡ τῆς θαλάττης, ἡ θάττων οὖσα ἢ ἡ τοῦ ἀέρος κίνησις.

[2] Cp. Plut. *Quaest. Conviv.* i. 9, which appears to be a direct reference to this passage.

[3] Cp. chapter 32.   [4] Cp. above, 932[b] 4.

[5] *Ib.* [b] 18 ff.   [6] *Ib.* [b] 10 ff.

a thing is the more closely allied is it to heat;[1] and sea water possesses both these qualities of dryness and heat to a greater extent than fresh water.

16 Why is it that the wind blows cold in early morning from rivers, but not from the sea?[2] Is it because the sea extends over open spaces, but rivers are in narrow places? The breeze, therefore, from the sea is dispersed over a wide area 30 and is consequently weak; whereas the breeze from a river is carried along in a mass and is stronger and therefore naturally seems colder. Or is the reason other than this, namely, that the rivers are cold, but the sea is neither hot nor cold? Now a breeze or an exhalation is due to the 35 heating or cooling of liquids; for whichever of these two processes they undergo, evaporation takes place, and, when water evaporates, the resultant air is set in motion, and this is a breeze. That which is produced from cold liquids naturally blows cold, while that which blows from very hot 40 liquids cools and becomes cold. One would, therefore, find **933^b** that all the rivers are cold, but that the sea is neither very hot nor very cold. That which blows from it, therefore, is not cold, because it is not itself cold, nor does it cool quickly, because it is not very hot.

17 Why do waves calm down more slowly in the wider open 5 sea than in shallow waters? Is it because everything calms down more slowly after much motion than after little? Now in the wide open sea the ebb and flow is greater than in shallow waters; there is, therefore, nothing strange if that which is greater is more slow in calming down.   10

18 Why is it that salt water when it is cold is not drinkable, but becomes more drinkable when it is heated, and when it is heated and then cooled? Is it because a thing naturally changes from one opposite into the other? Now drinkable 15 water is the opposite of salt water; and, when salt water is heated, the salt is boiled out, and, when it cools, is precipitated.

---

[1] Reading with Bonitz τῷ ἐγγυτέρω τοῦ θερμοῦ εἶναι τὸ ξηρότερον. τῇ δὲ θαλάττῃ ἄμφω ταῦτα μᾶλλον ὑπάρχει.

[2] This problem occurs again in Book xxvi. chapter 30.

Why is it that waters near the sea are usually fresh and **19** not salty? Is it because water which is allowed to percolate becomes more drinkable, and the nearer water is to the sea 20 the more it percolates?

Why does salt water not flow readily? Is it because that **20** which is heavy is stationary, and salt water is heavy? Hence only warm salt waters flow readily, for they have lightness in them which prevails over the heaviness which is in their 25 saltness; for that which is hot is lighter. Furthermore, water which flows readily can percolate through the earth; and if water can percolate, the thickest and heaviest part of it is always carried to the bottom, while the light and clean element becomes separated. For salt water is heavy and 30 fresh water is light. And so flowing water is fresh. It is for the same reason that salt water, when it is set in motion and undergoes change, becomes fresher; for it becomes lighter and weaker owing to the motion.

Why is it that in Libya, if one digs a hole near the sea, **21** the water that first comes is drinkable, but afterwards 35 quickly becomes salty, but this happens less elsewhere?[1] Is it because the water which comes first is the water which was already there and has been concocted by the earth, but after a time the sea also percolates through[2] and, because it has had no time to undergo any change, makes the water more salty? [Elsewhere, however, there is[3] either no water 40 or abundant water, because the ground is not dried up.]

934[a] Why does salt water melt salt more quickly than drinking **22** water? Is it because the process of melting anything is its dissolution by moisture or heat penetrating into it so that it becomes liquid? Now those things do not cause melting which either cannot penetrate at all or penetrate in such a way as not to touch the substance. Those things which 5 pass through easily scarcely cause any melting, but those

---

[1] Cp. chapter 37.   [2] Reading προσδιηθουμένη.
[3] The Latin version of T. G. renders 'aqua vel nulla est vel plurima', but ἔχει can hardly be used thus intransitively by itself, and we must either read οὐκ ἔστι or else ὁ τόπος for τὸν τόπον. The sentence, how-ever, is quite out of place here and appears to have come in from some other problem.

which enter in with violence dissolve substances very quickly. Now those liquids which are composed of very large particles do not penetrate, for they are too large for the pores; while those which are composed of small particles pass through without touching. Now drinking water is rare, while salt water is thicker; and so the former, passing through easily owing to its rarity, scarcely causes any melting, whereas the latter penetrates, but percolates through [1] to a less extent, because it is composed of larger particles, and forces its way in more quickly.

23   Why does water appear less white when it is in motion, for instance when there is a ripple? Whence Homer says that, when the wind begins to blow,

the sea grows blacker beneath it.[2]

Are there two reasons? Firstly, because, when the sight is near to it, it can penetrate farther through the water when it is still, but when it is in motion the sight cannot pass directly through it. (And that which is transparent appears white, for that through which the sight cannot pass is what Homer calls black; therefore the air appears black from a distance but white near at hand, and the part of the sea which is near is white, while that which is distant is blue or black.) And, secondly, because,[3] when the sight is at a distance and is subject in any way to disturbance, it is refracted back in a mass towards the light, if the water is still,[4] but cannot be refracted when it is in motion.

24   Why is it that the waves do not ripple in the deep, open sea, but only on small expanses?[5] Is it because a small amount of water, as it is carried along, is more divided by the air than a large amount? Hence it beats more and is broken up. Now in deep water the quantity which is set in motion is great, but in shallow water it is small.

---

[1] Reading διαρρεῖ for διαιρεῖ, which contradicts the doctrine of ll. 5,6.
[2] *Iliad* vii. 64.
[3] Reading διὰ τὸ for καὶ τῷ (C[a], Y[a], and A[p] read τὸ) to correspond to the διὰ τὸ διιέναι in l. 16.
[4] Placing a comma after ἠρεμῇ.
[5] A longer version of chapter 1.

30   Why are the waters saltier in regions facing the south **25**
wind? Do they become mixed because the sea is driven
under the earth by the south wind?

Why does the salty element in water come to the **26**
surface more in sweet than in dry wine? Is it because
35 sweet wine, like raisin wine, has more earth in it? Or is it
because sweet wine is heavier and stickier and so mixes
less, and, as the wine does not mix[1] with the water, the salty
element comes to the surface?

Why does the salty element, being earthy, float on the **27**
surface at all (for its natural tendency is to sink)? Is it[2]
934^b owing to its heat, as happens with salt (for it resembles
an efflorescence)? Or is there some other reason? For if
it is for no other reason,[3] it is not unreasonable that it
should be for this reason that it floats specially on the
surface of sweet wine; for that is the hottest of wines.

Why do the waves sometimes begin to move before the **28**
5 winds reach them?[4] Is it because they also cease to move
later? For the first breath of wind as it were dies down
before the wave which has been impelled by it into motion;
and it is not the wave which is first set in motion that
arrives, but there is a[5] successive impetus given to the
adjoining water.

Why is it that the ground where the waves break more **29**
violently becomes solid, often to such an extent as to appear
10 to have been artificially levelled, and why is the ground
where the waves break solid, whereas further from the sea
it is loose? Is it because the fine sand is not cast up from
a long way off by the waves, but rather the coarser sand,
just as it is not possible to throw a very small object far
with the hand? Then, many objects being mingled in
15 confusion, the smallest particles fall out[6] and form into
a mass, and the motion of the wave, as it recedes, levels

---

[1] Reading μιγνυμένου (W. D. R.).
[2] Omitting ὅτι μᾶλλον ἔχει γῆν ὁ γλυκύς; ἢ with the best MSS. These
words obviously came in from the previous chapter.
[3] Placing a comma after οὐ and omitting that after μᾶλλον.
[4] Cp. chapters 2 and 12 above.   [5] Omitting ἡ before ὦσις.
[6] Reading ἐκπίπτοντα; the Latin version renders *interlapsa*.

them and no longer disturbs them. Since, then, the smallest
particles cannot leap far, a mass is formed of very small
objects; and since it is in frequent motion, it becomes continuous, the sand falling in amongst it until it unites it
together; it is then levelled by the last waves, and the [20]
slight moisture causes it to adhere together. But the
ground farther from the sea, being dry, becomes disinte-
grated, and is formed of larger pebbles and is unlevelled.

30 Why is it that the upper parts of the sea are saltier and
hotter than the depths? So, too, in wells of drinking water [25]
the upper water is saltier than that at the bottom; yet
salty water, being heavier, ought to stand at a lower level.
Is it because the sun and the air always attract the lightest
part of liquid? Now water which is suitable for drinking
is always lighter, and the sun can more easily attract it from
the part of the water nearest to it. And so that which is
left on the surface both of the sea and of drinking water is [30]
saltier (since the fresh element has been extracted) than
that from which little or nothing has been withdrawn. For
this reason the upper part is also hotter; for salt water is
hotter than drinking water. Therefore some of the followers
of Heraclitus declare that stones and earth are formed
from the drying and solidifying of fresh water[1] and that [35]
the sun draws up vapours from the sea.[2]

31 Why are the waters of the sea fresher which are nearer
the land? Is it because they are more continuously in
motion? Now salt water becomes fresher through motion.
Or is it because the water is saltier in its depths,[3] and the **935[a]**
part of the sea near the land is less deep? Wherefore also
water which shelves deeply near the shore is less fresh.
The reason of this is that the salty element being heavy is
carried down more into deep water.

32 Why is sea water the only kind of water that is com- [5]
bustible,[4] whereas drinking water and river water are not?
Is it because it has much earth in it, as is proved by the

---

[1] Diels, *Vorsokr.* i.[3] p. 434, 5.   [2] Cp. xxiv. 11.
[3] This directly contradicts the doctrine of chapter 30.
[4] Cp. above, chapter 15.

presence of the salt in it ? Or is it because it is of a fatty composition, as is proved by the oil which forms on the surface[1] of salt water ?

Why does sand not form in lakes, or at any rate less **33** than in the sea and in rivers ? Is it because rocks form in the sea and the earth has been to a great extent burnt out of them ? Now sand is rock which has been broken up into small and minute particles, and it is broken up by the impetus of the waves. But in lakes rocks free of earth are not formed to the same extent, nor are they broken to the same extent, because there are not waves to the same extent. But sand is formed more in rivers, because they carry down the earth and break up the rocks with their impetus.

Why is it that, when a lake either falls or dries up, the **34** corn in the adjoining plain is more likely to be cut off by frost ? Is it because the moisture in the lake evaporates and warms the air with its vapour, and so makes the frosts slighter and weaker than in hollow and marshy districts ? Or is it from the earth, as men say, that the cold begins and penetrates unnoticed ? If then the lake becomes dry, owing to the larger space of earth greater cold attacks the crops and freezes them and cuts them off to a greater extent ; and on such ground the cold comes from below, as is the popular belief. And yet the earth is warm in winter ; but the surface heat which is in the earth, owing to the fact that it is moist, becomes cooled, for the moisture is neither so far in as not to be affected by cold, owing to the heat which is present in liquids, nor so slight as to have no force, since the earth is permeated with water. For instance, owing to its becoming cold, one walks and lives upon ice.

Why is the sea salty and bitter ? Is it because the juices **35** in the sea are numerous ? For saltness and bitterness appear at the same time.

Why do shells and stones which are in the sea become **36** round ? Is it because the breaking off of their extremities

---

[1] Reading ἐφιστάμενον with Yᵃ and Aᵖ.

equally on every side causes them to assume a round form?
For this is the only shape in which the outer surface is the 935^a
same on all sides, and the sea by moving objects in every
direction breaks off their extremities equally.

37   Why is it that sometimes, if one digs a hole near the sea,
the first water which enters is drinkable but afterwards it
becomes salty?[1]   Is it because the water comes from the 5
sea itself which percolates under the earth?   The water
which first comes is, therefore, naturally fresh; for fresh
water is lighter than salt water, and the sea has some fresh-
ness in it, which mingling with the earth tends to come to
the surface. But the salt water, owing to its weight and to the
fact that it has power to penetrate, is carried downwards.
Whether this is so or whether the fresh water flows from 10
the mainland into the sea through the earth's veins, it
would naturally float on the surface of the sea which
mingles with it;[2] but, the passages being opened, the salt
water, owing to its greater volume, subsequently prevails and
makes the whole sea salty.   For if the passages are blocked
the result is that the inflowing salt water finds another way 15
higher up;[3] but when they are opened, it is all carried
there, just as happens in the veins in the body.

38   Why is it that the sea, which is heavier than fresh water,
is more transparent?[4]   Is it because of its fattier composition?   Now oil poured on the surface of water makes it
more transparent, and the sea, having fat in it, is naturally 20
more transparent.   Or is that which is lighter not always
more transparent also?   For oil itself is lighter than water
but not more transparent.   Or is the sea not really more
transparent, but only apparently so?   For fresh water comes
from the earth or from streams, and its source sends forth
earth also with the water, so that the streams, not being 25
pure, bring down with them the earth and sediment.   This
then is the reason why fresh water is less transparent.

[1] Cp. above, chapter 21.
[2] Reading αὐτῷ (W. D. R.) for αὐτῇ.
[3] Reading with the MS. A^p τῶν πόρων ἄνω.
[4] Cp. above, chapter 8.

Why do the bowels of those who swim in the sea open **39** readily? For if it is because they take violent exercise, those who run also take very violent exercise, yet their 30 bowels do not open. Or does not every form of exertion cause the bowels to open, but only such exercise as does not cause wasting? Now staying in the sea seems to make men, generally speaking, hungrier and opens the bowels; for the vapour given off by it is both hot and dry.

Why does the Lake of Paesus,[1] of which the water is **40** 35 drinkable, wash and also remove the stains from garments? For water which is fresh washes, but that which is bitter removes stains, and water cannot have both these qualities at the same time. Are stains removed not because the water is bitter, but by the quality of stickiness which has this power? Hence animals' hoofs have this effect, and any- thing which contains gelatinous matter; and so also any 936^a bitter substances which partake of this character do the same. Now in this lake it so happens that the bitter element of the quality of soda has been burnt out, but the fatty and sticky element remains. It is by virtue of this that it removes stains, and it washes because it is fresh.

5 Why does the part of the sea which is calm appear white, **41** while that which is agitated appears black? Is it because that which is less visible appears blacker, and water which is in motion is less seen than that which is still? Or is it because that which is transparent is white, while that which is not so is black, and that which is in motion is less 10 transparent?

---

[1] T. G. renders πᾶσα λίμνη (which is omitted by Bonitz from his *Index*) by *Lacus Paesa*, and we should probably read Παῖσα λίμνη here with Sylburg. The reference then will be to a lake at Paesus on the left bank of the Hellespont near Lampsacus. See Strabo, p. 589.

BOOK XXIV

PROBLEMS CONCERNING HOT WATER

1 WHY is it that, if one is anointed with oil, hot water poured over one seems less hot, in spite of the fact that oil contains heat? Is it because owing to the smoothness caused by the oil the water glides off and sinks in less?   15

2 Why is it that in the summer the water in wells becomes warm after midday? Is it because by that hour the heat has mastered the air, whereas before midday the heat is dissolving and putting an end to the cold; but the one does not prevail as soon as the other has ceased, but only after   20 time has elapsed?

3 Why is it that water, which sometimes becomes hotter than a flame, does not burn wood, whereas the flame does so?[1] Is it because the flame, and the breath which comes from it, consist of small particles, whereas water is made up of large particles and so does not penetrate? Now flame and the heat from coals owing to their rarity can   25 penetrate and destroy.

4 Why is it that boiling water has not the power to melt, while the stomach possesses this power?[2] Is it because the heat which is in the stomach penetrates owing to its rarity, whereas water cannot penetrate because of its density? Or is it because liquid prevents other things also from melting (for nothing melts in liquid)? In the stomach, however, the   30 liquid flows down into the bladder and so does not prevent the process of melting.[3]

5 Why is it that the bottom of a vessel containing boiling water does not burn, but one can carry it holding it by the bottom, whereas if the water be removed it burns? Is it

---

[1] Cp. Theophrastus, *de Igne*, § 40.   [2] *Ib.*, § 45.
[3] Reading οὐ κωλύει for οὕτω λύει.

because the heat as it is engendered in the bottom of the
35 vessel is extinguished by the water? Wherefore also substances which can be melted do not melt if any liquid is
added to them.[1]

Why is it that water does not boil over so much in 6
winter as in summer, although heated not only up to the
same temperature but even higher, and although equally
936ᵇ hot or even hotter?[2] Is it because boiling over is due to
the rising of bubbles? The water then itself becomes just
as hot in winter as in summer,[3] but the bubbles cannot rise
to the same extent, because the surrounding air is cold, but
5 they rise smaller in size, being compressed by the cold, and
soon burst, being broken by the air. They are, therefore,
smaller in bulk and fewer in number in the winter, and the
contrary in summer. Now boiling over is due to the
number and size of the bubbles forming the froth.

10 Why does hot water cause wrinkles, but fire, though it is 7
hot, not do so? Is it because fire produces breath and so
causes swelling (for it distends the skin), whereas it is the
curving of the skin which makes wrinkles?

Why is it that the bottoms of vessels in which water is 8
being heated are hotter while the water is still cold?[4] Is
15 it because, while the water is still cool, the heat is enclosed
and driven inwards,[5] being prevented from making its way
out, but, when the water in the vessel becomes thoroughly
heated, since the fire no longer holds the heat but expends
itself and becomes less, the bottom of the vessel becomes
cooler, just as a bath does? For a bath is hotter in winter
20 than in summer, because the heat is more enclosed in
winter than in summer by the surrounding air which is
cold.

---

[1] The words μὴ ψόφος appear hopelessly corrupt, but the right sense
is given by T. G., who renders *si quid humoris admittatur.*
[2] Punctuating, with Bonitz, οὐ μόνον ὁμοίως θερμαινόμενον ἀλλὰ καὶ
μᾶλλον, καὶ ὁμοίως θερμὸν ὂν καὶ ἔτι μᾶλλον. The source of this problem
is Theophrastus, *de Igne,* § 16.
[3] Reading with Bonitz θέρους for ψύχους.
[4] Cp. above, chapter 5.
[5] For the doctrine of ἀντιπερίστασις of heat and cold see note on
867ᵇ 32.

9 Why is it that water when it boils does not form a scum, as do pea-soup and lentil-soup? And yet water is lighter than these, and light substances ought to be able to project themselves more easily to a distance. The same thing[1] happens in the case of silver when it is being purified; for those who clean out the mint make gains by appropriating the remnants, sweeping up the silver which is scattered about. Is it because the heat causes the scum by vaporizing and subjecting to force anything which opposes its own natural impetus? Water, therefore, owing to its lightness and rarity is not subjected to force, and so no great heat is collected in it, but the heat which continually passes into it cuts its way through before it can become massed together. But substances which have body in them, like thick soups and silver, since, owing to their weight, they contain much corporeal matter and offer resistance,[2] because they are subjected to violent force as the heat tries to make its way out, form bubbles wherever the heat prevails; for, owing to their density, the heat cannot pass through them, but the density prevails until it is thrown off by the heat which flows into it. The result is a sudden impact, and not a continuous pressure, owing to the heat passing up quickly from below.

10 Why, if substances are moistened in hot water for a **937ᵃ** short time, do they swell, but, if for a long time, collapse and become wrinkled? Is it because the heat makes a thing liquid instead of solid and produces breath from liquid and rarefies what is dense? At first, therefore, it heats things which are solid and makes them moister, and producing breath from the moisture distends and swells them; but when it heats them still more, it rarefies their outer part,[3] so that the vapour is given off, and the drying up of moisture causes their bulk to collapse. Now, as anything collapses, its outer skin shrivels up, and where it shrivels up unevenly, wrinkles are formed.

11 Why are stones formed by hot water rather than by

---

[1] Deleting the comma after ταὐτό.
[2] Placing a comma after ἀνταπωθοῦντα instead of after βίᾳ.
[3] Putting the comma after θερμαίνῃ instead of after τὸ πέριξ.

cold ? Is it because a stone is produced from the failure of
moisture, and moisture fails more through the operation of
heat than of cold, in other words petrifaction is the result
15 of heat, as Empedocles says both rocks and stones come
into being through the action of [1] hot waters ? [2] Or, while
it is true that heat petrifies, can petrifaction also take place
through cold, because an extremely hard frost consumes
the moisture and causes hardening ? That cold, pure and
simple,[3] produces this effect is clear from the fact that its
excess does so.

20 Why is it that if one has one's foot in hot water, if the 12
foot is kept still the water appears to be less hot, but hotter
if it is moved? Does the same thing happen as in the body,
viz. that, when one runs in the wind, the opposing air
becomes increasingly colder, and the farther one continues
to go [4] the more one notices it ?

25 Why do hot things cool off more in the sun than in the 13
shade? Is it because the lesser heat is destroyed by the
greater ? [5] Or is it because in the shade the surrounding
cold represses the interior heat and does not allow it to
make its way out, producing the same effect as the pouring
of cold water produces upon those who are fainting [6] (for it
30 encloses the heat and prevents it from escaping); and
speaking generally the interior parts of anything are
warmer in the winter ? But in the sun, since there is
nothing which intercepts it, the heat is free to move and
vanishes more quickly.

Why is it that water heated by the sun is not more 14
35 wholesome for washing purposes ? [7] Is it because, owing to
the fact that it is cooling, it causes shivering while it is still

---

[1] Reading διὰ for καί.   [2] Diels, *Vorsokr.* i,[3] p. 211, 31.
[3] For this use of τὸ ἁπλῶς cp. *Top.* v. 135^a 2, where it is opposed to
τὸ μάλιστα.
[4] Reading with Bonitz ἀεὶ ἰὼν for εἰσιών.
[5] This is the doctrine of πῦρ ἐπὶ πῦρ which occurs so often in the
Problems.
[6] Cp. Theophrastus, *de Igne*, § 15, where the word λιποψυχήσασι
shows that we must read ἐκθνήσκουσι, with Bussemaker, here for
θνήσκουσι.
[7] Cp. below, chapter 15.

upon the body?[1] Or, while it has this effect, is it unhealthy if
used often for washing? For hot water, generally speaking,
produces concoction and has a drying effect, whereas cold
water has an astringent effect, and so both do good.
Therefore cold water and water heated over a fire are both **937^b**
beneficial to those who wash in them ; but water heated by
the sun owing to the weakness of its heat produces the
effect of neither of these, but merely has the effect of
moistening—like the light of the moon.[2]

15   Why is water which has been heated in the sun not
wholesome?[3]   Is it because that which is cooling causes
shivering?

16   Why are the hot waters at Magnesia[4] and at Atarneus[5]
drinkable? Is it because more water pours into the hot
water as it flows out, and so its saltness disappears, but its
heat remains?

17   Why is it that in Magnesia the hot waters ceased to be
hot but the water remained salty?[6] Is it because more
cold water from elsewhere was poured at the same time
into the springs and extinguished the heat? Now the
earth was salty,[7] but not hot owing to the abundance of
water flowing into it. (A similar process occurs in water
which is strained through hot ashes; for the water being
strained through the hot ashes cools the ashes and itself becomes cold, but[8] is salty and bitter owing to the ashes.) But
when the water which was added had become transformed,
the heat in the earth for a different reason prevailed over
the coldness of the water owing to its small volume, and
hot waters flowed again.

---

[1] Reading διὰ τὸ ψύχεσθαι καὶ ἔτι ἐπὶ τῷ σώματι ὄν. The Latin
version of T. G. renders *corpori adhuc insidens*.
[2] The light of the moon does not heat us because it is not hot
enough.
[3] Cp. above, chapter 14.
[4] i. e. Magnesia on the Maeander; cp. Strabo, p. 579.
[5] On the west coast of Asia Minor opposite Lesbos. The fact that
Aristotle resided for a time at or near Atarneus makes it possible that
this problem is Aristotelian (cp. Frag. 625, 1583^b 20, 30).
[6] The sense given by this problem as it stands is not clear and is
opposed to that of the preceding chapter.
[7] Cp. Strabo, *l. c.*   [8] Reading δὲ with C^a (according to Bekker).

Why are waters from hot springs all salty ? Is it because **18** they usually percolate through earth which contains alum [1] (as is shown by the smell of the water) and has been burnt ? Now the ashes of anything are salty and smell of sulphur. ²⁵ The earth therefore burns the water like a thunderbolt. Many hot springs therefore are due to strokes of thunderbolts.

Why are hot bathing-places sacred ? Is it because they **19** are due to two very sacred things, sulphur and the thunderbolt ?

[1] Or, perhaps, 'vitriol'.

BOOK XXV

PROBLEMS CONNECTED WITH THE AIR   30

I   WHY is it that pain is caused if the limbs are enclosed in
inflated skins? Is it due to the pressure of the air? For
just as the air does not yield to pressure applied to the
skin from outside but repels it, so the air also presses upon
the limbs enclosed within. Or is it because the air is held 35
within by force and is compressed, and so, having naturally
an outward impetus in every direction, it presses against the
body enclosed within?

2   Why is it that in marshes near rivers the so-called
'bellowings' take place, which according to the fable are
uttered [1] by the sacred bulls of the god? That which is **938^a**
produced is certainly a noise which resembles the roaring
of a bull, so much so that it has the same effect on cows
when they hear it as the bellowing of a bull. Is it due to
the fact that this phenomenon always occurs wherever rivers
stagnate into marshes,[2] or are driven back by the sea, or 5
give forth wind in unusually large quantities? The reason
is that hollows in the earth form, and the water making its
way in (for there is always a flow of water in marshy ground
of this kind) thrusts the air also through a narrow entrance
into a wider hollow, just as a noise like roaring is produced
if one makes a sound through the aperture into an empty 10
jar; for it is by a similarly shaped organ that a bull's
roaring is produced. Now, if the hollows have irregular
forms, a variety of strange noises is produced; for if one
takes off the base [3] of a vessel and rubs it against the

---

[1] Reading ἰέναι (W. D. R.) for εἶναι. With the whole passage compare *Meteor.* 368^a 23 ff.

[2] Omitting ἢ ὅσα ἕλη λιμνάζονται, in which the plural verb with a
neuter plural subject and the change to the middle voice are suspicious,
and which is probably due to dittography of the preceding clause.

[3] πύνδαξ, which by derivation is connected with πυθμήν, πύματος and
the Latin *fundus* can hardly mean 'lid' (L. and S.), and must mean
'base'.

15 bottom, drawing it in and out,[1] it makes enough noise to frighten away wild animals when orchard-watchers employ this device.

Why does the air not become moist when it comes into **3** contact with water?[2] For all other things become moist when they touch water. Is it because the extremities of the air and water meet, but the surface of each remains 20 distinct?[3] All other things then are heavier, but the air does not sink below the outer extremity of the water. It therefore touches it, because there is nothing between them; but it does not become wet, because it always remains above the water.

Why does calm weather occur most often at midnight **4** and at midday? Is it because calm is immobility of the air, and the air is most at rest when it either has the mastery or 25 is overmastered, and it is in movement when it is struggling? Now it has the mastery most at midnight and is over-mastered at midday; for at the former time the sun is farthest away and at the latter nearest at hand. Again, the winds begin to blow either about dawn or about sunset; and the wind which blows at dawn dies down when it is overpowered, and that which blows at sunset dies down 30 when it ceases to have the mastery. Consequently the former dies down at midday, the latter at midnight.

Why is it colder when dawn is breaking and it is already **5** early morning than at night, although the sun is nearer to us?[4] Is it because towards daybreak dew and hoar-frost 35 fall, and both of these are cold? The whole ground then being as it were sprinkled with cold moisture, a process of cooling takes place.

Why is it that in Pontus both intense cold and stifling **6** heat occur? Is it because of the thickness of the air?[5]

---

[1] εἰ τρίψει διὰ τοῦ καταδήματος has been omitted as a gloss. The word καταδημα is otherwise unknown and is probably a corruption of καταγματος (the break).

[2] Cp. below, chapter 10.

[3] Omitting οὐχ with Richards. *op. cit.*, p. 143, where see note.

[4] This problem is treated at greater length in Book viii, chapter 17.

[5] Cp. above, Book xiv, chapter 13.

For in the winter it cannot be thoroughly warmed, and in the summer, when it is heated, it burns because it is thick. It is for the same reason also that marshy regions are cold 938ᵇ in winter and hot in summer. Or is it because of the course of the sun? For in the winter it is far away, and in the summer near at hand.

7 Why is the sky finer at night than by day? Is the sun 5 the cause of wind and disturbance? For these occur when some movement takes place; the cause therefore is the heat. So, when the heat is not present, everything is at rest, and there is more rest when the sun is rising than when it is sinking. And the saying,

> Have no fear of a cloud from the land,[1] 10

means that, where there is most movement, there must be least permanence and consistency, that which is trying to hold together being inequable and unable to gain the mastery. And this is what happens on the sea in winter and on land in summer.

8 Why is it that when liquid which fills a jar is poured into skins the jar not only holds the liquid and the skins as well 15 but also has room for more liquid? Is it because there is air present in the liquid? This then, when it is in the jar, cannot be given off owing to the size of the jar; for the larger anything is the more difficult it is to press any moisture or air out of it, as can be seen in sponges. But when it is divided up into small portions, it is pressed out 20 of the skin together with the air already there,[2] so that the space occupied by the air becomes empty; and so the jar can hold the skins and additional liquid as well. This is more especially the case with wine, because there is more air in wine than in water. Similarly the same vessel can 25 hold the same quantities of ashes and water together as it can hold of each poured in separately. For there are apparently many empty spaces in ashes, and so the water,

---

[1] The whole proverb is given at 947ª 7-9.
[2] i. e. as the air in the skin is displaced by the liquid which is being poured in, it makes its way out, taking with it any air that there may be in the liquid.

being thinner,[1] sinks in more and saturates the ashes, so
that they become dense,[2] because the saturation takes place
in one part after another (for a thing always becomes more
30 thoroughly saturated if the process takes place little by little
than all at once), and, as this takes place, the ashes gradually
sink, at the same time absorbing the liquid because they
contain hollows. (But ashes thrown into water while still
hot cleave the water and cause it to evaporate.) And the
same thing happens if the water is poured in first and the
35 ashes put in afterwards, so that the water also would seem
to contain hollows and empty spaces. Or do the ashes take
up the water, and not the water the ashes? For it is only
natural that that which is composed of smaller particles
should be that which finds its way into something else.
(Further, this can be illustrated by an experiment; for
939ᵃ when ashes are sprinkled water[3] is attracted to any spot
where they are sprinkled; whereas the contrary would
have taken place if it were the water which takes up the
ashes.) Or does this process not occur if the water be
poured in first and fill the vessel to the brim, but, if anything then be added, does it overflow?[4] But if the water
5 once overflows and the ashes settle down,[5] then it does occur;
for it was the ashes which took up the water. There is
a parallel to this in the fact that trenches do not hold all
the earth which has been dug out of them; for apparently
some air occupies the space excavated, and for this reason it
does not hold all the earth.

10 Why is it that, though air is denser than light, it can pass **9**
through solids?[6] Is it because light travels in a straight

---

[1] Reading λεπτότερον ⟨ὄν⟩.   [2] Omitting καὶ after πυκνοῦσθαι.
[3] Omitting ἄλλο with Aᴾ.
[4] The argument here is not very clear, but the meaning is apparently
something like the following : the fact that when ashes are dropped in
an absolutely full vessel the water overflows is no argument against
the theory that a vessel can hold the same quantity of water and ashes
together as it holds of each separately ; for the ashes when first put in
naturally cause an overflow, but, when they become saturated and
settle down, there is room left for the amount of water which has over-
flowed, just as if earth is dug out of a trench and then replaced it takes
some time to settle down to its original level.
[5] Reading ὑποπέσῃ for ἐπιπέσῃ. The Latin version renders *descen-
derit*.
[6] Cp. above, Bk. xi. 49 and 58.

line only, and so the sight cannot see through porous substances like pumice-stone, in which the pores are irregular,
whereas they are not so in glass? The air, on the other
hand, is not obstructed, because it does not travel directly 15
through anything through which it passes.

10   Why is it that the air becomes cold by touching water
but not moist, even though one blows so hard upon water
as to cause waves?[1] That it becomes cold is clear from
the change which it undergoes; for the air from water[2]
causes cold. Is it because it is the nature of air to be cold
or hot, and it changes by touching anything with which it 20
comes into contact; but it does not also become moist,
because it is too light and so never penetrates below the
level of the water, but always remains in contact only with
the surface, even though it be forced downwards, and the
water then recedes still lower, so that the air can never
penetrate into its depth?

11   Why is the air from bubbles and the air which comes up 25
from beneath the water never wet? Is it because the
moisture is not retained, but the water drops off? The
water on the surface of a bubble is also too little to moisten
anything.

12   Why is it that air cannot saturate anything, but water
can? For water even when it is transformed into air is
moist. Is it for the same reason as that for which stone 30
cannot do so? For everything has not this faculty of
saturating other things, but only that which is viscous or
liquid.

13   ⟨Why is it that an inflated skin floats?⟩[3] Is it because
the air in it is carried upwards? For when the skin is
empty it sinks; but when it is inflated, it remains on the
surface, because the air supports it. But if the air makes 35
it lighter and prevents it from sinking, why does a skin
become heavier when it is inflated? And how is it that

---

[1] Cp. above, chapter 3.

[2] Reading ⟨ὁ⟩ ἀπὸ τῶν ὑδάτων (Bonitz).

[3] The statement of the problem has fallen out and must be supplied
from the Latin version of T. G. which reads: *Cur utres inflati valeant
fluitare?*

when it is heavier it floats, and when it is lighter[1] it sinks?

Why is it that the air does not rise upwards?[2] For if **14** **939**^b the winds are the result of air being moved by heat and it is the nature of fire to rise upwards, the wind ought to travel upwards, since that which sets it in motion rushes upwards and that which is set in motion has a natural tendency to travel in the same direction. As a matter of fact, however, the air obviously travels in an oblique direction.[3]

5   Why is the hour of dawn colder than the evening?[4] **15** Is it because the former is nearer to midnight and the latter to midday? Now midday is the hottest time, because it is nearest to the sun, and midnight the coldest[5] for the opposite reason.

Why is it that in hot weather the nights are more stifling **16** 10 than the days? Is it owing to the absence of wind? For the periodical winds and the 'forerunners'[6] blow less at night.

Why is it that substances enclosed in inflated skins and **17** closely covered vessels remain uncorrupted?[7] Is it because things which are in motion become corrupt, and all things that are full are without motion, and such skins and vessels are full?

15   Why is it that it is colder when the sky is clear than **18** when it is overcast, though the stars and the heaven are warm?[8] Is it because in clear weather there is nothing to hold the vapour, but it is diffused everywhere, whereas in cloudy weather it is contained?[9] For the same reason it is colder when the wind is in the North than when it is in the South; for the South wind attracts cloud, whereas the North

---

[1] i. e. empty.
[2] It is unnecessary to suppose with Klek that there is a lacuna in the statement of this problem.
[3] The explanation of this is given in Book xxvi, chapter 48, *ad fin.*
[4] Cp. above, chapter 5 and Book viii, 17.   [5] Reading ψυχρόταται.
[6] Cp. 946^a 15.
[7] A shorter version of the problem already dealt with in xxii. 4.
[8] Cp. below, chapter 21.   [9] i. e. in the clouds.

wind dispels it, and more evaporation appears to take place 20
when the wind is in the North than when it is in the South,
and in winter than in summer. Or is it because of dis-
similarity? Or because vapour is formed when that which
is hot cools?

19   Why is it that a smaller amount of air is warmer than
a larger quantity (for confined spaces are always warmer)?
Is it because a larger quantity is subjected to more motion, 25
and motion makes a thing cold? This can be seen from
the fact that hot things become cold if set in motion.

20   Why is it that water and earth become corrupt, but air
and fire do not? Is it because anything which is corrupted
must become hotter,[1] but there is nothing hotter than fire?[2]
Or is it because a thing must be chilled before it can be
corrupted, but fire is always hot and the air is full of fire? 30
So nothing becomes corrupted when it is hot, but only
when it is chilled. Now earth and water[3] can become hot
and cold.

21   Why is cloudy weather hotter than clear weather?[4]
Is it because, as the men of old said, the stars are cold?
Or is this too absurd a doctrine,[5] and is the real reason that
in clear weather vaporization takes place? That this is so 35
can be inferred from the fact that, when there is no wind,
dew and hoar-frost are formed. When, therefore, the weather
is clear, the hot substance, by which the moisture is taken
up, is blown about, and so the air becomes cold; for which
reason also the moisture which the hot substance lets fall
forms dew. But when the weather is cloudy the moisture
is contained; and therefore there is no dew or hoar-frost in
cloudy weather. The heat, therefore, remaining in the 940^a
neighbourhood of the earth makes the weather warm.

22   Why is it that in lofty rooms the air constantly ebbs and
flows, especially in calm weather? Is it because the air

---

[1] Reading θερμότερον for θερμότατον with Bonitz.
[2] And since fire cannot become hotter, therefore it cannot become
corrupt.
[3] Omitting καὶ ἀήρ with A^p.   [4] Cp. above, chapter 18.
[5] The contrary doctrine, that the stars are hot, is assumed in l. 16
above.

⁵ contains much void in its composition? When, therefore, it begins to flow in, the air inside the room gives way and contracts; and when in course of time this air becomes massed together, the air outside becomes more full of voids and contains much vacant space. Into this space then the air from the room rushes, since it is near at hand, and ¹⁰ passes into it, because it is in suspense and the nature of the void cannot resist. So when this happens in many parts of it, the adjoining air follows it owing to the forward impetus;[1] and then, since a large quantity of air rushes out,[2] the space within becomes full of voids, while the air outside is denser and so rushes in again from outside. Thus these two ¹⁵ currents continually interchange.

---

[1] Reading πρόκοψιν (W. D. R.) for πρόσοψιν.
[2] Reading ἔξω for ἔξωθεν.

BOOK XXVI

PROBLEMS CONNECTED WITH THE WINDS

1 WHY does the North-East wind (Caecias)[1] alone of the winds attract the clouds to itself?[2] Is it because it blows from higher regions? For the parts towards the East are higher than those towards the West,[3] as is shown by the 20

[1] Caecias does not strictly speaking correspond with our NE. wind, since the quadrants of the Greek compass were divided into three and

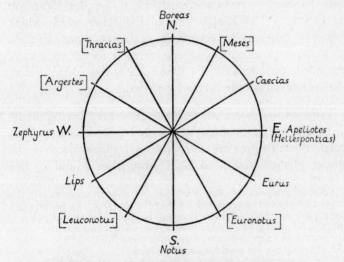

Chart of the winds to illustrate *Problems*, Bk. xxvi.

[The names in square brackets are supplied from other treatises.]

not four sections as in a modern compass ; Caecias is, therefore, 30° and not 45° north of the East wind. The chart of the Greek winds has been dealt with by Professor D'Arcy Thompson in *C. R.*, xxxii, p. 49 (1918), who has independently come to the same conclusion as I had previously formed in translating the *de Mundo* : he proves conclusively that Kaibel and Capelle's ' wind-rose ', which I had adopted when translating the *de Ventorum Sitibus*, is wrong, but he was apparently unaware that I had changed my view when translating the *de Mundo*.

[2] Cp. chapter 29. The source of both problems is Theophrastus, *de Ventis*, §§ 37, 39 ; cp. also *Meteor.* 364[b] 12.

[3] i. e. the earth is conceived of as sloping gradually from E. to W.

extent and depth of the sea towards the West. Now the
North-East wind (Caecias), blowing from above to a contrary
direction, describes in its course a line which follows an
upward curve in relation to the earth ;[1] and falling, as has
been said,[2] upon the western regions of the earth and
massing the clouds together as a result of the form of line
25 which it follows, on its return back it thrusts the clouds
before it towards itself.[3] It is the only one of all the winds
which does this, because for some the opposing regions
are higher,[4] towards which their course, either starting from [5]
a lower level or proceeding in a straight line, as a result
travels in a downward curve [6] towards the earth,[7] so that
30 there can be no return of the wind to its source because it
ends its course round the earth, where, besides, there are
no clouds.[8] The East wind and the other winds which
follow a less curving course do not form clouds because
they have no moisture. Since, then, it forms no clouds,
the effect produced by the East wind is less obvious than
that produced by the North-East wind.

35 Why do the North winds occur at a fixed period of the 2
year, whereas the South winds do not ?[9] Or do South winds
occur annually but are they not continuous, because the
source of the South wind is far away from us, and we live

---

[1] Reading κυρτὰ (T. G. has *convexum*) for κοῖλα in order to give the
required sense and to agree with the doctrine of 943ᵇ 1. Κοῖλα and κυρτὰ
appear to have changed places here and in l. 28. The meaning here is
that the N E. wind, descending from above, sweeps in a circular course
up into the sky and thence returns to the point from which it started.

[2] Nothing has yet been said on this point.

[3] i. e. to the point from which it started. ἐφ' αὑτὸν must be read for
ἐπὶ αὐτόν.

[4] Reading τοῖς μὲν ὑψηλοτέρους τοὺς ἐναντίους εἶναι τόπους (W. D. R.).

[5] Inserting ἐκ, omitted by error in the Teubner text, before τοῦ
κάτωθεν.

[6] Reading κοῖλα (T. G. has *devexus*) for κυρτὰ ; see note on l. 22.

[7] Reading ἔχουσαν for ἐχούσης and deleting the comma after συμβαίνει.
T. G. renders *quae versus, ut aut de imo aut e directo flatus feratur
devexus, terram versus necessum sit.*

[8] Reading τῷ περὶ τὴν γῆν (cp. 943ᵃ 37) ἔχειν τὴν τελευτὴν τῆς φορᾶς,
ἐν ᾧ οὐδὲ νέφη ἐστί (W. D. R.). The fact that the wind blows below
the cloud level gives an additional reason why it cannot form clouds.
περὶ τὴν γῆν appears to have been displaced from l. 30 by an emblema
from l. 29 and to have found its way into l. 31.

[9] The source of this problem is Theophrastus, *op. cit.*, § 11.

close to the North wind? Further, the annual North winds
blow when the air is still (for they blow in summer); 940^b
whereas the South winds occur in the spring, when the
region of the air is less stable. Again, the South wind is
moist, and the upper region of the atmosphere is unfavour-
able to moisture; so any moisture which is formed in it[1] is
quickly dissolved. Also moisture is erratic; and so the
South wind, because it does not remain in the same place, 5
helps to set up changes in the movement of the air. And
since the air does not remain in the same place when it
moves, other winds are consequently set up; for a wind is
a movement of air.

3 Why does the South wind blow after a hoar-frost?[2] Is it
because hoar-frost occurs when concoction takes place,
and after concoction and cleansing a change to the opposite 10
condition takes place? Now the South wind is the opposite
of the North wind. For the same reason also the South
wind blows after snow. In a word, both snow and hail
and rain and all such processes of cleansing are a sign of
concoction; therefore after rain and similar storms the 15
winds fall.

4 Why do the alternating winds blow?[3] Is it for the
same reason as causes the change of current in straits?
For both sea and air are carried along until they flow;
then, when the land-winds encounter opposition and can
no longer advance, because the source of their motion and 20
impetus is not strong, they retire in a contrary direction.

5 Why do the alternating winds come from the sea? Is it
because the sea is close at hand? Or is it because the
alternating wind is the opposite of the land-wind and as it
were the reverse of it? Now the land-wind is the breeze
which blows from the land towards the sea, and the
alternating wind is the reflux of the land-wind, so that it 25
must necessarily come from the sea. Or is it because[4] the

---

[1] Reading with Bekker αὐτῷ for αὐτῷ.
[2] The source of this problem is Theophrastus, *op. cit.*, § 50.
[3] This and the following problem are derived from Theophrastus,
op. cit., § 26.
[4] Reading ἢ διὰ κτλ., omitting ἡ θάλαττά ἐστι.

air which has been set in motion collects out at sea? The reason of its not collecting on land and of its being thrown back[1] is the fact that the sea is in a hollow, and air, like water, flows always into the deepest hollow it can find.

30   Why do cloud-winds[2] stop sooner when rain falls? Is it **6** because, when it rains, the hollows of the cloud, in which the source of the wind is formed, collapse?

Why are not the same winds everywhere rainy?[3] Is it **7** because the same winds do not everywhere blow against 35 mountains, but different winds are opposed to different mountains? For example, when the winds blow laboriously against steep mountains, the clouds are more likely to form there, since the wind cannot push them farther forward; and when the clouds form and are compressed, they burst.

941^a   Why are sunsets, if they are clear, a sign of fine weather; **8** if they are disturbed, a sign of stormy weather? Is it because a storm occurs when the air is dense and thick? When, therefore, the sun prevails, it breaks up and clears the air; but, if it is itself overpowered, an overcast sky 5 results. If, therefore, the density is excessive, a storm occurs as soon as the day dawns; whereas if it is weaker but not completely overpowered, the denseness which forms is driven towards the setting sun and remains there, because the air round the earth is thicker[4] than the storm. And the rest of the air quickly densifies, because 10 a beginning of the process has already been made and there is a rallying point to receive and collect anything which comes to it,[5] the same thing occurring in the air as happens in a rout, where, if one man makes a stand, the rest also remain firm. Hence the sky sometimes becomes quickly and suddenly overcast. When,

---

[1] Omitting ἀπιὸν as a dittography of αἴτιον.

[2] Cp. *de Mundo* 394^b 17.

[3] Cp. Theophrastus, *op. cit.*, § 5. This problem is more fully treated in chapter 56.

[4] Reading παχύτερον for παχύτατον, the comparative and superlative being frequently confused in the MSS.

[5] Omitting the meaningless καθάπερ ὄρθρος.

therefore, there is a disturbed sunset, it is a strong indication that the sun has not got the mastery over the density, 15
though it has struggled long against it, so that probably [1]
further condensation has taken place. This is a less alarming symptom when it occurs after a storm than in calm
weather ; for in the former circumstances it is probably the
remnant of a storm, but in the latter the beginning of
condensation.

9   What is the origin of the saying,   20

> Boreas blows not at night when once the third sun
>   hath arisen ? [2]

Is it because the breezes which come from the north are
weak when they blow at night?   A proof that the amount
of air which is set in motion is not great is the fact that
they blow at a time when there was a small amount of
heat ; and a small amount of heat was moving a small
amount of air.   Now all things terminate in multiples of
three,[3] and things which are very small terminate at the 25
end of the first triad ; and that is what this wind does.

10   Why does the North wind blow more frequently than the
South wind ? [4]   Is it because the North wind, being near the
inhabited portion of the world, attracts our notice in spite
of its short duration (for it is with us as soon as it begins to
blow), whereas the South wind does not reach us, because it 30
blows from a distance ?

11   Why does the South wind blow as much [5] on winter
nights as on winter days ?   Is it because during the night
the sun is near the southern region, and the nights there are
warmer than are the days in the north ?   Much air, therefore, is set in motion and not less than by day ; but the 35

---

[1] Reading εἰκὸς for εἰκότως.

[2] Cp. below, chapter 14. The source of both chapters is Theophrastus, *op. cit.*, § 49.

[3] Cp. *de Caelo* 268[a] 10 καθάπερ γάρ φασι καὶ οἱ Πυθαγόρειοι, τὸ πᾶν
καὶ τὰ πάντα τοῖς τρισὶν ὥρισται.

[4] Cp. below, chapter 15, and Theophrastus, *op. cit.*, § 9.

[5] Reading ⟨οὐχ⟩ ἧττον, which is demanded by the logic of the
problem. Whereas North winds blow less at night than by day
(chapter 9), South winds blow at least as much by night as by day.

warmer days prevent the wind from blowing more strongly
by drying up the moisture.[1]

Why does the South wind blow at the time of the Dog- **12**
star, and why does this happen regularly like any other
natural phenomenon?[2] Is it because the southern regions
are warm, since the sun is not far[3] away, and so the evaporation is considerable? The South winds would[4] blow fre-
941ᵇ quently if it were not for the annual winds; as it is, these
prevent their blowing.[5] Or is it because a sign occurs[6] at
the setting and rising of any star, and especially of the
Dog-star? It is clear that winds blow most at the time of
and after its rising, and since it causes stifling heat, it is
5 only natural that the hottest winds should be set in motion
when it rises; and the South wind is hot. And since things
are most accustomed to pass from contraries into contraries,
and the ' forerunners ',[7] which are northern winds, blow
before the rising of the Dog-star, the South wind naturally
blows after the Dog-star appears, since a sign then occurs,
10 and the occurrence of a sign[8] at the time when stars rise
means a change in the air. Now all winds change either
into their contraries or into those on their right; but since
the North wind cannot[9] change into the winds on its right,
the only thing left for it to do would be to change into
a South wind. Now on the fifteenth day after the winter
15 solstice the wind is in the south, because the solstice marks
as it were a fresh start and the sun sets in motion air which

---

[1] Cp. Theophrastus, *op. cit.*, § 49, *ad fin.*

[2] The source of the first explanation offered is Theophrastus, *op. cit.*,
48. The problem is repeated in chapter 32.

[3] Reading τοῦ ἡλίου ⟨οὐ⟩ πόρρω ὄντος, cp. Theophrastus, *l. c.*, αἴτιον
δ' ὅτι θερμὰ τὰ κάτω, τοῦ ἡλίου πάροντος, ὥστε γίνεται πολλὴ ἀτμίς.

[4] Reading πολλοὶ ἂν ἔπνεον.

[5] There should be a full stop in place of a comma after κωλύουσι.
The rest of this chapter occurs in the MSS. under chapter 32, whence
the editors have transferred it to this chapter as dealing with the same
problem.

[6] σημαίνει and ἐπισημαίνει (l. 9) are used impersonally as equivalent
to σημεῖόν ἐστι. The Latin *significat* has the same force, cp. Columella,
ix. 2 *Siderum occasus tempestates facit, interdum tantum significat.*

[7] So called because they precede the Etesian winds (946ª 15).

[8] Reading ἐπειδὴ ἐπισημαίνει μέν, ἐπιτέλλουσι δὲ τοῖς ἄστροις τὸ ἐπιση-
μαίνειν ἐστι κτλ.

[9] Reading ἐπιδεξίους ⟨οὐ⟩ μεταβάλλει (Bonitz); the Latin version of
T. G. inserts the negative.

is nearest to it[1] and at this solstice it is near the south. Just as, therefore, when it sets the region of the east in motion it stirs up the East winds, so when it sets in motion the southern region it stirs up the South winds. It does not do this immediately after the solstice, because the [20] changes which it sets up extend at first over a very small area, but only on the fifteenth day, because this date corresponds to the first sensible impression made by the change; for the said date is simply the most significant part of a whole.

13   Why are the days most changeable during the period of Orion, and why is there then such variability in the [25] wind?[2]   Is it because during a period of change all things are always most indeterminate, and Orion rises at the beginning of autumn and sets in the winter, so that, since there is not yet one settled season, but one is coming on and the other coming to an end, the winds must therefore necessarily be unsettled, because those of each season are [30] passing into one another?   And Orion is said to be dangerous both in his setting and in his rising owing to the uncertainty of the season; for it must needs be full of confusion and inconsistency.

14   Why does the North wind which blows at night cease on the third day?[3]   Is it because it comes from a small and [35] weak source and the third day marks the crisis? or is it because it expends itself all at once like the 'cloud-winds',[4] and therefore quickly dies down again?

15   Why do the North winds blow more than the other winds?[5]   Is it owing to the fact that the inhabited portion of the earth is near the region of the north, which is high 942[a] and outside the tropics and full of snow, which never leaves some of the mountains?   As, therefore, frozen matter is usually melting there, a wind often arises, and this wind is the North wind which comes from the region of the pole.

---

[1] Reading καθ' αὐτὸν for κατ' αὐτήν (cp. 944[a] 22).
[2] The source of this problem is Theophrastus, *op. cit.*, § 55.
[3] Cp. above, chapter 9.
[4] See above, 940[b] 30, and *de Mundo*, 394[b] 17.
[5] Cp. above, chapter 10.

5   Why do the South winds blow during winter and at the 16
beginning of spring and the end of the autumn,[1] and why
are they boisterous and whirling in their course and why
are they cold to the inhabitants of Libya in like manner as
the North winds are to us?[2]   Is it because, the sun being
near, the winds must necessarily be set in motion?   Now
10 during the winter the sun travels towards the south, and at
the beginning of the spring and at the end of autumn it is
giving forth heat; whereas during the summer the sun
travels towards the north and leaves those other regions.
The South wind is hot, because it mingles its breath with
the air in the region of Libya, which is hot; and so it is
15 boisterous[3] and makes the summer rainy, sweeping down
on the sea.

Why does the South wind cause evil odours?   Is it 17
because it makes bodies moist and hot, and they are then
most liable to corruption?   South winds, however, which
come from the sea are good for plants—for the South wind
reaches the Thriasian Plain in Attica from the sea[4]—and
20 the reason is that it is cooled before it arrives.   Now
mildew is caused by moisture which is hot and comes from
without.

Why does wind usually occur before eclipses, at nightfall 18
before midnight eclipses and at midnight before those
which occur at dawn?   Is it because the heat which comes
25 from the moon becomes faint, because its course is already
getting near the earth, and when it is quite near the eclipse
will take place?   Now when the heat, by which the air is
held back and kept still, is set free, the air begins to move
again and a wind springs up later in time according as the
eclipse is later.[5]

---

[1] Cp. Theophrastus, *op. cit.*, § 10.
[2] This is dealt with in chapter 49.
[3] Reading μεγαλοκύμων ⟨ὢν⟩ (Platt).
[4] Reading ἐκ θαλάττης γὰρ ὁ νότος (for αὐτοῖς) προσπίπτει καὶ τῆς Ἀττικῆς
τῷ Θριασίῳ πεδίῳ· αἴτιον δ᾽ ὅτι (for διότι) κτλ.   Unless ὁ νότος is read for
αὐτοῖς there is no subject for προσπίπτει; cp. the Latin version, *nam
et Thriasio campo terrae Atticae auster de mari occurrit.*
[5] The sense (cp. above, ll. 23, 24 ἀκρόνυχον . . . τῶν ἑώων) demands
some such reading as ὀψιαίτερον, τῆς ἐκλείψεως ὀψιαίτερον ⟨οὔσης⟩.

19   Why is the South wind rainy not when it is beginning but when it is ending?[1] Is it because it collects the air 30 from a distance? For the rain comes when the South wind masses the air together, and it masses the air together only after it begins to blow. Or is it because, when the South wind begins to blow, the air is still hot, because it comes from a hot region, but in course of time it becomes cool, and then tends to become massed into rain?

20   Why is it that the South wind, when it is less strong, brings clear weather, but, when it is strong, brings clouds 35 and lasts longer?[2] Is it, as some say, owing to the source from which it comes? For if it comes from a weaker source it brings clear weather, but if it starts from a stronger source it brings clouds. Or is it because it is weaker when it begins, so that it does not propel much air, but in the end it usually becomes strong? Hence **942ᵇ** comes the proverb,

When the South wind begins and when Boreas ceases his blowing.[3]

21   Why is it that in the winter the winds come forth from the east, but in the summer also from the west?[4] Is it because, when the sun no longer prevails, the air flows freely? 5 When, therefore, the sun sinks, it leaves clouds behind it, which cause the West winds, and anything which it carries with it to the inhabitants of the southern hemisphere becomes an East wind. And, contrariwise, when it sinks in the southern region of the earth, it will cause West winds for the inhabitants of that region and East winds in our part of the world from the air which accompanies it. For 10 this reason too, if it finds another wind blowing, that wind becomes stronger when the sun rises, because it adds something to it.

---

[1] Cp. Theophrastus, *op. cit.*, § 7.

[2] Cp. below, chapter 38, and Theophrastus, *op. cit.*, §§ 6, 7.

[3] The complete proverb is εὖ πλεῖν ἀρχομένου, &c.; cp. below, 945ᵃ 29.

[4] The source of this problem is Theophrastus, *op. cit.*, § 47. The subject is treated more fully in chapter 54 below.

Why are hounds least able to find the scent when a West **22** wind is blowing? Is it because it disperses the scent most owing to the fact that of all the winds it blows most 15 continuously and down on to the earth?

Why, when there are shooting stars, is it a sign of **23** wind?[1] Is it because they are carried along by the wind, and the wind occurs where they are, before it reaches us? For this reason also the wind rises in that quarter from which the stars are set in motion.

20 Why is it that of all the winds the West wind drives the **24** largest clouds?[2] Is it because it blows from the open sea and over the deep, so that it collects clouds from a large area?

Why are the winds strongest which are at their ending?[3] **25** Is it because when they expend themselves all at once, what remains is very little?[4]

25 Why is it that, if the South-West wind (Lips)[5] blows **26** about the time of the equinox, rain results? Is it because the sun sets the winds in motion from any part of the universe in which it is? Hence the succession of the winds corresponds to the course of the sun. Now since the equinox is the boundary between winter and summer, 30 when it happens that the sun, according to the equinox as it appears to us, has passed the exact boundary or falls short of it and is rather in the wintry region, the result is that the winds from that region blow, of which the first is the South-West wind (Lips), which is naturally moist. Now when the sun is rather in the wintry region of the universe 35 and stirs up the winds there, the result is that the functions of winter come into operation; one of which is wet weather. Again, since the equinox is as it were winter and summer

---

[1] Cp. Theophrastus, *op. cit.*, § 36.

[2] The source of this problem is Theophrastus, *op. cit.*, § 42.

[3] The source of this problem is Theophrastus, *op. cit.*, § 36.

[4] And therefore they come to an end. λοιπόν should be read for the meaningless θερμόν from Theophrastus, *l. c.*, ὅταν γὰρ ἀθρόοι ἐμπνεύσωσι, μικρὸν γίγνεται τὸ λοιπόν.

[5] Lips does not correspond exactly to our SW. wind, being 30° and not 45° south of the West wind. See note on 940^a 18.

equally balanced, if anything is added to either one of
them it causes a distinct inclination in one direction, just
as happens in the case of equally balanced scales. But,
since the South-West wind (Lips) is of the wintry order 943^{a}
and naturally moist, its addition at the equinox causes an
inclination towards winter and rainy weather; for rain is
the wintry weather most akin to the wind that has begun to
blow.

27 Why are the South wind and the South-East wind (Eu- 5
rus),[1] which are warmer than their respective contraries, the
North wind and the West wind, more rainy, although water
is engendered from the air by cold? For it is not true
that the clouds form because the North wind thrusts them
away from our part of the world; for the West and South-
East winds both alike—for they are similarly at the sides of
the world[2]—drive away clouds from the quarter from
which they blow, as also do all the other winds. Is it 10
because the more the heat exists outside, the more the cold
is driven within? Or is it due in some degree to the
quarter from which they blow that certain winds bring
clear weather? For the South-East wind rises from the
dawn (and the region is warm), while the West wind is
situated towards the evening.[3] But is there not a further
reason, namely, that air, like water,[4] cools most quickly and 15
thoroughly when it is previously heated? The air then
brought by the South-East wind arrives warm from the
rising sun, as does that brought by the South wind from
the midday sun; when, therefore, they reach the colder
region, they quickly condense and become massed into
rain. And the South-East wind has a greater tendency to

---

[1] Eurus does not correspond exactly with our SE. wind, being only
30° south of the East wind (see note on 940^{a} 18).

[2] πλάγιοι is contrasted with ἄνωθεν and κάτωθεν (north and south).
Cp. *Meteor.* 377^{b} 29.

[3] Reading ἀπ᾽ ἠοῦς ἐστίν· ἥδε δὲ ἡ χώρα ⟨θερμή⟩· πρὸς ⟨δὲ⟩ ἑσπέραν
κεῖται ζέφυρος. ἥδε ἡ χώρα can only refer to ἀπ᾽ ἠοῦς; it is therefore
impossible to take it with πρὸς ἑσπέραν, which must belong to ζέφυρος.
We must therefore suppose that something has fallen out after ἥδε δε
ἡ χώρα, apparently θερμή, cp. below, l. 17. Something may similarly
have fallen out between καὶ and ζέφυρος. The Latin version of T. G.
simply renders, *eurus namque ex ortu, favonius ex occasu adventat.*

[4] Cp. *Meteor.* 348^{b} 30 ff.

20 form rain, because it brings the air more directly from the sun and equally hot; but the South wind is rainy as it ceases to blow, because the first air that is brought comes cold from the sea, whereas the last air, which is very warm, is brought[1] from the land. Or is there not a further reason, namely, that the South wind is stronger as it ceases 25 to blow (hence the proverb applied to it, ' When the South wind begins . . . '[2]), and stronger winds are colder, and so the South wind masses the clouds together at the end of its duration?[3] Is not this why it is more rainy then than when it first begins to blow?

Why do the winds, though they are cold, cause dryness? **28** Is it because the colder winds cause evaporation? But why should they do so more than the sun? Is it because 30 they carry off the vapour, whereas the sun leaves it where it is and consequently causes more moisture and less dryness?

Why does the North-East wind (Caecias)[4] alone of all the **29** winds attract the clouds towards itself,[5] as the proverb has it, ' Drawing it to himself, as Caecias draws clouds'[6]? For the other winds simply drive forward the clouds from the quarter from which they blow. Is this phenomenon to 35 be attributed to the fact that the contrary wind blows at the same time? But would not this have been obvious, and is it not more likely that the North-East wind naturally follows a circular course? The other winds therefore **943^b** blow round the earth, but the North-East wind (Caecias)[7] has the concave side of its course towards the heavens and not towards the earth, and so, blowing towards its source, it attracts the clouds to itself.

Why is it that the wind blows cold in the early morn- **30** 5 ing from rivers but not from the sea?[8] Is it because the

---

[1] Reading κομίζεται for κομίζει.
[2] The complete hexameter is given at 945^a 29.
[3] Cp. chapters 20 and 38.
[4] See note on 940^a 18.   [5] Cp. above, chapter 1.
[6] Reading ὥστε for the sake of the metre instead of ὥσπερ, cp. *Meteor.* 364^b 13 (Nauck, *Frag. Trag. Adesp.* 50).
[7] Reading τούτῳ (W. D. R.) for τοῦτο.
[8] This problem also occurs in Book xxiii, chapter 16.

sea extends over open spaces, but rivers are in narrow
places? The breeze, therefore, from the sea is dispersed
over a wide area and is consequently weak; whereas the
breeze from a river is carried along in a mass and is
stronger and therefore naturally appears colder. Or is the
reason other than this, namely, that the rivers are cold, 10
but the sea is neither hot nor cold? Now a breeze or
exhalation is due to the heating or cooling of liquids;[1]
for whichever of these two processes they undergo,
evaporation takes place, and, when water evaporates, the
resultant air is set in motion, and this is a breeze. That
which is produced from cold liquids naturally blows cold, 15
while that which blows from very hot liquids cools and
becomes cold.[2] One would therefore find that all the rivers
are cold, but the sea is neither very hot nor very cold.
That which blows from it therefore is not cold, because the
sea is not itself very cold, nor does it cool quickly because 20
the sea is not very hot.

31 Why is the West wind always considered to bring fair
weather and to be the pleasantest of the winds?[3] So, for
instance, Homer says that in the Elysian Plains

> Ever the breezes blow of the Zephyr.[4]

Is it because in the first place it has an equable temperature? For it is neither hot like the winds from the south
and east, nor cold like that from the north, but is[5] on the 25
boundary between the cold and the hot winds; and, being
near to them both, it partakes of their qualities, and is
consequently temperate and breathes most of spring.
Furthermore, the winds change either into their contraries
or into those on their right;[6] blowing therefore after the
North wind (for the west is on the right of the north[7]), it 30
enjoys a good reputation, as being mild as compared with

---

[1] Reading ψυχομένων ⟨τῶν ὑγρῶν⟩, cp. 933^a 36.
[2] Cp. 943^a 15 and note.
[3] The same problem is dealt with in chapter 55 below.
[4] Hom. *Od.* iv. 567, where, however, the *textus receptus* reads
  ἀλλ' αἰεὶ Ζεφύροιο λιγὺ πνείοντας ἀήτας
  Ὠκεανὸς ἀνίησιν.
[5] Reading ἐστὶ for ἐπὶ, cp. 946^b 22.   [6] Cp. 941^b 10.
[7] This contradicts the doctrine of 941^b 12 as emended by Bonitz

an inclement wind. Also as soon as wintry weather ceases, fine weather usually follows; and the North wind is a wintry wind. [The East wind,[1] though it lies between the warm and the cold winds, partakes less of them; for, when 35 it blows, it sets in motion the winds towards the south (for when it changes it does so in that direction), but though it sets them in motion it does not mingle with them. The West wind is set in motion by the South winds, and when it 944ᵃ blows it sets the North winds in motion; for there the succession of the winds ceases. Hence the West wind, constituting as it does the end of some winds and the starting-point of others, justly is and is considered to be a pleasant wind.]

Why does the South wind blow at the time of the Dog- **32** 5 star?[2] Is it because a sign occurs[3] at the setting or rising of any star, and especially of the Dog-star? It is clear then that the wind blows most at the time of and after its rising. And since it causes stifling heat, it is only natural that the hottest winds should be set in motion when it rises; and the South wind is hot. And since, &c. (as 941ᵇ 6–23).

10 Why does the West wind blow towards evening and not **33** in the early morning?[4] Is the sun at its rising and setting usually the cause of breezes? For when it concocts and dissolves the air, which is moist, by thoroughly heating it, it dissolves it into breath; and if the air is full of breath, it becomes still more evaporated by the sun. When, there- 15 fore, the sun is in the east, it is far away from the West wind, for the latter blows from the setting sun; but when the sun is already near its setting, the breath is then thoroughly dissolved, and from midday onwards and towards evening the sun is most suitably situated for heating and dissolving the air. It is for this reason also 20 that the East wind begins to blow in the early morning; for since the air above the earth becomes charged with

---

[1] The remainder of the chapter does not occur in the best MSS. It certainly contradicts the doctrine just stated that winds change into those on their right, and in general it does not give satisfactory sense. The passage occurs again in chapter 55, where it is more relevant.
[2] Cp. above, chapter 12 and note.   [3] See note on 941ᵇ 2.
[4] The same problem is treated in the first part of chapter 35 below.

moisture during the night and owing to its weight approaches the earth, the sun from dawn onwards dissolves it and sets in motion first the air which is nearest to itself. Now the East wind get its name Apeliotes because it is the wind which blows from the rising sun.[1]

34 Why is it that when the sun rises the winds both rise 25 and fall? Is it because a wind is the movement either of the air or of moisture carried up? Now this movement, when it is only slight, is quickly absorbed by the sun, so that no wind occurs; but when it is greater, the movement is increased when the sun rises, for the sun is a source of movement.   30

35 Why does the West wind blow in the evening?[2] Is it because all the winds blow when the sun disperses the moisture? For the moisture being already in a mass, the power of heat, when it approaches it, concocts it.[3] Now the West wind blows from the setting sun; it is only natural then that it should rise in the evening, for then the sun 35 reaches the quarter proper to that wind.

The North and the South winds are the most frequent of winds,[4] because, when one contrary is overcome by its direct contrary, it is least able to continue,[5] whereas it is better able to resist a wind blowing against it from an angle.[6] Now the South and the North winds blow from **944ᵇ** regions on either side of the sun's course, while the other winds blow rather in a straight line with it.

36 Does the wind come from a source, as water does, and is it unable to rise to a higher level than that source, or is this 5

---

[1] i. e. the name Apeliotes is derived from ἀπὸ ἡλίου.

[2] Cp. above, chapter 33.

[3] Reading ἐκπέττει (cp. above, 11, 12, 13) for the meaningless ἐξάπτει.

[4] The latter part of the chapter deals with quite a different subject from the former portion. It is, indeed, quite possible that the Latin version of T. G., which renders, *Cur aquilo et auster saepissime spirant? An quia*, &c., translates a better reading, and that a new problem should begin here: 'Why are the North and the South winds the most frequent of all the winds? Is it because, &c.'

[5] And passes into its contrary, e. g. the North wind becomes the South wind and *vice versa* (cp. above, 941ᵇ 10 ff.).

[6] Cp. Theophrastus, *op. cit.*, § 2.

not so? And does it come from a single point or from
a wider area? There are indeed in the wind certain
similarities to that which seems to occur in water; for
water flows faster when it travels downhill, whereas it
stagnates on flat and level[1] ground, and the winds act
10 similarly, for on promontories and high ground the air is
always in motion, whereas in hollows it is often at rest and
there is a calm. Moreover on exceedingly high mountains
there is no wind at all—on Mount Athos, for example,
amongst others, as is proved by the fact that offerings
which persons sacrificing leave there one year are, so it is
15 said, found there still in the following year. It is clear then
that the course of the wind starts as it were from a source of
some kind.[2] It cannot, therefore, rise any higher. Hence
the above phenomenon occurs on high mountains, to which
what happens to water would be a close parallel; for
apparently neither a strong flow of water nor a violent
20 wind is found in high mountains.

Why is it that when the South wind blows the sea 37
becomes blue, but when the North wind blows it becomes
dark?[3] Is it because the North wind disturbs the sea less,
and that which is less disturbed appears to be all black?

25 Why do the South winds when they blow gently cause 38
no overclouding, but when they become strong overcloud
the sky?[4] Is it because, when they blow gently, they
cannot thrust many clouds along?[5] They therefore cover
only a small area with cloud; but, when they blow strongly,
they thrust along many clouds, and therefore seem to cause
more overclouding.

30 Why is the North wind strong when it begins to blow, 39
but weak as it ceases, whereas the South wind is weak when
it begins, but strong as it ceases?[6] Is it because the North
wind is near to us and the South wind distant? The former
then, when it begins, blows immediately in one part of the

---

[1] Reading ὁμαλῷ with X[a], A[P].   [2] Cp. *Meteor.* 360[a] 27.
[3] This problem is translated word for word by Aulus Gellius, ii. 30,
as from Aristotle's *Books of Problems.*   [4] Cp. above, chapter 20.
[5] Reading ἀπωθεῖν (W. D. R.) for ποιεῖν; cp. l. 29.
[6] Cp. below, chapters 41 and 45, and Theophrastus, *op. cit.*, § 5.

world, whereas the beginning of the latter becomes dispersed
owing to the long time it takes to travel, and little of its 35
first breath reaches us; and we feel the end of the North
wind, but that of the South wind not at all.　It is, therefore,
only natural that the North wind should be weak as it ceases
(for the end of all things is weak), while the South wind is
not weak at its close, since we do not feel its ending at all.

40　Why do alternating winds blow where there are bays, **945^a**
but not where there is a wide expanse of open sea?　Is it
because the wind, when it pours into the bays, is less broken
up and travels practically in a collected mass, whereas over
open expanses of sea the land-winds tend to be broken up 5
as they begin to flow, and when they move the same thing
happens to them, because they are free to travel in many
directions?　For an alternating wind is the reflux of a
land-wind.[1]

41　What is the origin of the saying,

> When the South wind begins and when Boreas ceases
>> his blowing?[2]

Is it because the North wind, owing to the fact that we live
near it and our habitation is towards the pole, immediately 10
blows strongly, for it is with us as soon as it begins?　Hence,
as it ceases, it blows pleasantly; for it then blows weakly.
The South wind, on the other hand, because it is far away,
reaches us later in greater strength.

42　Why is it that men feel heavier and weaker when the
wind is in the south?[3]　Is it because moisture becomes
abundant instead of scanty, being melted by the heat, and 15
moisture, which is heavy, takes the place of breath, which
is light, and under these conditions men's strength becomes
languid?

43　Why are men hungrier when the wind is in the north
than when it is in the south?　Is it because the North
winds are colder?

---

[1] Reading ἀπογέας (W. D. R.).
[2] Cp. chapters 39 and 45. The complete proverb is εὖ πλεῖν ἀρχομένου,
&c. (cp. l. 29).
[3] A longer version of this problem occurs in Book i. 24.

Why does the South wind not blow in Egypt itself in **44**
₂₀ the regions towards the sea nor for the distance of a day
and a night's journey inland,[1] while in the regions beyond
Memphis and for the distance of a day and a night's journey
it blows freshly; and does not blow to the west for the
distance of two days' and two nights' journey, while to the
east the South-West wind (Lips)[2] blows? Is it because
Egypt in its lower regions is hollow, so the South wind
₂₅ passes over above it, but to the south and farther away the
regions are loftier?

Why is it that the South wind is weak when it begins **45**
to blow, but becomes stronger as it ceases, while with the
North wind the contrary is the case, hence the proverb,

> Sail when the South wind begins and when Boreas
> ceases his blowing?[3]

₃₀ Is it because we dwell rather towards the pole than towards
the midday sun, and the North wind blows from the pole,
while the South wind blows from the midday sun? It is
only natural, therefore, that the North wind, when it
begins, immediately attacks with violence the regions
nearer to it, and afterwards transfers its violence to the
dwellers farther south. The South wind, on the contrary,
₃₅ when it begins, presses upon those who dwell towards the
midday sun, and, when it has passed them by, blows freshly
upon those who dwell towards the pole.

What is the origin of the saying,   **46**

> Straightway the winter comes, if the South wind call
> to the North wind?[4]

Is it because it is the nature of the South wind to collect[5]
clouds and much rain? When therefore the North wind
945ᵇ blows under these conditions, since there is abundant

---

[1] The source of this problem is Theophrastus, *op. cit.*, § 8.

[2] Lips is strictly speaking slightly to the north of the SW. wind,
being only 30° south of the West wind, see note on 940ᵃ 18.

[3] Cf. above, chapters 39 and 41. There should be a question mark
after βορέαο in place of a comma.

[4] Cp. Theophrastus, *op. cit.*, § 46.

[5] Reading συναιρεῖν; T. G. renders *colligat*.

material, the North wind freezes it and brings on the winter.   Hence the saying,

> When Boreas findeth the mire, soon cometh the season
> of winter.

Now mud and rain in general are usually, if not invariably, due to the South wind.

47   Why does the North wind follow quickly upon the South wind, but not the South wind upon the North wind?[1]   Is it because the North wind arrives from near at hand, but the South wind from a distance, since our habitation is towards the pole?

48   Why is it that the winds are cold, although they are due to movement caused by heat?[2]   Is movement caused by heat not invariably hot, but only when it occurs in a certain manner?   If it comes forth[3] in a mass, it burns with its heat the very thing which emits it; but if it passes out gradually through a narrow space, it is itself hot, but the air which is set in motion by this process completes the movement in accordance with whatever was its original nature.[4]   This can be seen in the mouth;[5] for there is a saying that from the same organ we breathe both hot and cold,[6] but this is untrue, since all that proceeds from the mouth is hot, as is shown by the fact that it appears hot if the hand is placed close to the mouth.   It is the manner in which it comes forth which makes the difference.   For if in yawning we emit breath from a wide opening, it appears hot because we can feel it; but if it be emitted through a narrow opening, being more violent, it impels the air in its immediate neighbourhood, which in its turn impels the adjoining air.   If the air is cold, its movement is also cold.   May not the same thing happen also in the winds, and their first movement be through a narrow channel and then set in

---

[1] The source of this problem is Theophrastus, *op. cit.*, § 9.
[2] The source of this problem is Theophrastus, *op. cit.*, §§ 19-20.
[3] Reading, with Theophrastus, ἐκπίπτῃ for ἐμπίπτῃ.
[4] i. e. temperature.
[5] Reading στόματος for σώματος (cp. Theoph. § 20).
[6] Cp. Aesop, *Fab.* 64 (ed. Halm).

motion[1] the adjoining air, and then other air begin to rush
onwards?   So in the summer the winds are hot, in winter
25 they are cold, because in each case this is the temperature
of the air which is already there; for that the air does not
follow this course because it is either set in motion by itself
or overpowered by the heat, is clear not only from the fact
that it heats the winds when there is more heat in it, but
also because it was originally being carried upwards.   For
30 fire is of this nature; whereas cold naturally travels downwards.   The winds move horizontally and for good reason;
for since the heat presses upwards and the cold downwards
and neither prevails, and the air cannot remain still, it is
only natural[2] that its motion should be sideways.

35   Why are the South winds cold in Libya as the North winds 49
are with us?[3]   Is it primarily because the sources of these
winds are respectively nearer to us and to them?   For if,
as we have already said,[4] the winds pass through a narrow
channel, they will be colder to those who are nearer to
them owing to the violence of their movement; for when
946^a their movement proceeds farther, they become dispersed.
Hence the North winds are cold in our part of the world,
because we are nearer to them and dwell quite near the
pole.

Why is it that those South winds which are dry and do 50
5 not bring rain cause fever?[5]   Is it because they engender
unnatural moist heat in the body?   For they are by nature
moist and hot, and this causes fever, which is due to a
combined excess of these two things.   When, therefore, the
South winds blow under the influence of the sun without
bringing rain, they engender this condition in us;[6] whereas,
when they bring rain with them, the rain cools us.

---

[1] For this meaning of διαφέρω cp. Soph. *Trach.* 323.
[2] Reading εἰκὸς for εἰκότως, cp. 941^a 16 and note.
[3] Cp. 942^a 7.   [4] In ll. 22 ff. above.
[5] This chapter (the source of which is Theophrastus, *op. cit.*, § 7) is
partly identical with i. 23.
[6] Reading ταύτην τὴν διάθεσιν ποιοῦσι (from 862^a 21) for the corrupt
ταύτην τὴν τάξιν.

51 Why do the periodical winds always blow at the season [10]
at which they do blow[1] and with the force with which they
blow?[2] And why do they cease at close of day and not
blow during the night? Is this due to the fact that the
melting of snow by the sun ceases towards evening and at
night? Now these winds blow in general when the sun
begins to prevail and melt the northern ice. When the ice [15]
begins to melt, the 'forerunners' blow; when it is already
melting, the periodic winds blow.

52 Why is the West wind at once the gentlest of winds and
also cold, and why does it blow mainly at two seasons,
namely, spring and autumn, and towards evening, and
usually in the direction of the land?[3] Is it cold because it [20]
blows from the sea and from extended areas? It is less
cold indeed than the North wind, because it blows from
evaporated water and not from snow; but it *is* cold, because
it blows either after the winter, when the sun is only just
beginning to prevail, or in the autumn, when the sun no
longer has power. For it does not have to wait for its
proper matter,[4] as it would if it were a land-wind, but [25]
wanders freely, because it has travelled over water.[5] For
the same reason it blows evenly; for it does not blow from
mountains or from forcibly melted matter, but flowing
gently as through a channel. For the regions towards the
north and south are mountainous; but towards the west
there is neither mountain nor land but the Atlantic Sea,
so that it travels in the direction of the land. Further, it [30]
blows towards evening owing to the quarter from which
it comes; for the sun then approaches that quarter. It
ceases at night because the movement set up by the sun
dies down.

---

[1] The form ταὐτήν, which Ruelle reads, does not exist; the MSS.
read ταύτην.

[2] The source of this problem is Theophrastus, *op. cit.*, § 11.

[3] The source of this problem is Theophrastus, *op. cit.*, §§ 38, 40, 41.

[4] Reading ὕλην, cp. 947ᵃ 2, 3. The lacuna in Theophrastus, *op. cit.*,
§ 40 *ad fin.* (ed. Wimmer), can be filled from this passage, viz. οὐ γὰρ
ὥσπερ ἐν γῇ ⟨ὑπομένει τὴν ὕλην⟩ ἀλλὰ κτλ.

[5] i. e. where there is evaporation everywhere going on, and therefore
matter for wind.

Why do all things appear larger when the South-East **53** wind (Eurus)[1] blows?[2] Is it because it makes the air gloomier?[3]

35 Why is it that during the winter the winds blow early **54** and from the east, but in summer in the evening and from the setting sun?[4] Is it because what happens in our part of the world during the summer occurs during the winter among those who inhabit the opposite hemisphere of the earth, and with us in the winter the winds blow early and from the east, because the air, which during the night is **946ᵇ** full of moisture,[5] is dissolved and set in motion by the sun in the early morning, the air nearest the sun being the first to be affected? The sun begins to produce this effect even before it rises; therefore the breezes blow just as much before sunrise. Since then the sun attracts the moisture to **5** itself and in the winter before its rising sets in motion in our part of the earth the air which is moist, it is clear that it would also attract the moisture when it is in the southern hemisphere, and it would be evening there when it is early morning with us. The result would be that the air, which the sun attracts to itself before its rising in our part of the world, would become a West wind to the dwellers in the **10** south and would blow in the evening. Now what happens during our winter at dawn happens to them in the evening, and what happens in the summer to them at dawn happens to us in the evening;[6] for when it is summer here, it is winter there, and our evening is their early morning, at which time they have breezes from the east,[7] while we have **15** West winds for the same reasons as are mentioned above. In the summer breezes do not blow from the east, because the sun, when it rises, finds the air in our part of the earth still too dry, owing to the short period of its absence; and

[1] See note on 943ª 5.   [2] Reading πνέη for πνεῖ.
[3] Reading ζοφωδέστερον (Platt).   [4] Cp. above, chapter 21.
[5] Reading κάθυγρον ⟨ὄντα⟩ (Richards).
[6] The sentence as it stands in the text is clearly incomplete, and something like the following must be read: ὁ δὲ ἐν τῷ παρ' ἡμῶν χειμῶνι τῆς ἕω, ἐκείνοις ⟨τῆς δείλης⟩ συμβαίνει· ὁ δὲ ἐν τῷ θέρει ⟨τῆς ἕω ἐκείνοις⟩, τῆς δείλης ἡμῖν.
[7] Reading ἕω for ἑώας.

West winds do not blow in the evening during the
winter, because East winds do not blow in the southern
hemisphere either at that time for the aforesaid reasons, in
virtue of which the sun attracts the moisture to itself and [20]
produces [1] the West wind in our part of the earth.

55   Why is the West wind always considered to bring fair
weather and to be the pleasantest of the winds? [2] Is it
because it is on the boundary between the hot and the cold
winds, and being near to them both it partakes of their
qualities, and is therefore temperate? The East wind,
though it also lies between the hot and the cold winds, [25]
partakes less of them; for when it blows it sets in motion
the winds towards the south (for, when it changes, it does
so in that direction), but, though it sets them in motion, it
does not mingle with them. The West wind is set in motion
by the South winds and, when it blows, it sets the North
winds in motion; for there the succession of the winds
ceases. Hence the West wind, constituting as it does the [30]
end of some winds and the starting-point of others, justly is
and is considered to be a pleasant wind.

56   Why are different winds rainy in different places; [3] for
example, Hellespontias [4] (the East wind) in Attica and the
islands, the North wind on the Hellespont and in Cyrene,
and the South wind round Lesbos? Is it because rain
occurs wherever there is a collection of clouds, since density [35]
collects wherever it can settle? It is for this reason that
there is more rain among the mountains than where the
mass of clouds can find a free passage, for that which is
confined becomes dense as a necessary consequence; also
it rains more in calm weather. In the Hellespont the North
wind, blowing from its upper end, masses together many **947[a]**
clouds, which Hellespontias (the East wind) drives towards
Attica and the islands, being thus provided with ample
material; for most clouds come round from the north.

---

[1] ποιῇ should perhaps be read here for ποιεῖ, 'for the sun to attract
the moisture to itself and cause', &c.

[2] This chapter is a shorter version of chapter 31 above.

[3] A longer version of chapter 7.

[4] Another name for Apeliotes, cp. *Vent. Sit.* 973[a] 22.

Round Lesbos the South-East (Eurus)[1] and South winds
5 bring much cloud from the open sea and drive[2] it against
the land. Similar instances might be quoted for the other
winds.

What is the origin of the saying,   57

> Have no fear of a cloud from the land in the season of
> winter,
> But if it come from over the deep have a care; and in
> summer
> Ever distrust the cloud that sweeps from the gloom of
> the mainland?[3]

Is it because in the winter the sea is warmer, so that, if any
10 cloud has formed, it must have done so from some powerful
cause, otherwise it would have been dissolved, because the
region in which it forms is warm? Now in the summer
the sea is cold, as also are the sea breezes, but the land is
hot, so that if any cloud comes from the land, it must have
been formed from some considerable cause; for it would
have been dissolved if it had been weak.

15   Why is it that in Arcadia, which is high, the winds are 58
no colder than elsewhere, but when there is no wind and it
is cloudy, it is cold, just as it is in flat, marshy districts?
Is it because Arcadia resembles a marshy district, since it
has no outlet for its waters to the sea, for which reason also
20 there are many chasms there? When, therefore, there is
a wind, it winnows away the exhalations from the earth,
which are cold, but the winds themselves are not cold,
because they arrive from the sea; but when there is no
wind the vapour which rises from the stagnant water
causes the cold.

25   Why is it that the wind lasts a long time when it begins 59
to blow at dawn? Is it because, when the sun rises, the
impetus given to the wind is very violent and can therefore
maintain its character? That this is so is shown by the
fact that it forms a strong mass.

---

[1] See note on 946^a 33.   [2] Reading with Sylburg προσβάλλουσι.
[3] The source of this problem is Theophrastus, *op. cit.*, § 60, where
ὡς ἀπὸ πόντου should be emended ἀλλ' ἀπὸ πόντου. Cp. 938^b 10.

60   Why is it that the North wind is keen during the day but falls at night? Is it because it is generated from frozen rain when this is evaporated by the sun? It falls at night, 30 because the process does not go on as before, but is reversed; for at night the North wind expends itself,[1] but it is less apt to do so during the day.

61   Why is it that when many spiders' webs[2] are borne through the air, they are a sign of wind? Is it because the spider works in fine weather, but the webs are set in 35 motion because the air, as it cools, collects on the ground, and this cooling process is the beginning of winter, so that the movement of the webs is a sign? Or is it because after rain and storms the spiders[3] are borne through the air in large numbers, since they work in fine weather (for they do not appear at all in the winter, the spider being an animal[4] which cannot support the cold), and as they are **947^b** borne along by the wind they unwind a quantity of web? Now after rain winds usually blow.

62   Why is it that the strong North winds[5] in winter cause clouds in the cold regions, but outside them bring a clear 5 sky?[6] Is it because they are at the same time cold and strong, and in the regions near the north they are colder and so congeal the clouds before they can drive them along, and the clouds, when they are congealed, remain where they are owing to their weight? Elsewhere, however, it is their strength rather than their coldness which takes effect.

---

[1] For this meaning of ἐκπνέω cp. 942^b 24, and the similar use of ἔκχυσις 941^b 36.

[2] i.e. gossamers.

[3] Reading ἀραχνῶν for ἀραχνίων. Though ἀράχνιον is frequently used in the sense of a 'small spider', in this passage it seems always to mean 'spider's web', and ἀραχνῶν must be read to agree with ἐργαζομένων and to provide a masculine plural to which φερόμενοι may refer.

[4] Reading τὸ θηρίον for τόδε (Bonitz).

[5] Reading οἱ βορέαι ⟨οἱ⟩ μεγάλοι.

[6] The source of this problem is Theophrastus, *op. cit.*, §§ 6, 7.

10 ## BOOK XXVII

PROBLEMS CONNECTED WITH FEAR
AND COURAGE

WHY do those who are afraid tremble?[1] Is it due to the **1**
process of chilling? For the heat fails and contracts; that
is also why the bowels usually are loosened.[2]

15 Why do men become thirsty under certain conditions, **2**
those, for example, who are about to be punished?[3] For
this ought not to be so, since they are chilled. Is it because
the chilling and heating do not occur in the same region,
but the former takes place on the surface of the body, from
which the heat departs, but the heating takes place in the
interior, so that it warms it, as is proved by the fact that
the bowels become loosened? For thirst occurs when
20 the sovereign region[4] of the body becomes dry. The same
thing seems to happen as occurs in those suffering from
ague,[5] who are thirsty and cold at the same time; for in
their case too the same part of the body is not hot and cold.

Why is it that under the influence of anger men become **3**
heated and bold (the heat collecting in the interior of the
body), whereas in a state of fear they are in a contrary
25 condition? Is it because they are not affected in the same
region, but in those who are angry the heat collects in the
region of the heart—hence they become courageous and
red in the face and full of breath—the course of the heat
being upwards, whereas in those who are afraid the blood
and heat both retreat in a downward direction—hence the
bowels become loosened. For the beating of the heart is

---

[1] This problem is dealt with more fully in chapters 6 and 7.
[2] See below, chapter 10.   [3] Cp. below, chapter 8.
[4] The region in which the most important organs are situated; cp.
κύρια μόρια, *Gen. An.* 744^b 31.
[5] The exact nature of this disease is doubtful; see W. H. S. Jones,
Malaria, a Neglected Factor in the History of Greece and Rome,
pp. 25, 36, 37.

different, since in those who are frightened it is frequent and 30
strongly punctuated, as would naturally occur from the
failure of heat, while in those who are angry it has the
character which one would expect when a greater quantity
of heat collects.   Hence the expressions about anger 'boiling up' and 'rising' and 'being stirred up' and the like
are apt and fitting.   Is the thirst also due to this cause,
since dry-spitting and the parching of the tongue and the 35
like are due to the simultaneous upward rush of breath
and heat?   Thirst, moreover, is clearly due to the body
becoming heated.   How then can the same region, namely,
that in which we feel thirst, become dried up both in one
who is afraid and in one who is angry?   That fear tends
to produce thirst is clearly shown in the case of routed **948ª**
soldiers; for under no other condition is such thirst experienced.   The same is true of those suffering from great
anxiety; therefore they wash out their mouths and swallow
liquid, as did Parmenon the actor.   Or is it in such cases
not thirst but dryness due to the flight of blood (whence
also they become pale)?   This is indicated by the fact that 5
they do not drink much but simply take a gulp; routed
soldiers on the other hand are undergoing violent exertion.[1]   So those who are about to be punished feel thirst,
and in this there is nothing strange.   In war some brave
men even, when they are drawn up in battle array, actually
tremble when they are not distraught but confident; and
they often beat their bodies with a flat cane or, failing 10
that, with the hand, in order that they may be warmed.[2]
It seems probable that owing to the violence and impetus
of the heat a disturbing inequality of the temperature is set
up in the body.

4   Why are brave men generally fond of wine?   Is it
because the brave are full of heat, and the heat is in the
region of the chest?   (For it is there also that fear shows 15
itself, acting as a process of cooling; with the result that[3]

---

[1] Which gives a reason for their excessive thirst in addition to the
effect of fear.

[2] Reading with Richards χερσὶν ⟨ἵν'⟩ ἀναθερμανθῇ.

[3] Omitting τοῖς μὲν, inserted by Ruelle without MS. authority.

less[1] heat remains in the region of the heart, and in some men the heart beats violently as it is cooled.) Those then who have an abundance of blood in their lungs have hot lungs, as though they were drunk, and so the presentiment of danger does not chill them. Such men are fond of drinking; for the desire for drink is due to the heat of this
20 region, as has been stated elsewhere,[2] and the desire is for that which has power to stop the heat. Now wine is naturally hot and satisfies the thirst better than water, particularly in those whom we are now considering;[3] the reason for this has been stated elsewhere.[4] Hence those who are suffering from inflammation of the lungs and those
25 who are mad both desire wine, though the lungs of the former are hot owing to the fever, and those of the latter owing to their state of disturbance. Since, then, the same people are usually of a thirsty and of a brave kind, and those who are thirsty desire wine and are therefore fond of drinking, it necessarily follows that the two characteristics of bravery and fondness for wine usually go together.
30 Hence those who are drunk are braver than those who are not.

Why do states honour courage more than anything else, **5** though it is not the highest of the virtues? Is it because they are continually either making war or having war made against them, and courage is most useful in both these circumstances? They, therefore, honour not that which is ideally best, but that which is best for themselves.

35 Why do those who are afraid tremble most in the voice, **6** the hands, and the lower lip?[5] Is it because this affection is due to the departure of heat from the upper parts of the body? If so, their pallor is due to the same cause. The voice, then, trembles owing to the departure of heat from the chest, the region in which the voice is set in motion

---

[1] Reading ἥττων (Bussemaker) and omitting μὲν, which is due to dittography.

[2] Cp. 872ᵃ 4 ff.

[3] Reading τῶν τοιούτων (sc. τῶν ἀνδρείων) for τῶν αὐτῶν which gives no sense: T. G. renders *maximeque id genus hominum*.

[4] The reference cannot be identified.

[5] Cp. chapters 1 and 7, and xi. 31.

thus becoming cooled. So too with the hands; for they are attached to the chest. The lower lip trembles, and not **948ᵇ** the upper, because the upper lip hangs downwards[1] in the direction of its natural tendency; but the upward direction of the lower lip is contrary to nature and it is held steady in that position by the heat. When, therefore, the heat is withdrawn as the process of cooling takes place, it trembles. For the same reason the lip hangs down when a man is angry, as can be seen clearly in children; for the heat 5 rushes together into the heart.

7 Why do those who are afraid tremble, especially in the voice, the hands, and the lower lip?[2] Is it because the heat fails in the region of the body in which the voice is situated, while the trembling of the lip and hands is due to the fact that they are very easily set in motion and contain very little blood? Those who are afraid also emit bile and their 10 sexual organs contract, the emission of bile being due to the heat which descends and causes liquefaction, while the contraction of the sexual organs is due to the fact that fear comes from outside, and therefore the rush of heat is in the contrary direction.[3]

8 Why do those who are afraid feel both thirst and cold, these being contrary affections?[4] Do they feel cold because they are chilled, and thirst because they are heated, since 15 under the influence of fear the heat and the moisture leave the upper parts of the body? That this happens is shown by the change of colour and by the effect on the bowels; for the face becomes pale and the bowels are sometimes loosened. The cold, therefore, is caused by the departure of the heat, and the thirst by the departure of the moisture,[5] from the upper parts of the body.

9 Why is it that, although both fear and pain are a kind of 20 grief, those who are in pain cry out, but those who are

---

[1] Reading τὸ δὲ κάτω χεῖλος ἀλλ᾽ οὐ τὸ ἄνωθεν ⟨τρέμει, διότι τὸ ἄνωθεν⟩ κάτω κρέμαται κτλ.

[2] Another version of the problem of chapter 6.

[3] Cp. 949ᵃ 15 ἅτε τοῦ θερμοῦ ἐκκεκριμένου.

[4] This question has already been touched upon in chapter 3.

[5] Reading διὰ τὸ ⟨τὸ⟩ ὑγρὸν (sc. ἐκλείπειν) with Bonitz and Richards.

afraid keep silence? Is it because those who are in pain
hold their breath (and so it is emitted all at once and comes
forth with a loud cry), whereas the body of those who are
afraid is chilled and the heat is carried downwards and
25 creates breath? It creates breath in the particular region
to which it is carried; hence those who are frightened
break wind. Now the voice is a rush of breath upwards
in a particular manner and through certain channels; and
the reason why those who are in pain hold the breath is
that when we suffer anything (just as the other animals use
their horns or teeth or claws in self-defence) we invariably
30 make use straightway and without thought of the resources
which we have in ourselves by nature, and against all or
most forms of pain heat is helpful. This is what occurs
when a man holds his breath; for he applies heat and concoction to the pain by collecting heat within him by means
of the breath.

35　　Why is it that in those who are afraid the bowels are 10
loosened and they desire to pass urine?[1] Is it because the
heat in us is as it were alive? It therefore flees whenever it
is afraid of anything. Since, then, the fears due to nervousness and the like come from without and pass from the upper
to the lower parts of the body and from the surface to the
949^a interior, the regions round the bowels and bladder becoming heated are loosened[2] and make these organs ready to
function. For anise and wormwood and all substances
which promote the flow of urine have heating properties.
Similarly the drugs which affect the bowels are those

---

[1] This problem is quoted as Aristotelian by Aulus Gellius (xix. 4):
*Aristotelis libri sunt qui problemata physica inscribuntur, lepidissimi
et elegantiarum omne genus referti. In his quaerit quam ob causam
eveniat, ut quibus invasit repentinus rei magnae timor plerumque alvo
statim cita fiant . . . ac de alvo quidem inter timendum prona atque
praecipiti causam esse dicit quod timor omnibus sit algificus, quem ille
appellat* ψυχροποιητικόν, *quae vis frigoris sanguinem caldoremque
omnem de summa corporis cute cogat penitus et depellat, faciatque simul
uti qui timent, sanguine ex ore decedente, pallescant. Is autem, inquit,
sanguis et caldor in ultima coactus movet plerumque alvum et incitat.*
While Aulus Gellius gives in the main the substance of this problem,
it is noticeable that the word ψυχροποιητικόν does not occur in the text
as we have it, nor indeed elsewhere in the Aristotelian Corpus.

[2] Reading δή for δέ, as suggested by Richards.

which cause heat in the lower parts of the body,[1] and some
of those which are applied merely [2] have a loosening effect,
while others set up a further process of liquefaction, like 5
garlic, which passes into the urine.[3] Now heat coming
from the surfaces of the body and meeting in these regions
has the same effect as such drugs.

11   Why do the sexual organs contract in those who are
afraid? For one would expect the contrary to happen,
namely, that they should become relaxed, since the heat 10
collects in this region in those who are afraid. Is it because
those who are afraid are almost always as it were chilled?
Their sexual organs therefore contract, because the heat
has left the surface of the body; hence also those who are
greatly frightened have internal rumblings. The surface
of the body and the skin of those who are cold seems to
contract, because the heat is driven out; and it is for this 15
reason too that they shiver. Now the scrotum too contracts
upwards and the testicles also are lifted up with it as it
is drawn in.[4] This is more readily seen in the effect on
the sexual organs; for fear causes excretion, and an emission of semen often occurs [5] in those who are nervous or 20
greatly alarmed.

---

[1] Reading τῶν κάτω.   [2] Reading μόνον with Xᵃ, Yᵃ, Aᵖ.
[3] Cp. above, 908ᵃ 28 ff.
[4] Reading αὐτῇ συστελλομένῃ for αὐτοῖς συστελλομένων (cp. the Latin
version of T. G. atque eo (sc. scroto) contracto una testiculi contra-
huntur). There is nothing for αὐτοῖς to refer to, and the view of
Bonitz (Index, sub voce συστέλλω) that συστελλόμενοι is equivalent to
φοβούμενοι can hardly be right. συνεσταλμένοι might conceivably mean
'downcast' (cp. Eurip. H. F. 1417 συνέσταλμαι κακοῖς), but this is
scarcely the sense required here, and the present participle could not
possibly bear this meaning.
[5] Reading συμβαίνει (Platt) for συγκινεῖ ἡ.

BOOK XXVIII

PROBLEMS CONNECTED WITH TEMPERANCE AND INTEMPERANCE, CONTINENCE AND INCONTINENCE

WHY is it that some men become ill when, after having 1 been accustomed to live intemperately, they adopt a tem- 25 perate mode of life? For example, Dionysius the tyrant, when during the siege[1] he ceased drinking for a short time, immediately became consumptive, until he changed his manner of life and began to drink again. Is it because in every one habit is a matter of importance, since it soon becomes a second nature? Just, then,[2] as a fish would fare ill if it continued long in the air or a man if he con- 30 tinued long in the water, so those who alter their manner of life suffer from the change, and a resumption of their accustomed mode of life is just as much their salvation as if they were returning to a natural condition. Furthermore, men waste away if they have been accustomed to large quan- tities of a particular diet; for if they do not receive their usual food, they are reduced to the condition in which they 35 would be if they had no nourishment at all. Moreover, the excretions, when mixed with a large quantity of food, disappear, but by themselves they rise to the surface and are carried to the eyes or lungs; whereas, if one takes nourish- ment, they mix with it and become diluted and harmless. 949^b But in those who live an intemperate life the excretions become superabundant up to a certain point, when they cease from their accustomed mode of life, owing to the fact that much undigested matter is still present in them from their former manner of living; and, when this is melted, like a mass of snow, by the natural heat, the result is that 5 violent fluxes take place.

---

[1] i. e. the siege of Syracuse by the Carthaginians in 397 B.C.
[2] Reading οὖν for ἂν (Richards).

2 Why is it that we speak of men as incontinent in connexion with two only of the senses, namely, touch and
taste?[1] Is it because of the pleasures that result from these
in us and in the other animals? Being then shared by the
animals, they are held in least honour and so are regarded
as the only pleasures deserving of reproach, or at any rate
more so than any others. So we blame a man who is a
slave to them and call him incontinent and intemperate, 10
because he is a slave to the worst pleasures.

3 Why are men called incontinent in respect only of their
desires, although incontinence is possible also in anger?
Is it because an incontinent man is one who acts in some
way contrary to reason, and incontinence is a mode of life 15
which is contrary to reason, and the desires are, generally
speaking, contrary to reason? Feelings of anger, on the
other hand, are in consonance with reason, not in the sense
that reason prompts them, but in the sense that reason
informs us of the insult or of the charge made against us.

4 Why is it that we approve most of continence and 20
temperance in the young and wealthy, and of justice in the
poor? Is it because we feel most admiration if a man
abstains from what he most desires, rather than from the
contrary? Now a poor man desires easy circumstances,
while a rich young man wants enjoyment.   25

5 Why can men tolerate thirst less easily than hunger?[2]
Is it because thirst is more painful? A proof that it is
so is the fact that there is more pleasure in drinking when
one is thirsty than in eating when one is hungry. Now
the contrary of what is more pleasant[3] is more painful. Or
is it because the heat whereby we live[4] requires moisture
more?[5] Or is it because thirst is a desire of two things, 30
namely, drink and food, but hunger is a desire of only one,
namely, food?

[1] Cp. below, chapter 7. The doctrine is that of *E. N.* 1148ᵃ 8–10.
[2] Cp. chapter 6.
[3] Reading τῷ ἡδίονι, since the comparative is demanded by the
sense.   [4] Heat being ἡ ψυχικὴ ἀρχή (*G. A.* 751ᵇ 6).
[5] Reading δεῖται τοῦ ὑγροῦ τὸ θερμὸν ᾧ ζῶμεν (W. D. R.). ἢ τὸ ξηρὸν
appears to be a gloss which has replaced τὸ θερμόν, and τὸ θερμόν has
been afterwards inserted in the wrong place.

Why can we endure thirst less than hunger?[1] Is it **6** because the former causes us more pain? A proof of the pain it causes is the fact that the pleasure it gives is more intense.[2] Further, he who is thirsty needs two things, 35 nourishment and cooling, and drink provides both of these; but he who is hungry needs one of them only.

Why are men called incontinent if they indulge to excess **7** in the pleasures connected with touch and taste?[3] (For **950**[a] those who are intemperate in sexual intercourse and the enjoyments of eating and drinking are called incontinent; and in the joys of eating and drinking the pleasure is partly in the tongue and partly in the throat; hence Philoxenus[4] longed for the throat of a crane.) And why is the term incontinent never extended to the pleasures of sight and hearing? 5 Is it because the pleasures of touch and taste are common to us and the other animals? Being, then, shared by the animals they are held in least honour and so are regarded as the only pleasures deserving of reproach, or at any rate more so than any others. So we blame a man who is a slave to them and call him incontinent and intemperate, because he is a slave to the worst pleasures. Now the senses being 10 five in number, the other animals find pleasure only in the two already mentioned; in the others they find no pleasure, or, if they do, it is only incidentally. For the lion[5] rejoices when he sees or scents his prey, because he is going to enjoy it;[6] and when he has satisfied his hunger, such things do not please him, just as the smell of dried fish 15 gives us no pleasure when we have eaten our fill of it, though, when we wanted to partake of it, it was pleasant.[7]

---

[1] Cp. chapter 5.   [2] Reading ἡ ἡδονὴ ⟨ἡ⟩ σφοδροτέρα.
[3] Cp. above, chapter 2. This problem is quoted in Greek by Aulus Gellius (xix. 2) as Aristotelian.
[4] Cp. *E. E.* 1231[a] 17.
[5] The repetition of ὁρῶν ... ὁρῶν here is unsatisfactory, and in any case we should expect a neuter to agree with ζῷον understood. In *E. N.* 1118[a] 18 ff., where the same subject is discussed, the example taken of an animal is the lion. We ought certainly, therefore, to read here ὁρῶν μὲν γὰρ ὁ λέων. [Richards (*op. cit.*, p. 144) makes the same suggestion.]
[6] Reading ἀπολαύσει (Bonitz).
[7] Reading ἡδεῖα (Sylburg) for ἡδέα.

The scent of the rose, on the other hand, is always pleasant.

8   Why are men less able to restrain their laughter in the presence of friends? Is it because, when anything is especially elated, it is easily set in motion? Now benevolence causes elation,[1] so that laughter more readily moves us.

---

[1] εἰπεῖν is clearly corrupt. The point of the solution of the problem appears to depend on the metaphorical use of ἐξαίρειν ; and something like the following seems to be required : ἡ δ᾽ εὔνοια ἐξαίρει, ὥστε κινεῖ μᾶλλον τὸ γελοῖον.

BOOK XXIX

PROBLEMS CONNECTED WITH JUSTICE AND INJUSTICE

WHY is it that, although injustice is greater according as 1 the good which is injured is greater, and honour is a greater good, yet injustice in the matter of money seems to be more serious and those who are unjust as regards money 25 are considered more unjust? Is it because men prefer money to honour, and money is common to all, whereas honour comes only to a few and its enjoyment is a rare occurrence?

Why is it a more terrible thing to rob a man of a deposit 2 than of a loan?[1] Is it because it is disgraceful to wrong a friend? Now he who robs another of a deposit does 30 wrong to a friend; for no one places a deposit with another unless he trusts him. A creditor, on the other hand, is not a friend; for, if a man is a friend, he gives and does not lend. Or is it because the injustice is greater, since, in addition to the loss inflicted, he also violates his plighted word, for the sake of which, if for no other reason, he ought to abstain from doing the wrong? Further, it is 35 base not to requite like with like; for the one party in making the deposit regarded the other as his friend, but the latter in robbing him treated him as an enemy; but a lender does not lend in the spirit of friendship. Again, a deposit is handed over to be guarded and returned, whereas the lender lends for his own advantage as well. Now we are less angry at losing if we are in pursuit of 950^b gain, like fishermen when they lose their bait; for the risk is obvious. Again, those who make deposits are generally the victims of plots or misfortune, but it is the rich who lend money; and it is more terrible to wrong the unfortunate than the fortunate.

[1] Cp. below, chapter 6.

3   Why is it that in some law courts the jury give their [5] verdict[1] in accordance with the birth of the litigants rather than the provisions of the will? Is it because about birth it is impossible to lie, but the truth must be declared, whereas before now many wills have been proved to be forged?

4   Why is it that poverty is more commonly found amongst the good than amongst the bad?[2] Is it because, being [10] universally hated and despised, she takes refuge with the good, thinking that with them she is most likely to find safety and a place of habitation; whereas she thinks that if she goes to the wicked, they would never remain content with the same condition but would steal or plunder, in which case she could no longer remain with them? Or [15] is it because she thinks that the good will treat her better than any one else and that she is least likely to be insulted by them? So, just as we place deposits[3] of money with good men, so she of her own accord[4] ranges herself with them. Or is it because, being of the female sex, she is more helpless, so that she needs the assistance of the [20] good? Or is it because, being herself an evil, she will not betake herself to that which is evil, since if she were to choose the evil, her position would be quite irremediable?

5   Why is it that wrongs in other matters are not so liable to be committed on a large scale[5] as those in respect of money?[6] For example, a man who has spoken a light word would not therefore necessarily divulge a secret, nor[7] would one who has betrayed an individual also betray [25] a city, as a man who has stolen an obol would steal a talent

---

[1] Reading ψηφίζονται for ψηφιοῦνται, as suggested by Bekker.
[2] Cp. below, chapter 8.
[3] In the Teubner Text τιθέμενα is a misprint for τιθέμεθα.
[4] Reading αὑτῆς for αὐτῆς.
[5] Reading αἱ ἀδικίαι ⟨αἱ⟩ μείζους (Richards).
[6] Reading χρήματα. Most MSS. read ῥήματα, but Yᵃ (which not infrequently preserves the correct reading) reads χρήματα, and the Latin version renders *iniuriae in pecuniis*. The origin of the change to ῥήματα may be found in the fact that εἰπὼν ... εἴποι occur below. If ῥήματα is read, no sense can be found for the concluding sentence of the chapter; whereas, if χρήματα is read, the argument is clear and resembles that of chapter 1.
[7] Reading οὐδὲ for ἀλλὰ; the Latin version renders *neque qui unum prodiderit*, &c.

also. Is it because, though there are forms of unjust disposition which are worse,[1] the acts resulting from them are
less serious owing to lack of power?

Why is it more disgraceful[2] to rob a man of a small **6**
deposit than of a large loan?[3] Is it because he who robs
30 another of a deposit is deceiving a man who thought him
to be honest? Or is it because he who commits the one
crime would commit the other also?

Why is it that man, who of all animals has the advantage **7**
of most education, is yet the most unjust of all? Is it
because he possesses the power of reasoning to the greatest
degree, and has therefore most carefully estimated the
35 pleasures and happiness, and these are impossible of attain-
ment without injustice?

Why is it that wealth is more often found in the hands **8**
of the wicked than in those of the good? Is it because,
being blind,[4] it cannot read men's hearts and choose the
best?

951^a   Why is it considered more just to defend the dead than **9**
the living? Is it because those who are alive can look
after themselves, but a dead man can no longer do so?

Why is it that a man who associates with one who is **10**
healthy does not himself become any healthier,[5] nor does
intercourse with the strong or beautiful improve a man's
5 condition, whereas association with the just and temperate
and good does have this effect? Is it because some qualities can, and others cannot, be imitated by the soul, good-
ness being a quality of the soul and health of the body?
A man can, therefore, accustom himself to feel pleasure
and pain under the proper circumstances; but his association with the healthy does not produce this result, for
health does not consist in taking pleasure or not in certain
10 things, since none of these things can produce health.

---

[1] Sc. than that involved in stealing a talent.
[2] Reading αἴσχιον for αἰσχρὸν with Bonitz (*Aristot. Stud.*, p. 418).
[3] Cp. above, chapter 2.
[4] Cp. above, chapter 4, where poverty is personified.
[5] Cp. 886^b 5.

11 Why is it more terrible to kill a woman than a man, although the male is naturally superior to the female? Is it because she is weaker and so he commits a greater [1] injustice? Or is it because it is not a manly act to use one's strength against that which is greatly inferior?

12 Why is the defendant given the position on the right hand in a law court? Is it from a desire to equalize matters? Since, then, the plaintiff possesses other advantages, the defendant is given the advantage of position. Further, as a rule defendants are under guard; and, if the defendant has the right-hand position, the guard is on his right.[2]

13 Why is it that, when the votes for the plaintiff and for the defendant are shown to be equal, the defendant wins the case? Is it because the defendant has heard only in court, during the course of the trial itself,[3] the charges against which he has to make his defence and produce the witnesses to refute the accusations,[4] if any advantage is to be obtained from them?[5] Now it is not easy for a man to foresee of what he ought to provide witnesses or some other kind of evidence to prove his innocence. The plaintiff, on the other hand, can act as he pleases, and can begin to take action before having the summons issued; and even after he has summoned his opponent he can invent and bring against him any plausible accusation he likes. The lawgiver then, recognizing that the defendant has the disadvantage in all these respects, has given him any advantage which may accrue from the disagreement of the jury. And, indeed, that defendants are at a disadvantage is shown by the fact that when men are in a state of alarm they omit much of what they ought to have said or done, and defendants are, generally speaking, always in greater danger; and so, if

---

[1] Reading μείζω (W. D. R.) for ἐλάττω, cp. 952ª 1.
[2] The meaning perhaps is that the accused is placed on the right hand of the judge and has on his own right hand the guard which has charge of him; he is, therefore, protected on both sides.
[3] Reading with Richards, αἰτῷ for αὐτοί.
[4] Omitting ⟨τὸ⟩ and ἔχεσθαι, which is probably due to the preceding παρασχέσθαι.
[5] Reading with Yª ὠφεληθήσεσθαι and taking μέλλουσι as a careless plural for singular.

35 they omit necessary parts of their defence, when they are put on a level with their opponents in respect of their claims, they would clearly have been victorious if they had not omitted anything.

Further, any one of us would prefer to pass a sentence 951ᵇ acquitting a wrong-doer rather than condemn as guilty one who is innocent, in the case, for example, of a man being accused of enslavement or murder. For we should prefer to acquit either of such persons, though the charges brought against them by their accuser were true,[1] rather than con-
5 demn them if they were untrue; for, when any doubt is entertained, the less grave error ought to be preferred; it is a serious matter to decide that a slave is free, yet it is much more serious to convict a freeman of being a slave.

Further, if one man brings a charge and another disputes his claim to any piece of property, we do not consider that
10 we ought to award the disputed property immediately to the plaintiff, but that the man in possession ought to enjoy it until the matter is decided. Similarly, when a number of persons are involved in a case and the numbers of those who declare that a wrong has been committed and of those who deny it are equal—just as in the case cited above when one man brought an accusation, while another denied the truth of it—we consider that the lawgiver is right in
15 not handing over the disputed property[2] to the accuser but allowing the defendant to remain in possession until the plaintiff[3] has established some superiority. Similarly, when the votes of the jury are equal and so neither side has the superiority,[4] the lawgiver has allowed matters to be left as they are.

Again, in serious crimes the punishments are also heavy,
20 so that, if the jury pass an unjust sentence and then change their mind,[5] it is impossible to take the opportunity of

---

[1] Punctuating τούτων γὰρ ἑκάστου, ὄντων ἃ κατηγορεῖ αἰτῶν, μᾶλλον κτλ.
[2] We should perhaps read προστίθεσθαι (cp. 951ᵃ 31) for προστιθέναι. The Latin version of T. G. renders *favere*.
[3] Reading διώκων for ἀδικῶν with Bonitz, *Aristot. Stud.*, p. 418.
[4] Reading οὐδεμία ὑπεροχὴ with Bonitz, *loc. cit.*
[5] Reading μεταγνοῦσιν (Richards).

remedying the mistake; if, on the other hand, they acquit
the accused when they ought not to do so, if he lives [1] so
circumspectly as never to commit any crime again, how can
the jury have made a serious mistake in failing to condemn
such a man to death? If, however, he subsequently commits a crime, the law [2] would consider [3] that he ought to be ₂₅
punished for both crimes.

Or is it because it is an act of greater injustice to bring
an unjust accusation than to commit an offence which may
easily be made the subject of an unjust accusation? [4] For
wrong-doing may be due to anger or fear or desire and to
many other causes, and not only to design, but an unjust
accusation is generally due to design. So when the votes ₃₀
have proved equal, indicating both [5] that the accuser has
brought an unjust charge and that the defendant is in the
wrong, the unjust accuser being judged the greater offender, [6]
the lawgiver has awarded the legal victory to the defendant.

Again, we ourselves adopt the attitude towards our
servants that, when we suspect that they have committed ₃₅
a crime and have no certain knowledge, but nevertheless
think that they have done the deed, we do not immediately
proceed to punish them; and when we cannot pursue our
inquiries any further, we acquit them of blame.   952^a

Further, he who designedly commits a crime does a
greater wrong than he who does not act designedly. Now
the man who brings a vexatious charge against another
always does wrong designedly, whereas he who commits
any other crime may happen to do so either under compulsion or through ignorance or by some other chance. But ₅
when the votes are equal, the prosecutor has been judged
by half the jury to be committing a wrong wilfully, while

---

¹ Reading εἰ μὲν οὕτως εὐλαβῶς ⟨ζᾴη⟩ or some similar verb.

² The subject is ὁ νομοθέτης supplied.

³ Reading ἀξιοίη (W. D. R.).

⁴ The text as it stands gives no sense either in itself or in view of
the rest of the argument, which seems to require something like the
following: ἢ ὅτι ἀδικωτέρου μέν ἐστιν ἀνδρὸς ⟨ἀδίκως ἐγκαλεῖν ἢ⟩ ταῦτα
ἀδικεῖν ἃ [ἧττον] εἰκός ἐστιν ἀδίκως ἐγκαλεῖσθαι.

⁵ Reading τό τ' for τὸ δὲ [so also Bussemaker].

⁶ Reading φαυλοτέρου for φαύλου (Richards).

the defendant is considered by the remainder to be in the wrong, but not wilfully ; and so, since the prosecutor is judged guilty of a more serious wrong than the defendant, the lawgiver has rightly decided that he who has committed
10 the less serious wrong wins the case.

Further, a man is always more unjust who does not expect to escape the observation of the man whom he wrongs and nevertheless commits the wrong, than he who expects to remain undiscovered. Now[1] he who brings a vexatious charge against another does not expect to escape the observation of the man whom he falsely accuses, whereas those who commit any other crime usually try to commit an injustice with the expectation of doing so with-
15 out the knowledge of their victims, so that plaintiffs ought to be regarded as more unjust than defendants.

Why is it that, if a man steals from the baths or the **14** wrestling-school or the market or any similar place, he is punished with death, whereas, if he steals from a house, he merely pays back double[2] the value of what he has stolen ?
20 Is it because in houses it is possible in some way or other to safeguard one's property ? For the wall is strong and there is a key, and it is the business of all the slaves in the house to see that the contents of the house are kept safe. At the baths, however, and in places which are similarly public, it is easy for any one who wishes to commit a crime ;
25 for those who place their property there have no sure means of guarding it except their own eyes, so that, if one takes one's eye off it for a moment, it is immediately placed at the mercy of the thief. Hence the lawgiver, considering that bathers are not able to guard their property, has set the law to guard against thieves by threatening that they
30 shall lose their lives if they appropriate the possessions of others.

Further, the owner of a house is responsible for admitting into it whom he wishes and for introducing[3] into it any one whom he does not trust ; but the man who deposits any

---

[1] Reading with Richards οὖν for γάρ.
[2] The Teubner Text misprints διπλοῦς for διπλοῦν.
[3] Reading εἰσφρέεσθαι (Richards).

property in a bath cannot prevent any one from coming in, nor can he prevent him, when he has entered, from placing his garments next to his own[1] when he has stripped himself;[2] but, contrary to his wishes, the clothing of the thief and of the man who is about to be robbed lie together 35 in a confused heap. Therefore the lawgiver has prescribed not very heavy penalties to help the man who of his own free will and by his own mistake has admitted the thief to **952ᵇ** his house, but has clearly fixed heavy penalties for theft to aid those who are obliged to share with others the right of entrance and the promiscuity of the baths.

Further, it is obvious that all those who commit theft in places the entrance to which is open to any one who wishes 5 to come are bad men,[3] and so, if they are allowed to live, do not desire to have the semblance of honest men even for the future advantage which they can gain from it, regarding it as useless to pretend to be honest in the eyes of those who know their real character; they therefore continue henceforward to be openly wicked. Those, on the other hand, whose wickedness is known to one person only, try to per- 10 suade that person by bribery not to make known their real character to the rest of the world; they are not likely therefore to be completely wicked for ever, and so the penalty which the lawgiver has fixed for them is less severe.

Further, of all crimes those which are committed in the most crowded meetings and assemblies bring most disgrace upon the city, just as public orderliness brings the greatest 15 credit; for it is at public gatherings that the citizens are most conspicuous to each other and the rest of the world. The result, therefore, of such thefts is that not only is the man who loses his property personally injured, but also abuse is heaped upon the city. This is why the lawgiver has fixed heavier penalties for such thieves than for those 20 who abstract property from a private house.

---

[1] Reading τὸ αἰτοῦ ⟨τὸ⟩ ἱμάτιον κτλ., and omitting κλέπτην as a gloss.

[2] Omitting ἄν.

[3] Reading πονηροί for φανεροί.

Again, the man who loses anything from a private house is in a place where[1] it is easy for him to bear his misfortune, since he is in his own home and neither suffers anything nor is jeered at by others. But the man who is robbed at the baths finds it difficult to leave without his 25 clothing, and, in addition, is usually jeered at by others; and this is harder to bear than the actual loss. Therefore the lawgiver has prescribed heavier penalties to assist such persons.

Again, many legislative parallels can be found for these penalties. For example, if any one speaks evil of a magistrate the punishment is severe, but there is no penalty for speaking evil of an ordinary individual; and rightly so, for 30 the legislator considers that the slanderer not only commits an offence against the magistrate but also insults the city. Similarly, a man who commits a theft at the harbour is considered not only to harm the individual whom he robs, but also to bring disgrace upon the city. And the same is 35 true of any crime committed in a place of public meeting.

Why is it that in law courts, if equal votes are given for 15 the two adversaries, the defendant wins the case?[2] Is it 953^a because the defendant has remained unaffected by the action of the plaintiff, and in a position of equality with him he would probably have won?

Why is it that for theft the punishment is death, whereas 16 for assault, which is a more serious crime, the penalty or fine is assessable in court? Is it because to commit an 5 assault is an act of human weakness, of which all more or less partake, whereas there is no force which compels us to theft? A further reason is the fact that a man who tries to commit theft would think nothing of committing assault also.

---

[1] ὅθεν can hardly be right and ὅθι should probably be read.
[2] This chapter gives an additional suggestion for the solution of the problem of chapter 13.

BOOK XXX

PROBLEMS CONNECTED WITH PRUDENCE, INTELLIGENCE, AND WISDOM

I   WHY is it that all those who have become eminent in 10 philosophy or politics or poetry or the arts are clearly of an atrabilious temperament, and some of them to such an extent as to be affected by diseases caused by black bile, as is said to have happened to Heracles among the heroes? [1] For he appears to have been of this nature, wherefore 15 epileptic afflictions were called by the ancients 'the sacred disease' after him.[2] That his temperament was atrabilious is shown by the fury which he displayed towards his children [3] and the eruption of sores which took place before his disappearance on Mount Oeta; for this often occurs as the result of black bile. Lysander the Lacedaemonian also suffered from similar sores before his death.[4] There are 20 also the stories of Ajax and Bellerophon, of whom the former became insane, while the latter sought out habitations in desert places; wherefore Homer writes,

> And since of all the gods he was hated,
> Verily o'er [5] the Aleïan plain [6] alone he would wander,
> Eating his own heart out, avoiding the pathway of 25
> mortals.[7]

---

[1] This problem is cited as Aristotelian by Cicero, *Tusc. Disp.* i. 33 *Aristoteles quidem ait omnes ingeniosos melancholicos esse; ut ego me tardiorem esse non moleste feram. Enumerat multos, idque quasi constet, rationem, cur ita fiat, adfert.* It is also quoted by Plutarch; see below, note 4.

[2] Called by Hippocrates and Galen νόσος Ἡρακλείη.

[3] i. e. his murder of the children borne to him by Megara.

[4] This passage is quoted as Aristotelian by Plutarch, *Vit. Lysandri* 2 Ἀριστοτέλης δὲ τὰς μεγάλας φύσεις ἀποφαίνων μελαγχολικάς, ὡς τὴν Σωκράτους καὶ Πλάτωνος καὶ Ἡρακλέους, ἱστορεῖ καὶ Λύσανδρον οὐκ εὐθὺς ἀλλὰ πρεσβύτερον ὄντα τῇ μελαγχολίᾳ περιπεσεῖν.

[5] Reading κἀπ πεδίον for καππεδίον.

[6] Cp. Herodot. vi. 95; Arrian, *Anab.* ii. 5; Strabo xiv, p. 963. It was situated near the city of Mallus in Cilicia, between the rivers Pyramus and Sinarus.

[7] *Iliad* vi. 200–2.

And many others of the heroes seem to have been similarly afflicted, and among men of recent times Empedocles, Plato, and Socrates, and numerous other well-known men, and also most of the poets. For many such persons have bodily
30 afflictions as the result of this kind of temperament, while some of them obviously possess a natural inclination to affections of this kind; in a word, they all, as has been said, are naturally atrabilious. The cause of this may be understood if we first take an example from the effect of wine, which if taken in large quantities appears to produce
35 such qualities as we attribute to the atrabilious, inducing, as it is drunk, many different characteristics, making men for instance irritable, benevolent, compassionate, or reckless; whereas no such results are produced by honey or milk or water or anything similar. One can easily see that wine has a variety of effects by observing how it gradually
953^b changes those who drink it; for, finding them chilled and taciturn as the result of abstinence, a small quantity makes them more talkative, while a larger quantity makes them eloquent and bold, and, when they proceed to action, reckless, and a still larger quantity makes them insolent and afterwards frenzied, while outrageous excess enfeebles
5 them and makes them stupid like those who have been epileptic from childhood,[1] and very similar to those who are exceedingly atrabilious. As, therefore, an individual as he drinks and takes wine in different quantities changes his character, so there are men who embody each character. For the temporary condition of one man when he is drunk is the permanent character of another, and one man is
10 loquacious, another emotional, another easily moved to tears; for wine has this effect also on some people[2] and therefore Homer writes,

> He says that I swim in tears, like a man that is heavy
> with drinking.[3]

Others become compassionate or savage or taciturn; for

---

[1] Placing a comma after ἐπιλήπτους.
[2] Cp. above, 874^b 8-10.
[3] *Od.* xix. 122, where the received text has φῇ δὲ δακρυπλώειν βεβαρηότα με φρένας οἴνῳ.

some maintain a complete silence, especially those atrabilious subjects who are out of their minds. Wine also makes men amorous; as is shown by the fact that a man who is drinking 15 is induced to kiss those whom, owing to their appearance or age, no sober person would kiss. Wine then gives a man extraordinary characteristics, but for a short time only, while nature gives them permanently for the period of a lifetime; for some men are bold, others taciturn, others compassionate, 20 and others cowardly by nature. It is therefore clear that each [1] characteristic is produced by wine and by nature by the same means; [2] for the whole body functions under the control of heat. Now both the juice [3] and the atrabilious temperament are full of wind; wherefore the physicians say that flatulence and disorders of the stomach are due to black 25 bile. Now wine has the quality of containing air; so wine and the atrabilious temperament are similar in nature. The froth which forms on wine shows that it contains air; for oil does not produce froth, although it is hot, but wine produces it in large quantities and dark wine more than white because it contains more heat and substance. It is 30 for this reason that wine excites sexual desire, and Dionysus and Aphrodite are rightly coupled together, and atrabilious persons are generally lustful. [4] For sexual desire is due to the presence of breath, as is shown by the fact that the virile organ quickly increases from a small to a large size by 35 inflation; also [5] boys before they are capable of emitting semen find a certain pleasure in rubbing their sexual organs through lust when they are approaching the age of puberty, and the swelling of the organ becomes manifest because breath passes through the passages through which the semen subsequently passes; also the effusion 954^a and impetus of the semen in sexual intercourse is clearly due to propulsion by the breath. [6] So those foods and liquids which fill the region of the sexual organs with breath are rightly regarded as aphrodisiac. Thus dark wine

---

[1] Reading ἕκαστον (Richards) as in l. 8.
[2] Reading διὰ τοῦ αὐτοῦ (Richards).   [3] i. e. wine.
[4] Cp. 880ᵃ 30–33.   [5] Omitting ἔτι with Burnet.
[6] Cp. *H. A.* vii. 7. 586ᵃ 16. It seems necessary to read with Richards φανερὸν ὅτι γίνεται.

₅ more than anything else produces the condition found in atrabilious persons.[1] This condition is obvious in some individuals; for most atrabilious persons are thin[2] and their veins stand out, the reason being the abundance not of blood but of breath. The reason why all atrabilious
₁₀ persons are not thin[3] or dark,[4] but only those who contain particularly unhealthy humours, is stated elsewhere.[5]

But to return to our previous subject of discussion, this humour, namely, the atrabilious, is originally mingled in the bodily nature, for it is a mixture of heat and cold, of which two things the bodily nature consists. Black bile,
₁₅ therefore, becomes both very hot and very cold, for the same thing naturally admits both heat and cold, like water, which, though cold, yet when it is sufficiently heated (for example, when it boils) is hotter than the actual flame which heats it, and similarly a stone or a piece of iron when thoroughly heated becomes hotter than charcoal, though
₂₀ they are naturally cold. (This subject has been dealt with more clearly in dealing with Fire.[6]) Now black bile, which is naturally cold and not on the surface,[7] being in the condition mentioned above, if it abounds in the body, produces apoplexy or torpor or despondency or fear; but when it is overheated, it produces cheerfulness accompanied by song,
₂₅ and frenzy, and the breaking forth of sores, and the like. In most people then black bile engendered from their daily nutriment does not change their character, but merely produces an atrabilious disease. But those who naturally possess an atrabilious temperament immediately develop
₃₀ diverse characters in accordance with their various temperaments; for example, those who are originally full of cold black bile become dull and stupid, whereas those who

---

[1] Omitting πνευματώδεις as a gloss on τοιούτους.

[2] Reading with Bussemaker σκληφροί.

[3] Reading σκληφροὶ with Aᵖ.

[4] Omitting οἱ before μέλανες with Bekker.

[5] This reference cannot be identified in the Aristotelian Corpus.

[6] Camotius at the end of Book 24 states that according to some authorities books on Fire and Light formerly found a place at that point, but are now lost. The reference here is possibly to a lost book on Fire.

[7] Reading ἐπιπόλαιος for ἐπιπολαίως with Sylburg and Platt.

possess a large quantity of hot black bile become frenzied
or clever or erotic or easily moved to anger and desire,
while some become more loquacious. Many too, if this
heat approaches the region of the intellect, are affected by 35
diseases of frenzy and possession; and this is the origin of
Sibyls and soothsayers and all inspired persons, when they
are affected not by disease but by natural temperament.
Maracus, the Syracusan, was actually a better poet when
he was out of his mind. Those in whom the excessive
heat dies down [1] to a mean temperature are atrabilious, but **954ᵇ**
they are cleverer and less eccentric and in many respects
superior to others either in mental accomplishments or in
the arts or in public life. In respect too of facing dangers
an atrabilious state causes great variation, in that [2] many of 5
those who are in this condition are inconsistent under the
influence of [3] fears; for they vary from time to time according
to the state in which their bodies happen to be in respect
to the atrabilious temperament. Now this temperament is
itself also inconsistent, just as it produces inconsistency in
those suffering from the diseases which it causes; for, like 10
water, it is sometimes cold and sometimes hot. And so the
announcement of something alarming, if it occurs at a time
when the temperament is rather cold, makes a man cowardly;
for it has already prepared a way for the entrance of fear,
and fear has a chilling effect (as is shown by the fact that
those who are greatly alarmed tremble). If, however, the
temperament is inclined to be hot, fear reduces it to a moderate temperature and causes a man to be in his senses and 15
unexcited. So too with the despondency which occurs in
everyday life (for we are often in the condition of feeling
grief without being able to ascribe any cause for it, while at
other times we feel cheerful without knowing why), such
feelings and those usually called superficial [4] feelings occur
to a slight degree in every one, for something of the force

---

[1] Reading ἐπανεθῇ ἡ ἄγαν θερμότης with Bywater. The Latin version
of T. G. has *ab quibus minus* (a misprint for *nimius*) *ille calor
remissus ad mediocritatem sit.*   [2] Reading τῷ for τοῦ.

[3] Reading ἐν for μέν. [So. too, Richards and Klek.]

[4] Reading ἐπιπόλαια (which is suggested by the contrast with ὅσοις
δ᾽ εἰς βάθος) instead of the meaningless παλαιά; T. G. renders
superius.

20 which produces them is mingled in every one; but those
who are thoroughly penetrated by them acquire them as
a permanent part of their nature. For as men differ in
appearance not because they possess faces but because they
possess certain kinds of faces, some handsome, others ugly,
others with nothing remarkable about them (those, that is,
who are naturally ordinary); so those who possess an atra-
25 bilious temperament in a slight degree are ordinary, but
those who have much of it are quite unlike the majority of
people. For, if their condition is quite complete, they are
very atrabilious; but, if they possess a mixed temperament,
they are men of genius. If they neglect their health, they
have a tendency towards the atrabilious diseases, the part
of the body affected varying in different people; in some
30 persons epileptic symptoms declare themselves, in others
apoplectic, in others violent despondency or terrors, in
others over-confidence, as happened to Archelaus, King of
Macedonia. The force which gives rise to such a condition
is the temperament according as it contains heat or cold.
If it be cold beyond due measure, it produces groundless
35 despondency; hence suicide by hanging occurs most
frequently among the young, but sometimes also among
older men. Many men too put an end to themselves after
drunkenness, and some atrabilious persons continue in a
state of despondency after drinking; for the heat of the
955^a wine quenches their natural heat. Heat in the region in
which we think and form hopes makes us cheerful; and for
this reason all men are eager to drink until they become
intoxicated, for abundance of wine makes all men hopeful,
just as their youth makes children sanguine; for old age is
5 despairing but youth is full of hope. There are a few who
are seized with despondency while they are drinking, for
the same reason as makes others despondent after drinking.
Those then who become despondent as the heat in them
dies down tend to hang themselves. Hence the young and [1]
the old are more likely to hang themselves; for old age
10 makes the heat die down, and so, in the young, does their

[1] Omitting ἤ with Richards.

condition, which is itself natural.[1]   When the heat is extinguished[2] suddenly, most men make away with themselves
to the general astonishment of all, since they have given no
previous sign of any such intention.   When the temperament caused by the admixture of black bile is colder, it
gives rise, as has been already remarked, to despondency 15
of various kinds, but when it is hotter to cheerfulness.
Hence the young are more cheerful, the old more despondent, the former being hot and the latter cold ; for old age
is a process of cooling.   Extinction takes place suddenly
from external causes, just as objects which have been heated
in the fire are cooled by unnatural processes, as for example
when water is poured over hot coals.   Hence men some- 20
times commit suicide after drunkenness ; for the heat of the
wine is introduced from outside, and when it is extinguished
the condition which leads to suicide is set up.   Also after
sexual intercourse most people tend to be despondent ;
those, however, who emit a considerable amount of excrement with the semen become more cheerful, for they are
relieved of an excess of excrement and breath and heat. 25
But those who indulge in sexual intercourse[3] are often
more despondent, for by so doing they become cooled,
because they lose something which is valuable, as is shown
by the fact that the amount of semen which is emitted is
not great.[4]

To sum the matter up, owing to the fact that the effect
of black bile is variable, atrabilious persons also show varia- 30
tion ; for the black bile becomes very hot and very cold.
And because it has an effect upon the character (for heat
and cold have such an effect to a greater extent than anything else in us), like wine mingling in a stronger or weaker
form in the body, it gives us our own special characters.
Now both wine and black bile are full of breath.   And 35

[1] Omitting τὸ μαραινόμενον θερμόν as a gloss on τὸ πάθος.

[2] ὅτοις δὲ σβεννυμένου can hardly stand here, and the required sense
is given by the Latin version, which renders *quibus autem calor
exstinctus subito est.* We should probably read ὅσοις δὲ σβέννυται
ἐξαίφνης, οἱ πλεῖστοι κτλ. ; cp. below, l. 18.

[3] ἐκεῖνοι will be equivalent to οἱ ἀφροδισιάσαντες. Possibly ἕτεροι
should be read ; the Latin version has *ceteri.*

[4] i. e. it has quality rather than quantity.

since it is possible for an abnormal state to be well
attempered and in a sense a favourable condition, and since
it is possible for the condition to be hotter and then again
cold, when it should be so, or to change to the contrary
owing to excess, the result is that all atrabilious persons
40 have remarkable gifts, not owing to disease but from
natural causes.

955^b   Why do we say that we acquire a habit as the result **2**
of pursuing some sciences but not others? Are we said to
acquire a habit only by such sciences as enable us to make
discoveries, since discovery is the result of a habit?

Why is it that of all the animals man has most practical **3**
5 wisdom? Is it because he has the smallest head in proportion to his body? Or is it because he is abnormally
small in certain parts? For that is why his head is small,
and among men those who have smaller heads are wiser
than those who have larger heads.

Why is it that a journey seems longer when we traverse **4**
10 it without knowing its length than when we know it, all
other conditions being equal?[1] Is it because to know its
length is to be able to connect a number with it? For that
which cannot be numbered is the same as the infinite, and
the infinite is always more than the determinate. Just as,
therefore, if one knows that a journey is a certain length
it must necessarily be finite, so if one does not know its
15 length one as it were converts the proposition[2] and the
mind draws a false conclusion, and this journey appears
infinite. Furthermore,[3] a quantity is determinate, and that
which is determinate is a quantity; therefore when a
thing does not appear determinate it will appear to be
as it were infinite, because that which is of a nature to be
20 determined, if it is not so, is infinite, and that which
appears not to be determined necessarily appears in a sense
unlimited.

---

[1] This problem has already been dealt with in V. 25.
[2] See note on 883^b 8.
[3] Reading ἔτι for ἐπεί and placing a full stop before it, cp. 883^b 9.

5   Why is it that, whereas we become wiser as we grow
older, yet the younger we are the more easily we can
learn? Is it because God has given us two instruments
within ourselves, which enable us to use external instruments, providing the body with the hand and the soul 25
with intelligence? For intelligence is among the things
implanted in us by nature, being as it were an instrument;
and, whereas the sciences and arts are among the things
created by us, intelligence is one of the gifts of nature.
So just as we cannot use the hand to the best advantage
immediately after birth, but only when nature has perfected
it (for the hand can perform its particular function best as 30
age progresses), in like manner of our natural endowments
reason is of most assistance to us not in early life but as we
get old, and is then at its highest perfection, unless it becomes
incapacitated by anything, as may happen also to the other
natural endowments. Intelligence comes to us later than
the faculty of using the hands, because the instruments 35
used by the intelligence are posterior to those used by the
hands. For science is an instrument of the intelligence
(for it is useful to the intelligence just as flutes are useful
to the flute-player), and many things in nature are instruments of the hands, but nature itself and its creations are
prior to science. Now it is natural that where the instruments are prior, the faculties should also come into being 40
in us first (for it is by using the instruments that we acquire
a habit); and the instrument of each faculty is related 956^a
similarly to that faculty,[1] and conversely, as the instruments
are to one another, so are the faculties of which [2] they are
the instruments to one another.[3] Intelligence then for this
reason comes to us when we are older; but we learn more 5
quickly when we are young because we do not yet know
anything, and when we know more we are no longer so
well able to acquire knowledge,[4] just as we remember best

[1] i. e. as the instrument of any other faculty is related to that faculty.
[2] Reading with Richards οὗτως ⟨ὦν⟩ τὰ ὄργανα.
[3] Reading αὐτά (Richards). The reasoning resembles that of E. N.
1131^b 5–7: A' is to A as B' is to B; and, therefore, as A' is to B' so
is A to B.
[4] Reading with Richards οὐκέτι ὁμοίως δυνάμεθα δέχεσθαι κτλ.

what we come upon early in the day, and then, as the day
10 goes on, are less able to remember what happens, because
we have come into contact with a number of incidents.

Why should man be obeyed more than any other animal? 6
Is it because, as Plato answered to Neocles, he alone of all
the animals can count? Or is it because he is the only
animal that believes in gods? Or is it because he is the
most imitative (for it is for this reason that he can learn)?

15 Why is it that we feel no pleasure in the contemplation 7
or anticipation of the fact that the interior angles of a
triangle are equal to two right angles, and similar geometrical truths—except in so far as we enjoy the specula-
tion, and the pleasure of this is always the same and would
be equally great if these angles were equal to three or more
right angles—but we rejoice at the recollection of an Olympic
20 victory or the sea-battle at Salamis, and at the anticipation
of such events, but not in their opposites? Is it because[1]
we rejoice in such events as having taken place or taking
place, but as regards what happens in the course of nature
the contemplation of the real state of affairs alone causes us
pleasure, whereas actions[2] give rise to the pleasure caused
25 by their results? Since, then, actions are various, their
results too are sometimes painful and sometimes pleasant;
and we avoid and pursue anything in accordance with
pleasure and pain.

Why do doctors continue their treatment only until 8
health is restored?[3] For the doctor reduces[4] the patient,
and next dries his body, then creates a healthy condition
30 and at that point stops. Is it because[5] it is impossible for
any other condition to be produced from health? Or, if it
is possible, is it the task of another science, and will what
is produced from health be something different? Now,

---

[1] Reading τοιούτοις; ἢ ὅτι.

[2] Reading φύσιν ⟨ἡ⟩ ὡς κατ' ἀλήθειαν ἔχει θεωρία ἡδονὴν μόνη ἡμῖν ποιεῖ, αἱ δὲ πράξεις κτλ. (W. D. R.).

[3] The text of this chapter is unsatisfactory, but the general sense is clear.

[4] The Teubner text misprints ἰσχναίναι for ἰσχναίνει.

[5] Reading πότερον ⟨ὅτι⟩ οὐκ (Richards.)

if health is produced from conditions which are its opposite
or are intermediate between health and sickness, it is obvious
that the patient is sick because he is too moist or too dry
or something else.[1] The doctor, then, from a state of cold
creates a less extreme condition and, finally,[2] a condition of
a certain heat or dryness or moisture by change from the 35
opposite or intermediate condition,[3] until he achieves a state
which is such as to constitute a condition of health; and
from this no condition can be produced except one which
is intermediate between health and sickness. The possessor
of the art can, then, create some new condition; for, when
he has reached a certain point, he can retrace his steps
and undo his work; but the doctor's *art* has nothing to do
with such a course, for its aim is always to create a better 40
condition.[4] So neither the doctor's art[5] nor any other art
will create anything else out of health; for either nothing 956ᵇ
would be being produced,[6] or else the opposite of health,
if the same science were being employed (so too out of a
house nothing could make its contrary): nor is there any
other art[7] which can make anything out of health, except
as making a whole out of a part, as, for example, when the
cobbler's art makes a shoe out of the front part of a shoe;[8]
for these two things can be produced out of one another
by two processes, one of composition and the other of 5
destruction.

9   Why is it generally considered that the philosopher is
superior to the orator?[9] Is it because the philosopher
spends his time in studying the actual forms of things,
while the orator deals with the embodiments of these
forms—the former considering what injustice and tyranny
are, the latter urging that a certain individual is unjust or
dealing with the character of a tyrant?   10

---

[1] Reading τοιοῦτον ⟨ὤν⟩.
[2] Reading τέλος for τέλεον: T. G. renders *postremo*.
[3] Deleting the comma after ἐναντίων.
[4] Reading βελτίονος (Richards).
[5] Reading ὥστε οὔτε ἄλλη οὔτε αὕτη.
[6] Reading ἐγίνετο ⟨ἂν⟩ (Richards).
[7] Reading οὐδ' ἔστιν ἄλλη τέχνη (from T. G.).
[8] Cp. *Rhet.* 1392ᵃ 31 ff.
[9] A shorter form of this problem occurs in xviii. 5.

Why are theatrical artists generally persons of bad 10 character?[1] Is it because they partake but little of reason and wisdom,[2] because most of their life is spent in the pursuit of the arts which provide their daily needs, and because the greater part of their life is passed in incontinence 15 and often in want, and both these things prepare the way to villainy?

Why did the men of old institute prizes for physical 11 contests but none for wisdom? Is it because in all fairness the judges should in the intellectual sphere be either the superiors or at any rate not the inferiors of the competitors? Now if those who were pre-eminent in wisdom had to 20 compete and a prize had been offered, they would have no one to act as judges.[3] In athletic contests, however, anyone can judge by merely using his eyes. Further, the original institutor of the games did not wish to propose to the Greeks such a contest[4] as would be likely to produce 25 violent disputes and enmity; for when one is rejected or accepted in a contest of bodily strength, men do not altogether harbour any grievance nor feel sentiments of enmity towards the judges, but they feel great wrath and indignation against those who decide their relative wisdom or worthlessness; and this is a quarrelsome and bad state of affairs. 30 Furthermore, the prize ought to be better than the contest; for in athletic games the prize is more desirable than, and superior to, the contest. But what prize could be found superior to wisdom?

Why is it that man in particular thinks one thing and 12 does another? Is it because the same science deals with contraries? Or is it because the reason has many objects, 35 desire one? Now man usually lives by the intelligence, the animals by appetite, passion, and desire.

---

[1] This problem is quoted by Aulus Gellius (xx. 4) with slight textual variations as from the προβλήματα ἐγκύκλια of Aristotle.

[2] Reading λόγου ⟨καὶ⟩ σοφίας, which is supported by Aulus Gellius, who reads λόγου καὶ φιλοσοφίας.

[3] Reading αὐτοῖς.

[4] Reading ἐξ ἧς for ἐξ ὧν.

13 Why is it that some prudent men spend their time acquiring rather than using? Is it because they are following the habit of doing so? Or is it due to the pleasure of anticipation?

14 ⟨Why do those who sleep deeply and most pleasantly see no visions? Is it⟩ [1] because sensation and thought function because the mind is at rest—hence the word knowledge (ἐπιστήμη) seems to be derived from the fact that knowledge 40 checks the mind (ἵστησι)—[2] since when it is in motion and being carried along it can neither have sensation nor 957^a think? Hence it is that children and those who are drunk and the insane are senseless; for, owing to the abundance of heat present in them, they are in a state of considerable and very violent movement, but when this ceases they 5 become more sensible; for, when the thought is undisturbed, they can control it better. Those who have visions during their sleep dream because thought is checked, and in proportion as it is at rest. For the mind is greatly moved during sleep, since, when heat collects in the interior from the rest of the body, there is a very considerable and 10 violent movement; and it is not true, as most people suppose, that it is most at rest and by itself, and especially so when no vision is seen. The contrary is really true; for because it is in considerable movement and never rests for a moment, it cannot think. And it is naturally in most movement when 15 it sleeps most pleasantly, because it is then in particular that the greatest amount of heat collects in the interior of the body. That, when it is in motion, the mind cannot think, not only in its waking hours but also in sleep, is proved by the fact that one is least likely to see visions during the 20 sleep which follows the taking of food; now this is the time when the mind is most disturbed owing to the nourishment which has been introduced into the body. A vision occurs when sleep comes over us while we are thinking or letting

---

[1] Reading, with the margin of X^a A^p, Διὰ τί οἱ βαθέως καὶ ἥδιστα καθεύδοντες οὐδὲν ἐνύπνιον ὁρῶσιν; ἤ. This reading is also translated in the Latin version.

[2] The word ἐπιστήμη, which is really derived from ἐπίσταμαι, is here derived from ἵστημι or rather ἐφίστημι (cp. below, 957^a 6).

things pass before our eyes. Hence we usually see things
which we are doing or intend or wish to do; for it is on
25 these things that our thoughts and fancies most often dwell.
And the better men are, the better are their dreams, because
they think of better things in their waking hours, while
those who are less well disposed in mind or body have
worse dreams. For there is a close correspondence between
the disposition of the body and the images of our dreams;
30 for, when a man is ill, the ideas proposed by his thoughts
are bad, and furthermore, owing to the disturbance which
reigns in his body, his mind cannot rest. It is for this
reason that atrabilious persons start in their sleep, because,
owing to the excess of heat, the mind is in a state of too
much movement, and, when the movement is too violent,
35 they cannot sleep.

BOOK XXXI

PROBLEMS CONNECTED WITH THE EYES

1 WHY does rubbing the eye stop sneezing?[1] Is it because by this means evaporation is given to the moisture? For the eye sheds tears after friction, and sneezing is due to an 40 abundance of moisture. Or is it because the lesser heat is 957ᵇ destroyed by the greater? Now the eye when it is rubbed acquires more heat than is contained in the nose; and for this reason even if we rub the nose itself the sneezing stops.

2 Why can one see more accurately with one eye than 5 with both eyes? Is it because more movements are set up by the two eyes,[2] as certainly happens in those who squint? The movement of the two eyes, therefore, is not one, but that of a single eye is one; therefore one sees less accurately with both eyes.

3 Why do the eyes tend to become very red in those who are angry, and the ears in those who are ashamed? Is it 10 because the eyes are chilled in those who are ashamed (for 'shame dwells in the eyes'), so that[3] they cannot look straight in front of them? (Cowardice also involves a cooling in the same region.) Now the heat[4] travels in a direction away from the forepart of the head, and the ears are situated in the opposite part of the head, and therefore they redden most under the emotion of shame.[5] But under 15

---

[1] This problem is verbally repeated in xxxiii. 8; cp. also xxxiii. 2.
[2] Reading πλείους αἱ (Platt).
[3] Reading (ἐν ὀφθαλμοῖς γὰρ αἰδώς) ⟨ὥστ'⟩ ἀντιβλέπειν κτλ., ὥστ' having probably fallen out by haplography owing to the αἰδώς preceding. The quotation is from the *Cresphontes* of Euripides, Nauck[2] fr. 457.
[4] Reading τὸ θερμὸν (cp 961ᵃ 11) for τὸ ὄπισθεν. The Latin version of T. G. has *calor autem in partem transit adversam*, &c. The meaning will be that under the influence of shame the eyes become cold, and therefore the heat is driven backwards and so reddens the ears.
[5] Cp. xxxii. 1, 8, and 12, where additional reasons are given.

the influence of provocation assistance is sent [1] to the more
sensitive and easily affected part,[2] as though it were suffering violence; for in those who are frightened it fails altogether there.

Why is it that, if one eye is held down, the other has a **4**
more intent gaze?   Is it because the origins of sight in the
two eyes are connected at one source?   So when one eye
20 moves, the common source of sight is also set in motion;
and when this moves, the other eye moves also.   When
one eye therefore is held down, all the movement will be
concentrated on the other eye, which consequently will be
able to gaze more intently.

Why is it that those who are blind from birth do not **5**
become bald?   Is it because the eye is injured by the
presence of a large quantity of moisture in the region of
25 the head?   This is why they cauterize the veins round the
temples of those who suffer from running at the eyes (thus
closing the ducts through which the humours flow), and
scrape the head, cutting into the skin upon it.   Since,
therefore, it is the excretion gathering in the head which
injures the eyes, this same excretion by collecting in too
great quantities in the head might prevent the eyes [3] from
30 originally coming into being at all.   And since the hair
grows from excretions, and the excretion in the head of
those who are blind from birth is abundant, it is only
natural that they are not bald.

Why are those whose eyes protrude affected more than **6**
others by smoke?   Is it because smoke reaches the pro-
jecting parts most quickly?

35   Why is it that we can turn the gaze of both eyes simul- **7**
taneously towards the right and the left and in the direction
of the nose, and that of one eye to the left or to the right, but
cannot direct them simultaneously one to the right and the
other to the left?[4]   Similarly, we can direct them downwards
and upwards; for we can turn them simultaneously in the

---

[1] i. e. there is a rush of heat.   [2] i. e. the eyes.
[3] The Teubner text misprint αὐτοὺς for αὐτούς.
[4] i. e. outwards away from the nose.

same direction, but not separately. Is it because the eyes, 40
though two, are connected at one point,[1] and under such
conditions, when one extremity moves, the other must follow **958ᵃ**
in the same direction, for one extremity becomes the source
of movement to the other extremity? Since, therefore, it is
impossible for one thing to move simultaneously in contrary
directions, it is impossible also for the eyes to do so;
for the extremities would move in opposite directions if
one moved up and the other down, and the source of the 5
movement of both of them would have to make corresponding movements, which is impossible.[2] The distortion of
the eyes is due to the fact that the eyeballs possess a
moving principle and turn, to a certain extent,[3] upwards
and downwards and sideways. When, therefore, being so
placed that they are in a similar position to one another
and midway between an upward and a downward and an 10
oblique movement,[4] the two eyeballs catch the visual ray
on corresponding points of themselves, they are not distorted and their gaze is quite mobile[5] (though when[6] they
catch the visual rays on corresponding points of themselves, although the vision is not distorted it does not
follow that the position of the eyes is the same.)[7] Yet, if
you turn up the whites of the eyes, part of the pupil is 15
obscured, as for example in those who are about to sneeze;
others have oblique vision, madmen for example; in others
the gaze is turned towards the nose, as in tragic masks and
in those who are nervous, for their glance denotes concentrated thought. But those who keep their gaze fixed on
one point without[8] having their eyeballs similarly situated,
or who have them similarly situated but do not keep them

---

[1] Cp. above, 957ᵇ 19 ff.

[2] The movement of each eye corresponds with a movement of their
common point of connexion; if, therefore, the two eyes move simultaneously in contrary directions, the point of connexion must make
two contrary movements at the same time, which is impossible.

[3] Reading μέχρι του.

[4] Placing the comma after πλάγιον instead of κινεῖσθαι.

[5] Reading κινητοί: T. G. renders *mobiles*.

[6] Reading ὅσαι δ' ⟨ἂν⟩, as suggested by the Teubner editors.

[7] The point of this sentence seems to be that the previous proposition
is not convertible.

[8] Reading μὴ for μήθ'. The Teubner text misprints ὑμοίως for
ὁμοίως.

20 fixed on the same point, both these have distorted vision;
they therefore scowl and screw up the eyes, for they try
to fix one eyeball in the same position as the other; so
they leave one eye alone and try to b ing the other into
position. If the vision of both eyes does not rest on the
same point,[1] they must be distorted; for the same thing
25 happens as in those to whom, when they press under the
eye,[2] a single object appears double, for in these too the
source of vision is disturbed. If, therefore, the eye is moved
upwards, the terminus of the vision is lowered; if downwards, it is raised. And if the position of one eye is
changed, the object of the vision therefore seems to move
30 up or down, because the vision also does so, but it does not
appear double unless the vision of both eyes is in use.
A similar distortion[3] occurs also in one whose eyes do not
correspond,[4] causing him to see double; but this is due
to the position of the vision, because it is not in the middle
of the eye.

35 Why do those who are short-sighted write in small **8**
characters?[5] For it is strange that those who have not
acute vision should do what requires such vision. Is it
because small things appear large when they are near at
hand, and the short-sighted hold what they are writing
close to their eyes? Or is it because they screw up their
eyes when they write? For owing to the feebleness of
their sight, if they write with their eyes wide open, the
958ᵇ vision, being dispersed, can only see dimly; but when the
eyes are screwed up, it all falls on one point, and, since it
forms a small angle, it necessarily causes the writing of
small characters.

---

[1] Reading κατὰ ταὐτὸ with Bussemaker.
[2] The full phrase would be ὑποβάλλουσι τὸν δάκτυλον ὑπὸ τὸν ὀφθαλμόν;
cp. *de Insomniis* 441ᵇ 31, and *Met.* 1063ª 8. The reference is to the
experiment of slightly displacing the eyeball by pressing the finger
under it.
[3] Putting a full stop after ὦσι and reading καὶ διαστροφὴ τοιαύτη.
[4] ἑτερόφθαλμος in Classical Greek means 'having only one eye'; in
later Greek it can mean 'having different eyes'; see L. and S. *s.v.*
and cp. ἑτερόγλαυκος, ἑτερόπους, &c.
[5] Cp. below, chapter 15.

9   Why can some people see more clearly after suffering from ophthalmia ? Is it because their eyes are thus purged ? 5 For often the external thickening blocks the vision, but is dissolved when the eye discharges. Hence also it is beneficial that the eyes should be made to smart, with onion for example ;[1] but a substance of the opposite kind, such as marjoram, has an adverse effect.[2]

10   Why are those who see with only one eye less liable to disturbance of the vision ? Is it because their mind is less 10 affected, and so the disturbance of the vision is less felt ?

11   Why do objects appear double to those whose eyes are distorted ?[3] Is it because the movement [4] does not reach the same point on each of the eyes ? So the mind thinks that it sees two objects when it really sees one twice. A similar phenomenon occurs if one crosses the fingers ; for a single object appears to be two to a single person 15 touching it twice.[5]

12   Why is it that the senses on the right side of the body are not superior to those on the left side, but in all other respects the right side of the body is superior ?[6] Is it a question of habit, namely, that we accustom ourselves immediately to perceive equally well with the senses on both sides of the body ? And it seems that the superiority of the right-hand parts of the body is due to habit, for we can accustom ourselves to be ambidextrous. Or is it 20 because to feel sensation is to be passive, and the right parts of the body are superior in that they are more active and less passive than the left ?

13   Why is it that in all other respects the right side of the body is superior, but in sensation the two sides are alike ?[7]

---

[1] Cp. 959^b 11, 12. It seems necessary to read κρομμύῳ for κρόμμυον.
[2] The reading here is uncertain, but the sense is clear.
[3] Reading διεστραμμένοις (cp. ^a20) for διιστάμενοις, which can hardly bear the meaning given by Bonitz (*Index* 196^a 22) of *distractis oculis*.
[4] i.e. of the visual ray from the object seen.
[5] This phenomenon is referred to again in 959^a 15; cp. also *Met.* 1011^a 33, and *de Somniis* 460^b 20 ff. It appears necessary to read ἁπτομένῳ.
[6] Cp. below, chapters 13, 18, and 29.
[7] Cp. chapters 12, 18, and 29.

₂₅ Is it because we habitually practise the equal use of sensation on both sides ? Moreover, to feel sensation is to be passive, and the superiority of the right side of the body is shown in activity, not in passivity.

Why is physical exercise detrimental to acuteness of **14** vision ? Is it because it makes the eye dry, as it does the ₃₀ rest of the body ? Now dryness hardens every kind of skin ; so it has that effect also on the skin covering the pupil. This is also the reason why the aged have not acute vision ; for their eyes have a hard and wrinkled surface, and so the vision is obscured.

Why do the short-sighted, though they have not acute **15** ₃₅ vision, write in small characters ?[1] Yet it is characteristic of acute vision to see what is small. Is it because, having weak sight, they screw up their eyes ? For when the sight proceeds forth in a concentrated glance it sees better, but when the eye is wide open its vision is dispersed. So owing to the feebleness of their sight they bring their eyelids close together, and, because their vision proceeds from a small area, they see magnitude on a small scale, and **959ᵃ** the characters which they write are on the same scale as their vision.

Why do the short-sighted bring their eyelids close **16** together when they look at anything ? Is it due to the weakness of their sight, so that, just as a man in looking at ₅ a distant object puts his hand up to his eyes, they close the eyelids to look at objects near at hand ? They do so in order that the vision may proceed forth in a more concentrated form, since it passes through a narrower opening, and that it may not be immediately dispersed by passing out through a wide aperture. A wider vision, however, covers a larger field.

Why is it that if the eye be moved sideways a single **17** ₁₀ object does not appear double ? Is it because the source of sight is still in the same line ? It can only appear double when the line is altered upwards or downwards ; and it

---

[1] Cp. above, chapter 8.

makes no difference if it is altered sideways, unless it is
also at the same time altered upwards or downwards.[1]
Why, then, is it possible in sight for a single object to
appear double if the eyes are in a certain position in
relation to one another, but impossible in the other senses?
Is it not possible also in touch that one thing becomes[2] [15]
two if the fingers are crossed?[3]   But with the other senses
this does not happen, because they do not perceive objects
which extend to a distance away from them, nor[4] are they
duplicated like the eyes. It takes place for the same
reason[5] as it does with the fingers; for then the touch is
imitating the sight.[6]

18   Why is it that, though in the rest of the body the left [20]
side is weaker than the right, this is not true of the eyes,
but the sight of both eyes is equally acute?[7]   Is it because
the parts of the body on the right side are superior in
activity but not in passivity, and the sight is passive?

19   Why is it that when we keep our gaze fixed on objects
of other colours our vision deteriorates, whereas it improves
if we gaze intently on yellow and green objects, such as [25]
herbs and the like?   Is it because we are least able to gaze
intently on white and black (for they both mar the vision),
and the above-mentioned colours come midway between
these,[8] so that, the conditions of vision being of the nature of
a mean, our sight is not weakened thereby but improved?
Perhaps, just as we take harm from over-violent physical [30]
exertion but moderate exercise is beneficial, so too is it with
the sight; for we over-exert the sight if we gaze intently
on solid objects, but we do not strain it in looking at objects
which contain moisture, since there is nothing in them to
resist the vision. Now green things are only moderately
solid and contain a considerable amount of moisture; they [35]

---

[1] Reading ἐὰν μὴ ἅμα καὶ ἄνω ⟨ἢ κάτω⟩.
[2] We should perhaps read φαίνεται for γίνεται.
[3] Cp. above, 958[b] 14, 15, and note.
[4] Reading οὔτε for οὐδέ.
[5] Reading, with Richards, διὰ ταυτό.
[6] i. e. the two crossed fingers resemble the two eyes.
[7] Cp. chapters 12, 13, 29.
[8] Black and white being contraries (cp. de Sensu 445[b] 25, &c.).

therefore do not harm the sight at all, but compel it to rest upon them, because the admixture of their colouring is well attempered to the vision.

Why is it that we see other things better with both eyes, 20 but we can judge of the straightness [1] of lines of writing 40 better with one eye, putting it close to the letters? Do 959ᵇ both eyes falling on the same point cause confusion, as the writers on optics say, whereas, when we look with one eye, straightness is more apparent to the straight vision, just as it is when a measuring rod is used?

5   Why does smoke make the eyes smart more than any 21 other part of the body? Is it because they alone are very weak, since the inner parts of the body are always the weakest? (This is shown by the fact that vinegar and anything pungent causes not the outer but the inner flesh to smart, because [2] the latter is the rarest flesh in the body and contains most pores.) For the vision finds its exit 10 through certain pores, and so what causes most stinging within is drawn away [3] from the outer flesh. The onion too has a similar effect and anything else which causes the eye to smart, and of liquids olive-oil more than any other, because it is composed of very small particles and so sinks in through the pores. Vinegar is used as a medicament for the rest of the flesh.

15   Why is it that the eye, although it is very weak, is the only 22 part of the body which does not feel the cold? Is it because the eye is of a fatty consistency and does not partake of the nature of flesh, and such substances are unaffected by the cold? For if the eye is really a fire,[4] this is not the reason

---

[1] Reading τὸ δὲ εὐθὺ with Xᵃ.

[2] The Latin version implies a new solution beginning at this point, which would necessitate a full stop after ἐντός and the reading ἢ ὅτι ἀραιότατον (ἀραιότατον being read by several MSS., including Yᵃ). This second question is, however, hardly likely, since, where alternatives are offered, the first is almost invariably introduced by πότερον, whereas here in l. 5 we have ἢ ὅτι.

[3] ἀποπίπτει is certainly corrupt: the Latin version of T. G. has *itaque quod his mordacissimum est, ceteris corporis partibus obvium subire densiora non potest sed perreptat et decidit*, which implies a longer text.

[4] Cp. below, 960ᵃ 32, and *de Sensu* 437ᵃ 22 ff., where this view, at

why it does not feel cold, for its fire is not at any rate
of such a character as to engender heat.

23   Why are tears warm when we let them fall in weeping, 20
but cold when we shed them owing to an affection of the
eyes? Is it because that which is unconcocted is cold,
while that which is concocted is hot? Now every malady
certainly proceeds from lack of concoction, and the tears of
those whose eyes are affected are unconcocted and therefore cold. It is for this reason that physicians regard cold 25
sweating as a sign of serious illness, while on the contrary
they consider that hot sweating tends to get rid of disease.[1]
For if the excretion is abundant, the internal heat cannot
concoct it,[2] so that it must necessarily be cold; but when it
is scanty, the internal heat prevails over it. Now all diseases 30
are caused by excretions.[3]

24   Why is it that, though the parts of the body on the right
side are more easily moved, the left eye can be closed more
easily than the right? Is it because the parts of the body
on the left always contain more moisture,[4] and things that 35
are moist naturally close up more easily?[5]

25   Why is it that though both a short-sighted and an old man
are affected by weakness of the eyes, the former places an
object, if he wishes to see it, near the eye, while the latter
holds it at a distance? Is it because they are afflicted with
different forms of weakness? For the old man cannot see 40
the object; he therefore removes the object at which he is **960[a]**
looking to the point at which the vision of his two eyes
meets, expecting them to be able to see it best in this
position;[6] and this point is at a distance. The short-
sighted man, on the other hand, can see the object but
cannot proceed to distinguish which parts of the thing

---

which Empedocles appears at times to hint, is criticized at great
length.
    [1] Cp. 870[a] 15 ff., and note.
    [2] δύνανται in the Teubner text is a misprint for δύναται.
    [3] Cp. 856[a] 1.   [4] Cp. 961[a] 2.
    [5] The following sentence εἶτα . . . καθ᾽ αὑτό appears to be hopelessly
corrupt. The Latin version of T. G. apparently translates a different
text.
    [6] Reading ἅτ᾽ ἐκεῖ (Richards).

at which he is looking are concave and which convex,
5 but he is deceived on these points. Now concavity and
convexity are distinguished by means of the light which
they reflect; so at a distance the short-sighted man cannot
discern how the light[1] falls on the object seen; but near at
hand the incidence of light can be more easily perceived.

Why is man alone, or at any rate more than the other **26**
animals, liable to distortion of vision?[2] Is it because he
10 alone, or more than the other animals, suffers from epilepsy
in his youth,[3] at which time distortion of the vision always
begins?

Why are men alone among the animals liable to distor- **27**
tion of the vision?[4] Is it because they have the smallest
distance between their eyes and their eyes are in a straight
15 line, so that any perversion is very obvious? Or is it because
the eyes of the other animals tend to be of one colour only,
and if the eyes were of uniform colour there could be no
distortion? Or is it because man alone in the animal
world is liable to epilepsy, and epilepsy, whenever it
occurs, causes distortion in the eyes as in the other parts
of the body? Distortion, however, sometimes occurs quite
20 late in life, namely, in those to whom the illness comes
late.

Why is it that we can see better against the light of **28**
a lamp or the sun, if we place the hand in front of the
light? Is it because the light of the sun or of the lamp falling on our vision makes it weaker by its excess of brightness,
since by this excess it destroys those very things[5] which
25 are akin to it?[6] But if the light is shaded by the hand, it
does not hurt the sight, and the object seen is equally in
the light; so the sight sees[7] better and the object seen is
just as visible.

---

[1] Reading τὴν αὐγὴν for τῇ αὐγῇ with Bonitz.
[2] This problem is more fully treated in the next chapter.
[3] Cp. *de Somno* 457ᵃ 3-10 and J. I. Beare's note.
[4] Cp. above, chapter 26.
[5] Reading καὶ αὐτὰ τὰ συγγενῆ (Richards).
[6] i. e. the brightness of the eye, which is a fire; cp. 959ᵇ 17-19 and note.
[7] Reading ὁρᾷ for δρᾷ (Richards).

29 Why is there a difference between the left and the right
hand [1] and foot, while this is not so with the eyes and ears ? [2] 30
Is it because the elements, when they are pure, show no
variation, but variations occur where the elements are com-
pounded? Now these senses consist of pure elements—the
sight of fire [3] and the hearing of air.

[1] Reading πρὸς τὰ δεξιὰ τὰ ἀριστερά.
[2] Cp. chapters 12, 13, 18.   [3] Cp. above, 959^b 17 and note.

BOOK XXXII

PROBLEMS CONNECTED WITH THE EARS

WHY is it that, though the ears are the most bloodless part **1** of the face, they are most affected by blushing in those who feel shame?[1] Is it because extraneous moisture naturally makes its way most easily into a void, and so, when the moisture is dissolved by the heat engendered in those who 40 feel shame, it collects in the ears? Or is it because the ears **960^b** are near the temples, where the moisture most collects? Now under the emotion of shame the moisture flows into the face and causes blushing. But the ears have less depth than any other part of the face and are naturally very warm and fresh coloured, unless they have been long numbed 5 by the cold ; they are then the most fresh coloured of all the parts of the face, and so the heat, when it is dispersed, being nearest the surface in the ears, makes them red.

Why is it that the ear-drums of divers burst in the sea? **2** Is it because the ear, as it fills with water, is subject to violent pressure, because it retains the breath? Surely, if this 10 is the reason, the same thing ought to happen in the air. Or is it because a thing breaks more easily if it does not yield, and more readily under pressure from what is hard than from what is soft? Now that which is inflated is less yielding, and the ears, as has been said, are inflated because the breath is retained in them ; and so the water, which is harder than the air, when it presses upon them bursts them.

15 Why do divers tie sponges round their ears?[2] Is it in **3** order that the sea may not rush violently in and burst the ear-drums? For thus the ears do not become full, as they do when the sponges are removed.

[1] Cp. above, xxxi. 3, and below, chapters 8 and 12.
[2] Cp. above, chapter 2.

4   Why is the dirt in the ears bitter ? [1] Is it because sweat is corrupt ? It is, therefore, a salty, corrupt substance ; and that which is corrupt and salty is bitter.   20

5   Why do sponge-divers slit their ears and nostrils ? Is it in order that the breath may pass more freely ? For it is by this way that the breath seems to pass out ; [2] for it is said that they suffer more from difficulty of breathing by being unable to expel the breath, and they are relieved 25 when they can as it were vomit the breath forth. It is strange, then, that they cannot achieve respiration for the sake of its cooling effect; this appears to be a greater necessity. Is it not quite natural that the strain should be greater when the breath is held, since then they are swollen and distended ? But there appears to be a spontaneous passage of the breath outwards ; and we must next consider 30 whether breathing inwards is so also. Apparently it is ; for they enable the divers to respire equally well by letting down a cauldron ; [3] for this does not fill with water, but retains the air, for it is forced down straight into the water ; since, if it inclines at all from an upright position, the water flows in.[4]

6   Why do some people cough when they scrape their ears ? 35 Is it because the hearing is connected with the same duct as the lungs and the wind-pipe ? This is shown by the fact that, if these parts are filled up, a man becomes deaf.[5] When, therefore, heat is set up by the friction, moisture is caused by melting and flows downwards from the duct [6] into the wind-pipe and causes coughing.

7   Why is it that, if a hole is pierced in the left ear, it generally 40 closes up more quickly than in the right ear ? It is for this 961^a

---

[1] Apollonius, *Mirab.* 28, seems to be referring to this problem, which he cites as occurring ἐν τοῖς φυσικοῖς προβλήμασι.

[2] Omitting ἀνατέμνουσι δέ . . . εὔπνοιαν, which is not rendered by T. G., and is almost certainly a gloss on ὅπως εὐπνούστεροι ὦσι. Also πονεῖν γὰρ κτλ. clearly explains ἐξιέναι δοκεῖ τὸ πνεῦμα and should follow immediately after it.

[3] i. e. used as a diving-bell.

[4] Reading ὀρθοῦ γὰρ ⟨ἂν⟩ ὁτιοῦν παρεγκλιθῇ, εἰσρεῖ (W. D. R.).

[5] Reading ὅτι, ⟨ἂν⟩ ἀναπληρῶνται, [καὶ] γίνονται ἐνεοί (W. D. R.).

[6] Reading πόρου with A^p.

reason that women call the right ear the ' male ' and the left the ' female '. Is it because the left parts of the body are moister [1] and hotter, and such things close up very quickly ? This is why green plants grow together again ; and why 5 wounds close up more readily in the young than in the old. That the parts on the left side of the body are moister is shown by the fact that they are softer and, generally speaking, partake rather of feminine characteristics.[2]

Why is it that in those who feel shame the extremities of **8** the ears turn red, but in those who are angry it is the eyes that do so ? [3] Is it because shame is a cooling in the eyes 10 accompanied by fear, so that the heat naturally leaves the eyes ? So, when it withdraws thence, it travels to the region best adapted to receive it, and this is the extremity of the ears ; for the region of the face is otherwise bony. In those who are angry the heat travels in the other direction and 15 makes itself most manifest in the eyes owing to their white colour.

Why is it that buzzing in the ears ceases if one makes a **9** sound ? Is it because the greater sound drives out the less ?

Why is it that, if water has flowed into the ear, one pours **10** olive oil in, though the moisture in the ear cannot pass out 20 through another liquid ? Is it because the oil floats on the surface of the water and, owing to the adhesive nature of the oil, the water clings to it when it comes out, the object being to make the water come out with the oil ? Or is it in order that the ear may be lubricated and the water therefore come out ? For oil being smooth acts as a lubricant.

Why is it that the [4] ear-drums of divers are less liable to **11** 25 burst if they pour olive-oil beforehand into them ? [5] Does

---

[1] Cp. above, 959ᵇ 33.

[2] The text makes no sense, since it merely repeats as a σημεῖον what has already been assumed in l. 2 above. The right sense is certainly that of the Latin version of T. G., *argumentum partes sinistras esse humidiores quod molliores sunt atque effeminatiores*, and we must read σημεῖον δὲ ὅτι ὑγρὰ μᾶλλον ⟨ὅτι μαλακώτερα⟩ καὶ ὅλως θηλυκώτερα τὰ ἀριστερά.

[3] Cp. chapters 1 and 12 and xxxi. 3.

[4] Reading ⟨τὰ⟩ ὦτα as in 960ᵇ 8.

[5] Cp. above, chapters 2 and 3.

the reason for their bursting already mentioned[1] still hold
good, but the oil poured into the ears cause the sea-water,
which subsequently enters the ear, to glide smoothly over
its surface, just as happens on the exterior parts of the
bodies of those who anoint themselves? The sea-water
gliding smoothly along does not make a violent impact
upon the inside of the ear, and so does not break the drum. 30

12 Why is it that, although the ears are the most bloodless
part of the face, they turn red in those who feel shame?[2]
Is everything carried to that part which is most devoid of
it? Now in a man who feels shame the blood seems to be
carried upwards in a heated condition; it therefore passes[3]
into the part which is most devoid of it and causes it to
become red. The same thing happens also in the cheeks.
A further reason is that the skin of the ears, which is tightly 35
stretched, is very thin and therefore very transparent.[4]

13 Why is it that no one scrapes out the ear while yawning?
Is it because, when one yawns, the drum of the ear, by
means of which he hears, is inflated? That this is so is
shown by the fact that one hears least well while yawning;[5]
for the breath, as happens also in the mouth,[6] finds its way 40
into the interior of the ears and thrusts the membrane outwards and prevents the sound from entering. If, therefore, 961^b
one touches the seat of hearing when in this condition in
such a way as to scrape it, one might cause considerable
damage to it; for the impact would be against a resisting
and unyielding surface inflated by the breath,[7] and it is
obvious that the skin[8] and the membrane are far from being 5
solid; and so great pain is caused and a wound might
result.

---

[1] 960^b 9 ff.   [2] Cp. above, chapters 1 and 8 and xxxi. 3.
[3] Reading with Bonitz εἰς οὖν τὸ κενώτατον ⟨ἰὸν⟩ ἐρυθριᾶν ποιεῖ.
[4] Reading δι' αὐτοῦ (Richards).   [5] Cp. 902^b 9, 904^a 16.
[6] Putting a comma instead of a full stop after στόμα.
[7] Cp. above, 960^b 10 ff.
[8] Reading τὸ δὲ ⟨τὸ⟩ δέρμα (Richards).

BOOK XXXIII

PROBLEMS CONCERNING THE NOSE

WHY is it that sneezing stops hiccuping but does not **1**
10 stop eructation?[1] Is it because they are not affections of
the same region, but eructation is a cooling and lack of
concoction in the stomach,[2] while hiccuping is a similar
affection of breath and moisture in the region of the lungs?
Now the regions about the head (the ears,[3] for example)
are closely connected with the lungs. This is proved by
the facts that deafness and dumbness are found together,
15 and that the diseases of the ears become diverted into
affections of the lungs; also in some persons coughing
results when the ears are scratched.[4] That there is a
connexion between the region of the nose, in which the
sneeze takes place, and the lungs is shown by the fact that
both share in respiration; and so, while the nose sneezes
when that region becomes hot, the lower region,[5] where
hiccuping takes place, also sneezes in sympathy. Now
20 heat causes concoction; hence vinegar stops hiccups, as
also does holding the breath if the hiccup is only slight,
for it heats the breath which is constricted.[6] So too in
sneezing the counter-constriction of the breath has this
effect and expiration takes place properly and from the
upper region; for it is impossible to sneeze without expiring.
25 The impetus then dispels the enclosed breath which is the
cause of the hiccup.

Why is it that if, when one is about to sneeze, one rubs **2**
the eye, one sneezes less?[7] Is it because what causes the
sneeze is a kind of heat, and friction produces heat, which,
30 owing to the close proximity to the eyes of the region in

---

[1] Cp. below, chapters 5, 13, and 17.
[2] Which is too far away to be affected.
[3] Reading τὰ ὦτα for τοῖς ὠσίν.   [4] Cp. 960^b 35.
[5] i. e. the lungs.   [6] Reading ⟨τὸ⟩ κατεχόμενον.
[7] Cp. chapter 8 and xxxi. 1.

which the sneeze occurs, destroys the other heat, just as the lesser fire fades away before the greater?

3 Why is it that one generally sneezes twice, and not once or many times? Is it because there are two nostrils? The channel, therefore, through which the breath passes is 35 divided between the two.[1]

4 Why is it that one sneezes more after one has looked at the sun? Is it because the sun engenders heat and so causes movement, just as does tickling the nose with a feather? For both have the same effect; by setting up movement they cause heat and create breath more quickly from the moisture; and it is the escape of this breath which 40 causes sneezing.

5 Why do sneezing and holding the breath and vinegar **962ᵃ** stop hiccups?[2] Does sneezing, since it is a displacement of the lower breath, act in the same sort of way as medicines which, though applied to the upper part of the body,[3] affect the lower part of the stomach? Holding the breath stops weak hiccups, because the slight impetus of the 5 breath which comes forth represses and stifles and completely dispels the hiccup, just as happens in coughing, which[4] ceases if you hold it back. Vinegar stops hiccuping because by its heat it vaporizes the surrounding moisture, which prevents eructation; for eructation takes place when the moisture in the upper part of the stomach is vaporized 10 and concocted, whereas hiccuping occurs when by the action of moisture breath is retained in an excessive quantity in the region of the lungs; for this, gaining impetus and being unable to break through, causes a spasm, and this spasm is called a hiccup. Hence hiccuping seizes those who are cold, because the cold causes the moisture to acquire consistency[5] from the breath, and the rest of the 15 breath, being still[6] enclosed, gives a leap, and its movement is hiccuping.

---

[1] Reading καθ᾽ ἑκάτερον ; the MSS. read καθ᾽ ἕτερα.
[2] Cp. chapters 1, 13, and 17.   [3] i.e. through the mouth.
[4] Reading περὶ τὴν βῆχα ⟨ἥ⟩, ἐάν κτλ.
[5] Reading συνεστάναι (Yᵃ reads συνιστάν), since ποιεῖ requires an infinitive.   [6] Punctuating πνεύματος· ἔτι περιλαμβανόμενον κτλ.

Why do we sometimes pour cold water over a person's **6**
face when his nose is bleeding? Is it because the heat is
20 thus driven inwards? If, therefore, the blood is near the
surface, it tends to liquefy it.

Why do we regard sneezing as divine,[1] but not coughing **7**
or running at the nose?[2] Is it because it comes from the
most divine part of us, namely, the head, which is the seat
of reasoning? Or is it because the other affections are the
results of disease, but sneezing is not?

25　Why does rubbing the eye stop sneezing?[3] Is it because **8**
by this means evaporation is given to the moisture? For
the eye sheds tears after friction, and sneezing is due to an
abundance of moisture. Or is it because the lesser heat is
destroyed by the greater? Now the eye when rubbed
30 acquires more heat than is contained in the nose; and for
this reason, even if we rub the nose itself, the sneezing stops.

Why is it that the emission of other kinds of breath, of **9**
wind, for example, and of eructation are not regarded as
sacred, but that of a sneeze is so regarded?[4] Is it because
of the three regions of the body—the head, the thorax, and
35 the lower stomach—the head is the most divine? Now
wind is breath from the lower stomach and eructation is
from the upper stomach, but sneezing is from the head;
because, therefore, this region is most sacred, the breath also
from it is revered as sacred. Or is it because all discharges
of breath show that the above-mentioned parts are in a
40 better state generally (for without any discharge of excre-
962^b ment[5] the breath in its passage out lightens the body), and
so too sneezing shows that the region of the head is in a
healthy condition and capable of concoction? For when
the heat in the head overcomes the moisture, the breath
turns into a sneeze. This is why men test the dying by

---

[1] Reading θεῖον (Richards).
[2] This problem is dealt with at greater length in chapter 9.
[3] This chapter is verbally identical with xxxi. I; cp. also chapter 2.
[4] Cp. chapter 7.
[5] Cp. the impersonal use of διαχωρεῖν in Xen. *Anab.* iv. 8. 20 κάτω
διεχώρει αὐτοῖς ('they were suffering from diarrhoea'), and Plato,
Phaedrus 268 B.

applying something which will cause sneezing, with the idea that, if this does not affect them, their case is indeed 5 desperate. Thus sneezing is revered as sacred as being a sign of health in the best and most sacred region of the body, and is regarded as a good omen.

10 Why does man sneeze most of all animals?[1] Is it because in him the ducts are wide through which the breath and scent[2] pass in? For it is with these when they are full 10 of breath that he sneezes. That these ducts are wide is shown by the fact that man has a weaker sense of smell than any other animal, and those who have narrow ducts[3] have a keener sense of smell. If, therefore, the moisture, the evaporation of which causes sneezing, enters in larger quantities and more often into wide ducts, and man more than any other animal has such ducts, he might naturally be expected to sneeze[4] more often. Or is it because[5] his 15 nostrils are particularly short, and so the heated moisture can quickly become breath and be expelled, whereas in other animals owing to the length of their nostrils it cools before it can evaporate?

11 Why is sneezing between midnight and midday regarded as a bad thing, but between midday and midnight as a good 20 thing? Is it because sneezing seems rather to check those who are commencing anything and are at the beginning? And so, if it occurs when we are intending or beginning something, we are deterred from action.[6] Now early morning and the period after midnight are as it were a new beginning; therefore we carefully avoid sneezing so as not to hinder the action which has been begun.[7] But towards 25 evening[8] and up to midnight there is as it were an ending

---

[1] This problem is almost verbally identical with x. 18. The subject is more fully treated in x. 54.

[2] Reading ὀσμή for ῥύμη (Bussemaker), cp. 892^b 23.

[3] Reading λεπτόποροι for λεπτοὶ πόροι (Bussemaker).

[4] Reading πταρνύοιντο for πτάρνυντο.

[5] Reading ἢ ὅτι for ὅσοις, cp. 892^b 30.

[6] ὅταν μέλλωσιν ἀρχομένοις συμβῆναι of the MSS. gives no sense, and ὅταν μέλλουσιν ἢ ἀρχομένοις συμβῇ or something similar must be read. The Latin version of T. G. renders: *itaque cum rem agere pergimus atque inter initia sternuisse acciderit.*

[7] Reading ⟨τὸ⟩ ὡρμημένον.   [8] Reading δείλην (Richards).

and the contrary of the earlier period, so that the same thing that was undesirable becomes, under contrary conditions, desirable.

Why do the old sneeze with difficulty? Is it because the 12 ducts through which the breath passes have become partially closed? Or is it because they are no longer able to 30 raise the breath [1] up with ease, and, when they have done so, they expel it downwards with a violent effort?

Why is it that, if one holds the breath, hiccuping ceases? [2] 13 Is it because hiccuping is the result of cooling (hence those who are frightened and those who are chilled hiccup), whereas the breath when it is held back warms the interior region?

35 Why do the deaf usually talk through their noses? [3] Is it 14 because they suffer from lung trouble, since deafness is simply a congestion in the region of the lungs? The voice therefore does not easily find a passage; but, just as the breath of those who are panting or gasping accumulates owing to their inability to exhale it, so it is with the voice of the 40 deaf. It therefore forces its way even through the nostrils, 963^a and, as it does so, owing to the friction, causes the echoing sound. For talking through the nose takes place when the upper part of the nose, where the openings to the roof of the mouth are situated, becomes hollow in form; it then resounds like a bell, its lower part being narrow.

5 Why is sneezing the only phenomenon which does not 15 occur when we are asleep, but takes place practically always while we are awake? Is it because sneezing is the result [4] of heat of some kind causing motion in the region from which the sneeze proceeds (and this is why we look up at the sun when we want to sneeze [5]), whereas [6] when we are asleep the heat is driven inwards? [7] This is why the lower 10 parts become warm in those who are asleep, and the large

---

[1] Reading αὐτὸ for τὰ (Richards). [2] Cp. chapters 1, 5, and 17.
[3] The same problem is differently treated in xi. 2 and 4.
[4] Omitting καὶ after γίνεται. [5] Cp. 961^b 36 ff.
[6] Reading καθευδόντων δὲ for ⟨ἢ⟩ ὅτι καθευδόντων, the δὲ being implied by the preceding μέν. [Bussemaker confirms this reading from *Prob. Ined.* (in his edition) ii. 40.]
[7] Cp. 867^b 32.

quantity of breath which collects there is the cause of the emission of semen during sleep.[1] It is only natural, therefore, that we do not sneeze ; for when the heat (which naturally sets in motion the moisture in the head, the evaporation [2] of which causes the sneeze) is withdrawn from the head, it is only natural that the phenomenon which it causes does not take place. Men break wind and eruct rather than sneeze when they are asleep,[3] because, as the region about the stomach becomes hot during sleep, the moisture there becomes vaporized and, as it does so, is carried into the nearest parts ; for it is thrust together there by the breath engendered during sleep. For a man who is asleep is better able to hold than to expel the breath ; therefore he collects the heat within him. Now when a man holds his breath he forces it downwards ; for a downward course is unnatural to the breath, and that is why it is difficult to hold the breath. The same thing is the cause of sleep also ; for since waking is movement and this movement occurs to a great extent in the organs of sensation while we are awake, it is plain that we should go to sleep when our organs of sense are at rest.[4] And since it is fire which creates movement in our parts, and this during sleep is driven inwards and leaves the region of the head, where the seat of sensation is situated, our organs of sense would then be most at rest, and this must be the cause of sleep.

16   Why do people shiver after sneezing and passing urine?[5] Is it because by both actions the veins are emptied of the warm air which was previously in them, and, when they are empty, other air enters from without colder than that which was previously in the veins ; and such air entering in causes shivering?

17   Why does sneezing stop hiccuping?[6] Is it because hiccuping (unlike eructation, which comes from the stomach

[1] Cp 867ᵇ 9.   [2] Reading with Sylburg and Bekker ἐξαερουμένου.
[3] Omitting ἢ ἐγρηγορότες as a mistaken gloss on μᾶλλον. The position of καὶ ἐρεύγονται after πτάρνυνται is very awkward and perhaps ἢ πτάρνυνται is also a gloss—this time a correct one—on μᾶλλον.
[4] Omitting ἡμῶν as a gloss.
[5] A slightly longer version of viii. 8.
[6] Cp. chapters 1, 5, and 13.

40 when it receives food) comes from the lungs[1] and gene-
963ᵇ rally results from cooling as an effect of chill or pain or
medicine entering from above ? For the region of the lungs,
being naturally hot, when it is cooled does not emit all the
breath but forms as it were bubbles. This is why hiccup-
5 ing stops if the breath is held (for the region then becomes
warm) ; and the application of vinegar, which is heating,
has the same effect. Heat then collecting from the heat of
the brain also (for the upper regions are connected by
passages with the lungs) and the lungs being warm, the holding of the breath which precedes the sneeze, and the downward impetus from above, dissolve the hiccuping.

10 Why is it that those who have crisp hair and whose hair **18**
curls are usually rather snub-nosed ? Is it because crisp-
ness resides in fatness, and fatness is accompanied by hardness, and the blood being hard is hot, and heat does not
produce excrement, and boniness is formed from excrement,
and the cartilage of the nose is bony—therefore a scantiness
15 of this part is a natural result ? This theory is supported
by the fact that young children are always snub-nosed.

---

[1] Reading πνεύμονος for πνεύματος [so too Bussemaker], cp. 961ᵇ 11
ὁ δὲ λυγμὸς τοῦ περὶ πνεύμονα κατάψυξις ; also the mention of some part
of the body is required to which ὁ τόπος (963ᵇ 2) may refer.

BOOK XXXIV

PROBLEMS CONCERNING THE MOUTH AND THE PARTS THEREIN

1 WHY is it that those who have spongy teeth are not long-lived?[1] Is it because the long-lived have more teeth, for instance males have more than females, men than women, and rams than ewes? Those then who have spongy teeth apparently resemble those who have fewer teeth.

2 Why is it that, though the teeth are stronger than the flesh, yet they are more sensitive to cold? Is it because they are closely connected with the pores, in which the heat, because it is small, is quickly overcome by the cold and causes pain?

3 Why are the teeth more sensitive to cold than to heat, while the contrary is true of the flesh? Is it because the flesh partakes of the mean and is of moderate temperature, but the teeth are cold and therefore more sensitive to cold?[2] Or is it because the teeth consist of narrow pores in which the heat is scanty, so that they are quickly affected by the opposite of heat? Now the flesh is warm, so that it is unaffected by·the cold, but is quickly sensitive to heat; for it is a case of 'fire added to fire'.

4 Why is it that the tongue is indicative of many things? For in acute diseases it indicates fever by the presence[3] of

---

[1] This is the same problem as that of x. 48, differently answered. The solution of the problem presented here is taken direct from *Hist. Anim.* 501^b 20 ff.

[2] Reading ψυχροῦ for ἐναντίου. The reading of the MSS., οἱ δὲ ὀδόντες ψυχροί, ὥστε τοῦ ἐναντίου (i. e. τοῦ θερμοῦ) μᾶλλον αἰσθητικοί, is quite impossible, since (1) the problem is discussing why the teeth are more susceptible to *cold*, (2) the flesh, being hot, is stated (in ll. 30, 31) to be more susceptible to heat, therefore the teeth, being cold, ought to be more susceptible to *cold*. The Latin version, which renders *rem frigidam sentire plenius possunt*, evidently translates ψυχροῦ.

[3] Omitting καὶ before ἐάν.

blisters upon it ; also the tongues of sheep are particoloured
35 if the sheep are so. Is it because the tongue is capable of
taking up moisture and is situated near the lungs, which
are the seat of fevers ? Now all things which are particoloured are so because their humours are particoloured,
and that part first takes on colour through which the humour
first passes ; and this is what happens to the tongue. Now
blisters collect on the tongue because it is spongy ; for a
40 blister is as it were an eruption which has not been concocted within.[1]

964ª Why is it that the tongue becomes bitter and salty and 5
acid, but never sweet ? Is it because these qualities are
corruptions and so the tongue cannot perceive its own real
nature ?

Why is it that the coloration of the tongue corresponds 6
5 with that of the skin ?[2] Is it because it is really an external
part of the body, though it is enclosed in the mouth, and is it
because the skin on it is thin that even a slight variegation
of colour makes itself visible ? Or is it because it is liquid
that causes change of colour, and the tongue is most affected
by what is drunk ?

10 Why is it that one can emit both hot and cold breath 7
from the mouth ? For one can puff out cold breath and
breathe out warm breath.[3] That the breath is warm can
be demonstrated by placing the hand near the mouth.[4] Or
is the air which is set in motion warm[5] in both cases, but
does he who puffs out breath not set the air in motion all
at once but blow through a partly closed mouth, so that,
15 though he emits but little breath, he sets up motion over
a large area of the outer air, in which the warmth from his
mouth is not apparent owing to its scantiness ? But one
who breathes out breath emits it all at once, and therefore
it is warm. For it is characteristic of puffing out breath

---

[1] Cp. 965ᵇ 16.
[2] This subject has been already dealt with as part of the problem of
chapter 4 above.
[3] Cp. 945ᵇ 15 and note.   [4] Putting a full stop after χεῖρα.
[5] Reading θερμός (Ruelle) for ψυχρός.

to[1] pack the air into a particularly small space; whereas breathing out air is emitting it all at once.

8 Why is it that, if one expires violently and with all the breath at once, it is impossible to expire again? So too with violent inspiration, which cannot be repeated again immediately. Is it because expiration is a local dilatation, and inspiration a local contraction, both of which can be carried out within certain limits? Clearly, therefore, the two processes must be carried out one after another, but neither can be performed twice consecutively.

9 Why is it that, though there is one passage through which meat and drink pass and another through which we breathe, if we swallow too large a morsel we choke? In this there is nothing strange; for not only do we choke if something penetrates into this passage, but we choke still more if it be blocked. Now the passages through which we take food and through which we breathe are parallel to one another; when, therefore, too large a morsel is swallowed, the respiration is also blocked, so that there is no way out for the breath.

10 Why is it that men are very long-lived who have a cut right across the hand?[2] Is it because those animals which are badly articulated are short-lived and weak? As an instance of weakness we may take young animals, and of shortness of life the aquatic creatures. Clearly then those who are well articulated must be the opposite,[3] namely, those in whom even those parts are best articulated which are by nature badly articulated. Now the inside of the hand is the least well articulated part of the body.

11 Why is it that, in deep breathing, when we draw in the breath the stomach contracts, but when we expire it fills **964ᵇ** out? Now the contrary of this might be expected to occur. Is it because in breathing the stomach is compressed downwards by the flanks and then appears to expand again, like bellows?

---

[1] Reading τό for τῷ, but the corruption is perhaps deeper, though the sense is clear.

[2] The so-called 'line of life'. The same problem is treated in a slightly different form in x. 49.   [3] i. e. long-lived.

5   Why do we respire ?   Does the breath dissolve into fire, 12 just as the moisture dissolves into breath ?   The heat, then, of nature, when the greater part of the breath produces fire, causes pain and pressure upon the ducts ; and that is why we emit the fire with the breath.[1] Now when the breath and fire go forth, the ducts contract and are 10 cooled, and pain results ; we therefore draw the breath in again.   Then when we have opened the breath-ducts[2] and given them relief, fire is again engendered and we again feel discomfort, and therefore expel it and continue to do so indefinitely ; just as we continually blink as the part 15 round the eye cools and becomes dry.   Also we walk without[3] giving attention to the manner of our walking, the intellect by itself[4] guiding us.   In like manner, therefore, we carry out the process of breathing ; for we do so by contriving to draw in air, and then continue to draw it in.

[1] The Teubner text omits a whole line here by haplography and should read τὸ πῦρ ⟨μετὰ τοῦ πνεύματος. ὅταν δὲ ἐξέλθῃ τὸ πνεῦμα καὶ τὸ πῦρ⟩, συμπιπτόντων κτλ.

[2] Reading πνεύματος with Y^a X^a.

[3] Reading οὐ for οὖν with Bussemaker.

[4] Reading αὐτῆς for αὐτοῖς, unless we suppose a lacuna after τῆς διανοίας αὐτοῖς.

BOOK XXXV

PROBLEMS CONNECTED WITH THE EFFECTS
OF TOUCH

1 WHY do we shudder more when some one else touches us than when we touch ourselves? Is it because the touch of a part of some one else has more power to produce sensation than that of a part of oneself, since that which is connected by growth with the sense-organ is imperceptible? Also anything which occurs unawares and suddenly is more 25 frightening, and fright is a process of cooling; and both these qualities are possessed by the touch of another as contrasted with one's own touch. And, speaking generally, passive sensation is produced either solely by some one else or at any rate in a greater degree[1] than by oneself; as happens for example in tickling.

2 Why do we feel tickling in the armpits and on the soles 30 of the feet? Is it owing to the thinness of the skin? And do we feel it most where we are unaccustomed to being touched, as in these parts and the ears?

3 Why is it that every one does not shudder at the same things?[2] Is it because, just as we do not all feel pleasure or pain at the same things, so we do not shudder at the same things? For the same sort of cooling process takes 35 place.[3] So some people shudder when a garment is torn, others when a saw is being sharpened or drawn through wood, others when pumice-stone is being cut, others when the millstone is grinding on stone.[4]

4 Why is it that, though the summer is warm and the winter cold, bodies are colder to the touch in summer than 965^a

[1] Transposing ἡ μᾶλλον and ἡ μόνον (Richards).   [2] Cp. vii. 5.
[3] i. e. when we shudder and when we feel pain.
[4] i. e. when there is no grist in the mill. ὄνος is always used of the upper millstone.

in winter? Is it because perspiration and the act of perspiring cool the body, and this takes place in summer
but not in winter? Or is it because cold and heat are
5 driven inwards[1] inversely to the seasons,[2] and in the
summer the cold takes refuge within and therefore causes
perspiration to be given off, whereas in winter the cold
keeps the perspiration in and the body vaporizes it, as does
the earth?

Why do the hairs bristle upon the skin?[3] Is it because 5
they naturally stand erect when the skin is contracted,[4]
10 and this contraction occurs owing to cold and certain other
conditions?

Why is it that no one can tickle himself? Is it because 6
one also feels tickling by another person less if one knows
beforehand that it is going to take place, and more if one
does not foresee it? A man will therefore feel tickling
least when he is causing it and knows that he is doing so.
Now laughter is a kind of derangement and deception (and
15 so men laugh when they are struck in the midriff; for it is
no ordinary part of the body with which one laughs[5]).
Now that which comes unawares tends to deceive, and it is
this also which causes the laughter, whereas one does not
make oneself laugh.

Why is it that we feel tickling in particular on the lips? 7
Is it because the part which feels tickling must be situated
20 not far from the seat of sensation? Now the lips are
essentially in this position, and so of all parts of the head
the most sensitive to tickling are the lips, which are fleshy,
and therefore very easily set in motion.

Why is it that a man bursts out laughing if one scratches 8
the region of his armpits, though he does not do so when

---

[1] For the doctrine of ἀντιπερίστασις see note on 867ª 32.
[2] i. e. cold drives heat inwards and vice versa; cp. 888ª 34 ff., where
hot water is said to drive cold inwards.
[3] The same problem occurs in viii. 12.
[4] Reading συσπάσωσι for σπάσωσι, cp. 888ª 39.
[5] Laughter being a contraction of the muscles of the midriff or
diaphragm, which according to the Greeks enclosed the seat of
intelligence.

any other part is tickled? And why does a man sneeze if he tickles his nostrils with a feather? Is it because these 25 parts are regions where the small veins are situated, and when these are cooled or undergo the opposite process [1] they become moist or dissolve [2] into breath as the result of the moisture? (Similarly, if one compresses the veins in the neck of one who is asleep, an extraordinarily pleasant sensation is caused.[3]) And when the breath is engendered in greater abundance, we emit it in a single mass.[4] Simi- 30 larly also in sneezing, when we warm the moisture in the nostrils and scratch them with a feather, we dissolve it into breath; and when the breath becomes superabundant we expel it.

9 Why is it that we often shudder after taking solid food? Is it because when food which is cold enters the body it prevails at first over the natural heat rather than vice 35 versa?

10 Why is it that an object which is held between two crossed fingers [5] appears to be two? Is it because we touch it at two sentient points? For when we hold the hand in its natural position we cannot touch [6] an object with the outer [7] sides of the two fingers.

---

[1] i. e. become hot.
[2] Reading ὑγραίνονται ... διαλύονται.
[3] Reading ὥσπερ ἐὰν ... φλέβας καθεύδουσιν ἡμῖν, ἡδονὴ θαυμασία τίς ἐστιν (W. D. R.).
[4] And this causes an explosion of laughter.
[5] Reading τοῖς ἐναλλὰξ δακτύλοις (T. G. renders *digitis vice mutata implicatis*), cp. 958ᵇ 14, 15 and note.
[6] Reading θιγεῖν (W. D. R.) for εἰπεῖν.
[7] Reading ἐκτός, from T. G., for ἐντός.

BOOK XXXVI

PROBLEMS CONNECTED WITH THE FACE

965^b WHY is the face chosen for representation in portraits? **1**
Is it because the face shows best what the character of a
person is? Or is it because it is most easily recognized?

Why is it that one perspires most freely on the face, **2**
though it is far from being fleshy?[1] Is it because parts
5 which are rather moist and rare perspire freely, and the
head has these characteristics? For it contains an abundance of natural moisture; this is shown by the veins
which extend from it and the discharges which it produces,
and the fluidity of the brain and the numerous pores.
That there are numerous pores extending outwards is
10 shown by the presence of the hair. The perspiration
then comes not from the lower parts of the body but
from the head; and so one perspires most readily and
freely[2] on the forehead, for it is highest in position and
moisture flows down and not up.

Why do eruptions occur more frequently on the face **3**
than elsewhere? Is it because this part contains rarities
15 and moisture? That this is so is shown by the growth of
hair on it and by its power of sensation; and an eruption
is as it were an efflorescence of unconcocted moisture.

---

[1] This problem occurs also in Bk. ii. 17.
[2] Reading πρῶτον ⟨καὶ⟩ μάλιστα, cp. 868ᵃ 2.

BOOK XXXVII

PROBLEMS CONNECTED WITH THE WHOLE BODY

1 WHY is it that, though the body is in a state of continual 20 flux, and effluvia are given off from the excrements, the body is only lightened if it perspires?[1] Is it because the excretion in the form of effluvia is too little (for when liquid is transformed into air, much air is formed out of little liquid)? For what is excreted[2] is more, which 25 accounts for the excretion taking longer to begin.

2 And what is the reason of this? Is it because its exit takes place through smaller pores? For the viscous and the adhesive matter is expelled with the moisture because it mingles with it, but it cannot be expelled with the breath; and it is this thick matter in particular which causes pain. Therefore also vomiting lightens the body more than sweating, because that which is vomited, being thicker and 30 more substantial, carries away this viscous matter with it. Or is there a further reason, namely, that the region in which the viscous and the adhesive matter is, is situated at a distance in relation to the flesh (and so it is difficult to make it change its position), but near to the stomach? For it is engendered either in or close to it; and therefore 35 it is difficult to get rid of[3] it in any other way.

3 Why is it that friction produces flesh? Is it because heat has great power to increase what is in the body? For the bulk of what already exists in it becomes greater if the

---

[1] This and the following chapter are almost verbally identical with ii. 22, but the problem is here divided into two.

[2] i.e. in sweat.

[3] Reading δυσεξάγωγον from 868^b 11.

body is in continual motion and if our internal humours are carried upwards and vaporized, and this occurs as **966^a** a result of friction; whereas in the absence of this, the body wastes away and decreases. Or is it because the flesh increases in bulk by nutriment[1] as the result of heat (for anything which is hot has the power to attract moisture, 5 and the nutriment distributed in the flesh is moist and the flesh takes up moisture better by being rare, for the rarer a thing is the more it can absorb, like a sponge), whereas friction makes the flesh well ventilated and rare and prevents congestion in the body? Now if there is no congestion, there can be no wasting either; for atrophy and 10 wasting are the result of conglomeration. But the better ventilated and the rarer and the more homogeneous the parts of the body are the more likely they are to acquire bulk, for they are better able to take up nutriment and to get rid of excrements, since the flesh must be rarefied and not densified in order to promote health.[2] For just as a city or 15 locality is healthy which is open to the breezes (and that is why the sea too is healthy), so the body is healthier if the air can circulate in it than when it is in the contrary condition. For either there ought to be no excrement[3] in the body, or else the body ought to be able to get rid of it as soon as possible and be in such a condition that it can reject the excrement as soon as it receives it and be always 20 in a state of motion and never at rest. For that which remains stationary putrefies (standing water, for example), and that which putrefies creates disease; but that which is rejected passes away before it becomes corrupt. This then does not occur if the flesh is dense (the ducts being as it were 25 blocked up), but it does happen if the flesh is rare. One ought not therefore to walk naked in the sun; for the flesh thereby solidifies and acquires an absolutely fleshy consistency; for the internal moisture remains, but the surface moisture is expelled in the form of vapour, just as in roast meat the inner portions are moister than in boiled meat.

---

[1] Reading τῇ τροφῇ (W. D. R.).

[2] 966^a 13-34 is almost verbally identical with 865^b 18-37 and 884^a 24-^b7.

[3] Reading μηδὲν ⟨περίττωμα⟩, ἢ τούτου, cp. 865^b 21, 884^a 29.

Nor ought one to walk in the sun with the chest bare, for then the sun draws out the moisture from the best 30 constructed parts of the body, which [1] least require to be deprived of it; but it is rather the inner parts which need to be dried,[2] for, because they are remote, it is impossible to produce perspiration except by a violent effort; but it is easy to exhaust the moisture in the chest, because it is near the surface.

4   Why is it that, when we are chilled, the same heat causes 35 more burning and pain?[3] Is it because owing to its density the flesh holds the heat which comes into contact with it? This is the reason why lead becomes hotter than wool. Or is the passage of the heat violent because the body is congealed by cold?

5   Why does dry friction render the flesh solid? Is it 966^b because heat is engendered by the friction and the moisture is used up? Furthermore, the flesh when rubbed becomes dense,[4] and everything becomes denser and solider the 5 more it is rubbed. This can be seen in many examples; dough, for instance, and clay and similar substances, if you pour water into them and spread them out, remain moist and fluid, but, if you apply more friction, they quickly densify and solidify and become viscous.

6   Why does friction produce more flesh than running? Is 10 it because running cools the flesh and makes it less absorbent of nutriment, but part of the nutriment is shaken downwards, while the part on the surface,[5] owing to the

---

[1] Reading ἅ, as in the parallel passage 865^b 34.

[2] Punctuating (as in the parallel passage 865^b 32-5) οὐδὲ τὰ στήθη γυμνὰ ἔχοντα βαδίζειν ἐν ἡλίῳ· ἀπὸ γὰρ ... ἀφαιρέσεως, ἀλλὰ μᾶλλον τὰ ἐντὸς ξηραντέον.

[3] i. e. than it would if we were not chilled. This chapter is almost verbally identical with viii. 19.

[4] This is a direct contradiction of the doctrine of chapters 3 and 6 (^a 7, ^b 15), where it is stated that friction rarefies the flesh.

[5] Reading ἐπιπολῆς [so too Bussemaker] for the meaningless ἐπὶ πολλοῦ, which probably arose from the dittography of the λ and the subsequent assimilation of the gender to that of θερμοῦ; cp. ^a 27 τὸ δὲ ἐπιπολῆς ἀπαλλάττεται ἐξατμιζόμενον.

exhaustion of the natural heat, becomes quite thin and is
expelled in the form of breath? But the hand by friction
¹⁵ makes the flesh rare and able to take up nutriment. Moreover, the external contact, opposing by its pressure the
natural impetus of the flesh, makes it compact and drives
it back upon itself.

BOOK XXXVIII

PROBLEMS CONCERNING THE COLORATION 20 OF THE FLESH

1 WHY is it that the sun bleaches wax and olive oil, but darkens the flesh?[1] Is it because it bleaches the former by extracting the water from them (for that which is moist is naturally black owing to the admixture of the earthy element), whereas it scorches the flesh?

2 Why have fishermen reddish hair, and purple-fishers and 25 in short all who work on the sea? Is it because the sea is hot and full of dryness because it is salty? Now that which is of this nature, like lye and orpiment, makes the hair reddish. Or is it because they are warmer in their outer parts, but their inner parts are chilled, because, owing 30 to their getting wet, the surrounding parts are always being dried by the sun? And as they undergo this process, the hair being dried becomes fine and reddish. Furthermore all those who live towards the north have fine, reddish hair.

3 Why is it that running in clothing and anointing the body under the clothing with oil makes men pale skinned,[2] 35 whereas running naked makes them ruddy? Is it because ventilation produces a ruddy colour, while suffocation has the opposite effect and causes[3] pallor, because the moisture on the surface is heated up and does not cool? Now perspiring in clothes and anointing the body under the clothing both have the same effect, namely, that the heat is enclosed. But running naked makes the flesh ruddy for 967^a the opposite reason, because the air cools the excrements

---

[1] Cp. below, chapter 11.
[2] The same subject is dealt with in Hippocr. *de Diaet.* ii. 63 and Theophrastus *de Sudore*, § 39.
[3] Reading τοὐναντίον, διὰ δέ.

which form[1] and ventilates the body. Further, the oil, which is moist and thin, being smeared over the body under the clothing and blocking up the pores, does not 5 allow either the moisture and breath from the body to escape or the external air to penetrate inwards. Therefore the moist excrements being choked in the body decay and produce pallor.

Why is it that the ventilation of the flesh makes it **4** ruddy? Is it because pallor is as it were a corruption of the flesh? When, therefore, the surface is moist and hot, 10 it becomes yellow unless it is cooled and gives off the heat in the form of breath.

Why is it that those who perspire are ruddy as a result **5** of their exercises, whereas athletes are pale? Is it because as the result of moderate exertion the heat is burnt up and comes to the surface, whereas by constant exertion it is 15 drained off with the perspiration and breath, the body being rarefied by exertion? When, therefore, the heat comes to the surface, a man becomes ruddy, just as he does when he is hot or ashamed; but when the heat fails, he is pallid. Now ordinary persons indulge in moderate exercise, whereas athletes are constantly training.

20 Why are men more sunburnt who sit still in the sun than **6** those who take exercise?[2] Is it because those who are in motion are as it were fanned by the breath owing to the movement of the air which they set up, whereas those who are sitting still do not undergo this process?

Why does the sun scorch, while fire does not? Is it **7** 25 because the heat of the sun is finer and can penetrate farther into the flesh?[3] Fire, on the other hand, if it does scorch, only raises the surface of the flesh by creating what we call blisters, and does not penetrate within.

967ᵇ Why is it that fire does not make men black, whereas **8** the sun does so, and why does fire blacken earthenware,

---

[1] And so causes them to evaporate.
[2] Cp. Theophrastus, *de Igne*, § 36.
[3] Cp. Theophrastus, *op. cit.*, § 38.

while the sun does not? Or do they produce their effects by dissimilar means, the sun blackening the flesh by scorching it and the fire permeating the earthenware with the soot which it sends up? (Now soot consists of fine ember-dust, 5 formed by the simultaneous breaking-up and burning of the charcoal.) The sun, then, makes men black, while the fire does not do so, because the heat of the sun is gentle and owing to the smallness of its parts it can scorch the flesh itself; and so, because it does not set the flesh on fire, it does not cause pain, but it blackens it because it scorches it. 10 Fire, on the other hand, either does not kindle at all or else penetrates within; for what is burnt by fire also becomes black, but it does not burn merely that part of the body in which the colour is situated.

9 Why do men become darker complexioned as they become older?[1] Is it because anything which decays becomes blacker, except mildew? And old age and decay are the same thing.[2] Further, since the blood when it 15 dries up becomes blacker, it is only likely that the older men are the darker they are; for it is the blood which naturally gives colour to our bodies.

10 Why is it that, of persons engaged in the preparation of cereals, those who handle barley become pale and are 20 subject to catarrh, while those who handle wheat are healthy?[3] Is it because wheat is more easily concocted than barley, and therefore its emanations are also more easily concocted?

11 Why is it that the sun bleaches olive oil but darkens the flesh?[4] Is it because it extracts the earthy element from the olive oil, and this, like the earthy element in wine, is 25 the black part of it? Now it darkens the flesh because it burns it; for that which is earthy always becomes black when burnt.

---

[1] Cp. 890ª 16 ff. [2] Reading ταὐτὸ for τοῦτο.
[3] This problem is identical with xxi. 24, where see note on 929^b 28; cp. also 863^b 1 ff.
[4] The problem here dealt with is the same as that of chapter 1 above, but somewhat differently answered.

INDEX

B b

Gall-stones, man alone suffers from, 895ᵃ 37 ff.

Garlic, 865ᵃ 22, 903ᵇ 29, 907ᵇ 7, 908ᵃ 28, ᵇ 4, 925ᵇ 10, 926ᵃ 3, 11, 16, 26, 949ᵃ 6.

Geometrical truths, contemplation of, gives no pleasure, 956ᵃ 15 ff.

Geryone (play by Nicomachus), 922ᵇ 13.

Gestation, period of, 891ᵇ 11, 25, 896ᵃ 14, 898ᵇ 10; varies in man, 895ᵃ 24.

Glass, 905ᵇ 7, 18, 939ᵃ 14.

Gnomon, 912ᵃ 40, ᵇ 7.

Goats, milk of, 891ᵃ 4; change of colour in, 891ᵇ 13; prolific, 898ᵃ 12.

Gourds, grow well if buried, 923ᵇ 16 ff.; keep fresh in wells, 924ᵃ 36 ff.; methods of producing early, 924ᵇ 10 ff.

Grafting, 924ᵇ 36 ff.

Grapes, 909ᵃ 21; dried sweeter than fresh, 925ᵇ 15; stones of, ᵇ 24.

Grass, 923ᵃ 31.

Green objects, beneficial to the sight, 959ᵃ 24 ff.

Growth, in different dimensions, 916ᵃ 12 ff.

Gruel, 929ᵇ 1; see also *Barley-gruel*.

Gums, inflammation of the, 863ᵇ 11, 887ᵇ 1.

Hail, 940ᵃ 13.

Hair, growth of, at puberty, 876ᵇ 33 ff.; men with thick h. are lustful, 880ᵃ 34 ff., 893ᵇ 10 ff.; cause of bristling of, 886ᵇ 24, 888ᵃ 39, ᵇ 16 ff., 889ᵃ 26 ff., 965ᵃ 8 ff.; does not grow on human scars, 890ᵇ 38, 893ᵇ 28, 894ᵃ 13 ff.; turns grey through leprosy, 891ᵇ 1, 894ᵇ 6; grows harder if plucked out, 893ᵃ 18; soft in northern, hard in southern people, ᵃ 31; softer when long, ᵃ 36; grows on scars upon animals, ᵇ 27, 894ᵃ 12 ff.; distribution of, in man and animals, 896ᵇ 29 ff., 898ᵃ 20 ff.; turns white in man only, ᵃ 31 ff; curliness of, 909ᵃ 30, 963ᵇ 11 ff.; reddish, of those who work on the sea, 966ᵇ 25 ff., of those who live in the north, ᵇ 33.

Halo, solar, 912ᵇ 34.

Hare, prolific, 892ᵇ 1.

Head, the, sores on, 861ᵃ 33, 909ᵃ 35; effect of running on, 881ᵇ 7; movement of, by animals, 892ᵇ 19; some animals live after their h.s have been cut off, 898ᵇ 21; the most divine part of man, 962ᵃ 23, 35.

Health, a state of rest, 886ᵇ 6; fatness a condition of h., 888ᵃ 30; not communicable to others, 951ᵃ 4 ff.

Hearing, often defective from birth, 898ᵇ 28; has the same source as the voice, ᵇ 29; better in those who hold their breath, 903ᵇ 34, 904ᵇ 11; prevented by yawning, 902ᵇ 9 ff., 904ᵃ 16 ff.; see also *Ears*.

Heart, the, not controlled by the mind, 882ᵃ 35; effect of fear upon, 947ᵇ 29.

Heat, lack of, causes old age, 875ᵃ 13; feeds on moisture, ᵃ 14; the cause of motion in animals, ᵃ 25; excessive h. causes brutishness, 909ᵃ 13.

Heavenly bodies, nine in number, 910ᵇ 35; appear always to retain the same shapes, 911ᵃ 5 ff.

Hellebore, 864ᵃ 4.

Hellespont, 946ᵇ 34, 38.

Hellespontias (East Wind), 946ᵇ 33, 947ᵃ 2.

Hemlock, effects of, 874ᵇ 2.

Heracles, affected by melancholy, 953ᵃ 14.

Heraclitus, 908ᵃ 30, 934ᵇ 34.

Herbs, 923ᵃ 32.

Hesiod, quoted (*Works and Days*, 582, 586), 879ᵃ 28, (*ib.* 40) 892ᵃ 29.

Hesitation in speech; see *Speech*.

Hiccups, cause of, 963ᵃ 39: stopped by sneezing, 961ᵇ 9 ff., 963ᵃ 38 ff.; stopped by vinegar, 961ᵇ 20, 962ᵃ 1, 963ᵇ 6; other preventives, 962ᵃ 1 ff., ᵇ 31 ff.

Hoar-frost, 888ᵇ 30, 938ᵃ 34, 939ᵇ 36, 940ᵇ 8.

Homer, quoted (*Il.* v. 75), 890ᵇ 9; (*Od.* xx. 71) 894ᵇ 34; (*Il.* vii. 64) 934ᵃ 14; (*Od.* iv. 567) 943ᵇ 23; (*Il.* vi. 200-2) 953ᵃ 23; (*Od.* xix. 122) ᵇ 12.

'Homophony', less pleasant than 'antiphony', 921ᵃ 7 ff.: produces only a simple sound, ᵃ 12.

INDEX

Honey, 890[b] 25 ; mixed with flour, 928[a] 5.

Hoofs of animals, gelatinous matter in, 935[b] 38.

Horned animals, less hairy, 898[a] 24.

Horse-back, riders on, water at the eyes, 882[a] 3, 884[b] 22.

Horse-parsley, 923[a] 34, [b] 8.

Horses, 893[b] 27, 894[a] 12, 896[b] 10, 897[b] 35, 898[a] 11, 33, [b] 6 ; period of gestation in, 891[b] 28 ; colour of eyes of, 892[a] 1 ; wild, 895[b] 25.

Hunger, not felt immediately after exercise, 884[a] 1 ; stimulated by recollection, 886[a] 33 ; ravenous, in cold weather, 887[b] 38 ff. ; more tolerable than thirst, 949[b] 26, 32.

Hypate, 918[a] 14, 17, 919[b] 9, 12, 921[a] 10, 21, 24, 922[b] 4 ; easy to sing, 917[b] 35 ; stopped down produces *nete*, 918[b] 1 ; is double *nete* (in length of string), 919[b] 1 ; is half *nete* (in frequency of pitch), 920[a] 30 ; effect of *h*. produced by stopping down *nete*, 919[b] 15, 921[b] 14 ; one of the extremities of the scale, 922[a] 27.

Hypodorian mode, unsuited for tragic chorus, 920[a] 8, 922[b] 10 ff. ; characteristics of, [b] 15 ff.

Hypophrygian mode, unsuited for tragic chorus, 920[a] 8, 922[b] 10 ff. ; has a character of action, [b] 13.

Imitation, in music, 918[b] 17 ; by actors, [b] 28 ; of parents by young, 894[a] 30.

Inanimate Things, Problems connected with, 913[a] 19-915[b] 35.

Incontinence, only used of the pleasures of touch and taste, 949[b] 6 ff., 37 ff.

India, wild dogs in, 895[b] 25.

Infertility, of drunkards, 871[a] 23 ff. ; caused by varicocele, 878[b] 36 ff.

Inflammation, cured by salt and vinegar, 889[b] 19.

Injustice, varying degrees of, 952[a] 22 ff. ; in respect of money, [a] 20, [b] 23.

Instruments, wind, 919[b] 3 ; importance of *mese* in tuning, 919[a] 14 ff., 920[b] 7 ff. ; see also *Flute*, *Lyre*.

Intelligence and Wisdom, Problems connected with Prudence, 953[a] 8-957[a] 35.

Intelligence, use of the, 955[b] 26 ff.

Interval, musical, 917[b] 32, 36 ; see also *Fifth, Fourth, Octave*.

Jars, buried, cause resonance, 899[b] 25 ff. ; two, one full and the other half full, give an accord in the octave, 922[b] 35 ff. ; capacity of, 938[b] 14 ff.

Journeys, unfamiliar, seem longer, 883[b] 3 ff., 955[b] 9 ff.

Jumpers, weights held by, 881[b] 4.

Justice and Injustice, Problems connected with, 950[a] 21-953[a] 7.

Justice, association with, makes men just, 951[a] 5 ff.

Kidneys, 876[b] 20.

Knees, strain on, in ascending, 882[b] 25 ff.

Lacedaemonian, 953[a] 19.

Lame, the, are lustful, 880[b] 5.

Lameness, more common in man than in the animals, 895[a] 20 ff.

Language, 898[b] 30, 35.

Larynx, 901[a] 2, [b] 11, 903[a] 34, [b] 29, 906[a] 1.

Laughter, a deep sound, 900[a] 21, [b] 7 ; more difficult to restrain among friends, 950[a] 17 ff. ; nature of, 965[a] 14 ff. ; caused by tickling, 965[a] 23 ff.

Laws, originally sung, 919[b] 38.

Lead, 889[a] 13.

Leeks, make the voice loud, 903[b] 27 ; cannot endure salt water, 923[a] 7.

Left side of the body, more comfortable to lie upon, 886[a] 15 ff. ; moister and hotter than the right, 961[a] 3 ff. ; inferior to right except in the senses, 958[b] 16, 23, 959[a] 20, 960[a] 29.

Legs, sores on, 861[a] 34, 895[a] 31, 909[a] 36 ; of eunuchs, swollen, 876[b] 31 ; feel fatigue less than the thighs, 883[b] 13 ff.

Lentil-soup, 936[b] 24.

Leopards, never tame, 895[b] 26.

Leprosy, 887[a] 34 ; white l., 891[a] 26 ; found only in man, 894[a] 37 ; turns hair grey, 891[b] 1, 894[b] 6.

Lesbos, 946[b] 34, 947[a] 4.

Letters, use of, in speech, 895[a] 8, 905[a] 32.

INDEX

8 ff.; causes lisping, [b] 25 ff.; yields up its odour more quickly when diluted, 907[b] 13 ff.; effect of marjoram upon, 926[b] 32 ff.; taste of, after eating rotten fruit, 930[b] 5 ff., and sour fruit, 931[a] 6 ff.

Wine-skins, two, one double the size of the other, give an accord in the octave, 923[a] 2 ff.

Wisdom, Problems connected with Prudence, Intelligence, and, 953[a] 8–957[a] 35.

Wisdom, superior, of those who live in warm regions, 910[a] 26 ff.; practical, of man, 955[b] 4 ff.; increases with age, [b] 22 ff.; no prizes offered for, 956[b] 16 ff.

Woman, murder of a, more terrible than of a man, 951[a] 11 ff.; see also *Females.*

Words, uttered by man only, 905[a] 21.

Wormwood, 949[a] 2.

Wounds heal more readily in the young, 961[a] 5.

Wrestling-school, theft from, 952[a] 18.

Wrinkles, caused by hot water, 936[b] 10 ff., 937[a] 2 ff.

Yawning, 961[a] 37 ff.; why infectious, 886[a] 24 ff., 31 ff., 887[a] 4 ff.; prevents hearing, 902[b] 9 ff., 904[a] 16 ff.

Yellow objects, beneficial to the sight, 959[a] 24 ff.

Zephyr; see *West wind.*

PRINTED IN GREAT BRITAIN
AT THE UNIVERSITY PRESS, OXFORD
BY VIVIAN RIDLER
PRINTER TO THE UNIVERSITY